GREAT SONGS OF THE 90s
FOR GUITAR

THIS PUBLICATION IS NOT AUTHORISED FOR SALE IN THE UNITED STATES OF AMERICA AND/OR CANADA

Hal Leonard Europe
Distributed by Music Sales

S.E. EDUCATION & LIBRARY BOARD	
C210775332	
Bertrams	01.03.08
787.87166	£14.95

Guitar Notation Legend

Guitar Music can be notated three different ways: on a *musical staff*, in *tablature*, and in *rhythm slashes*.

RHYTHM SLASHES are written above the staff. Strum chords in the rhythm indicated. Use the chord diagrams found at the top of the first page of the transcription for the appropriate chord voicings. Round noteheads indicate single notes.

THE MUSICAL STAFF shows pitches and rhythms and is divided by bar lines into measures. Pitches are named after the first seven letters of the alphabet.

TABLATURE graphically represents the guitar fingerboard. Each horizontal line represents a a string, and each number represents a fret.

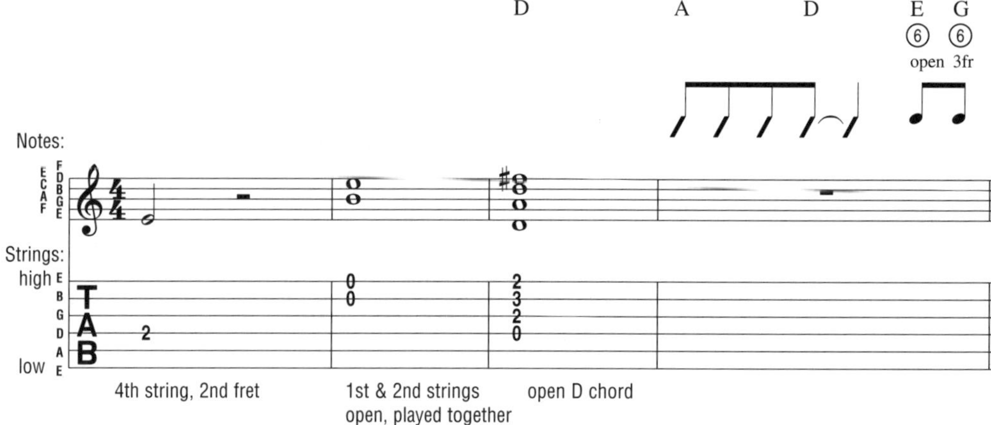

Definitions for Special Guitar Notation

HALF-STEP BEND: Strike the note and bend up 1/2 step.

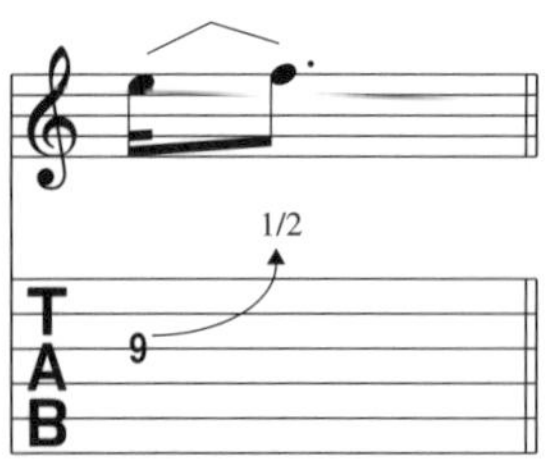

WHOLE-STEP BEND: Strike the note and bend up one step.

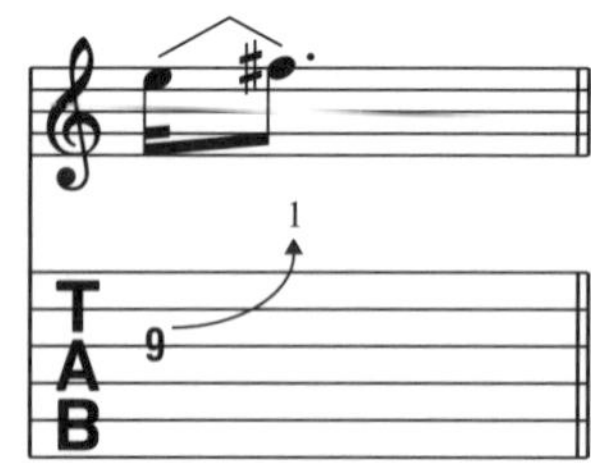

GRACE NOTE BEND: Strike the note and immediately bend up as indicated.

SLIGHT (MICROTONE) BEND: Strike the note and bend up 1/4 step.

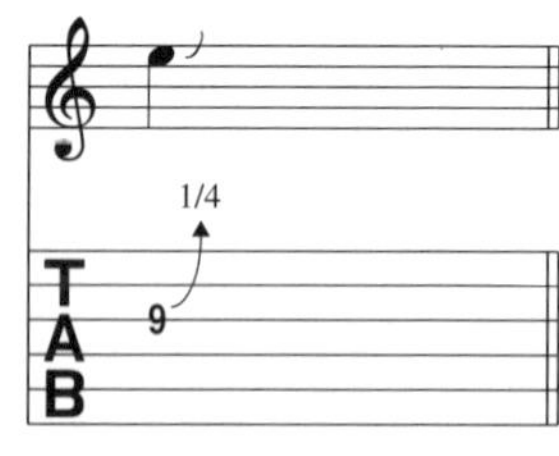

BEND AND RELEASE: Strike the note and bend up as indicated, then release back to the original note. Only the first note is struck.

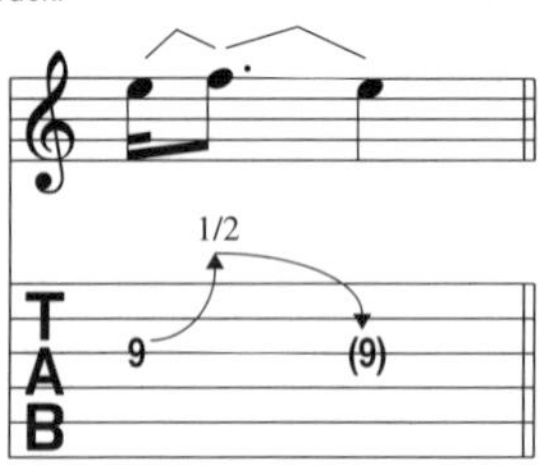

PRE-BEND: Bend the note as indicated, then strike it.

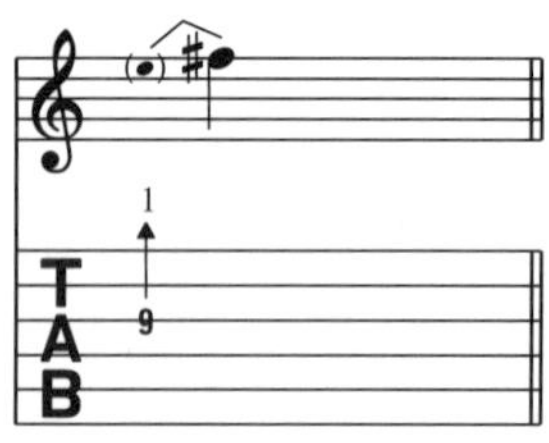

PRE-BEND AND RELEASE: Bend the note as indicated. Strike it and release the bend back to the original note.

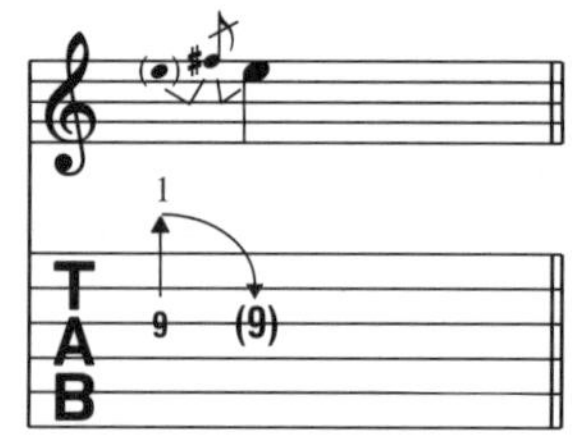

UNISON BEND: Strike the two notes simultaneously and bend the lower note up to the pitch of the higher.

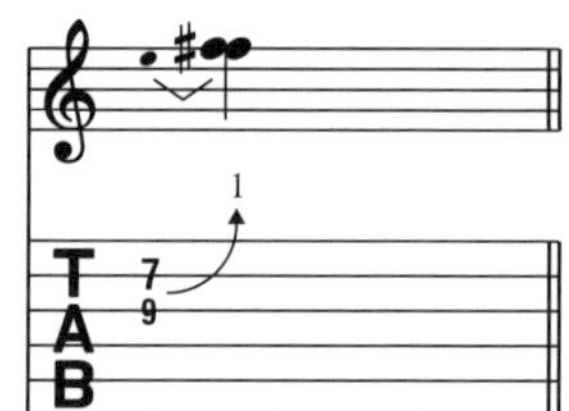

VIBRATO: The string is vibrated by rapidly bending and releasing the note with the fretting hand.

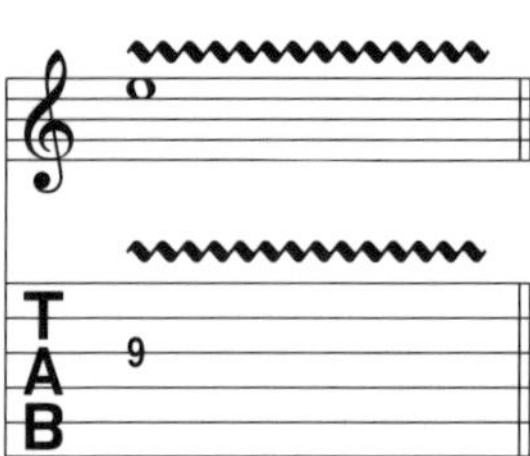

WIDE VIBRATO: The pitch is varied to a greater degree by vibrating with the fretting hand.

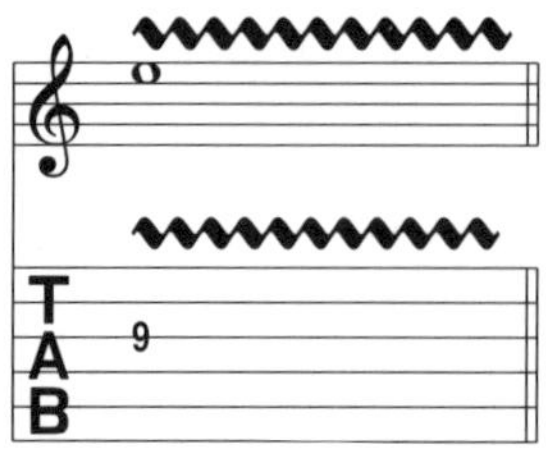

HAMMER-ON: Strike the first (lower) note with one finger, then sound the higher note (on the same string) with another finger by fretting it without picking.

PULL-OFF: Place both fingers on the notes to be sounded. Strike the first note and without picking, pull the finger off to sound the second (lower) note.

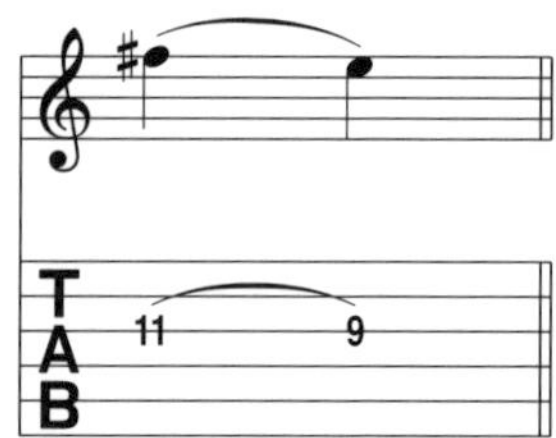

LEGATO SLIDE: Strike the first note and then slide the same fret-hand finger up or down to the second note. The second note is not struck.

SHIFT SLIDE: Same as legato slide, except the second note is struck.

TRILL: Very rapidly alternate between the notes indicated by continuously hammering on and pulling off.

TAPPING: Hammer ("tap") the fret indicated with the pick-hand index or middle finger and pull off to the note fretted by the fret hand.

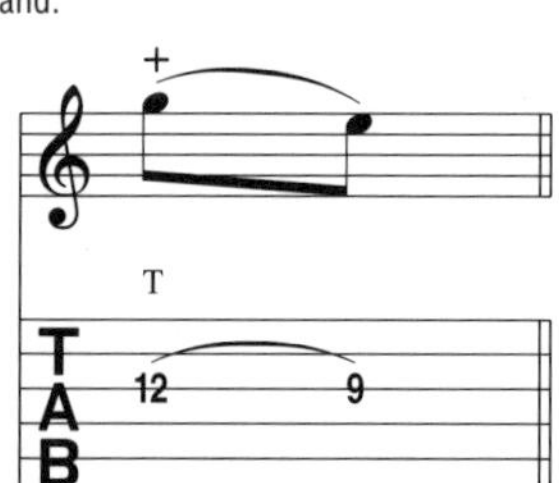

Loans

Helen Wilson
21 Sep 2024

New Stock
New Stock
Item barcode: C210775332
Due date: 12 Oct 2024

Guitar player book : 40 years of interviews, gea

Item barcode: C210777524
Due date: 12 Oct 2024

New Stock
New Stock
Item barcode: C901730798
Due date: 12 Oct 2024

Patchwork girls
Everest, Elaine
Item barcode: C903440707
Due date: 12 Oct 2024

Time to remember
Cox, Josephine
Item barcode: C903933655
Due date: 12 Oct 2024

Wedding bells for Woolworths
Everest, Elaine
Item barcode: C904060280
Due date: 12 Oct 2024

Woolworths girl's promise
Everest, Elaine
Item barcode: C904313094
Due date: 12 Oct 2024

NATURAL HARMONIC: Strike the note while the fret-hand lightly touches the string directly over the fret indicated.

PINCH HARMONIC: The note is fretted normally and a harmonic is produced by adding the edge of the thumb or the tip of the index finger of the pick hand to the normal pick attack.

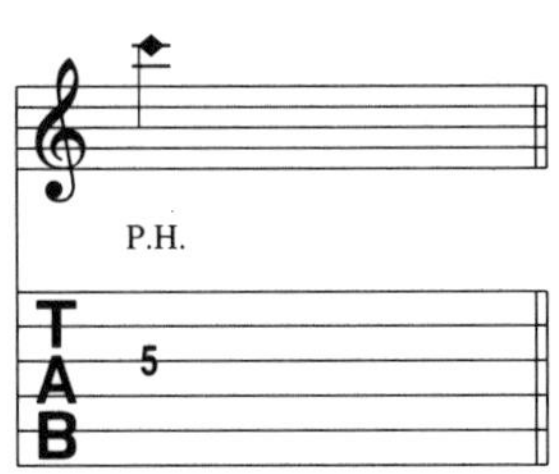

HARP HARMONIC: The note is fretted normally and a harmonic is produced by gently resting the pick hand's index finger directly above the indicated fret (in parentheses) while the pick hand's thumb or pick assists by plucking the appropriate string.

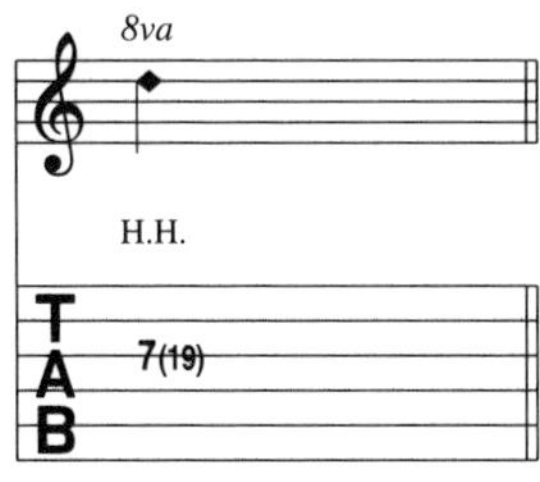

PICK SCRAPE: The edge of the pick is rubbed down (or up) the string, producing a scratchy sound.

MUFFLED STRINGS: A percussive sound is produced by laying the fret hand across the string(s) without depressing, and striking them with the pick hand.

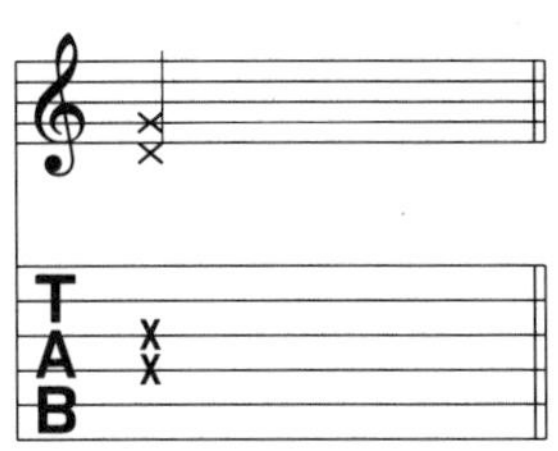

PALM MUTING: The note is partially muted by the pick hand lightly touching the string(s) just before the bridge.

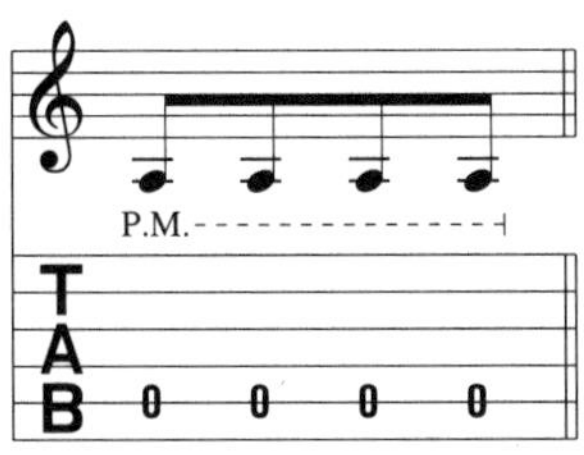

RAKE: Drag the pick across the strings indicated with a single motion.

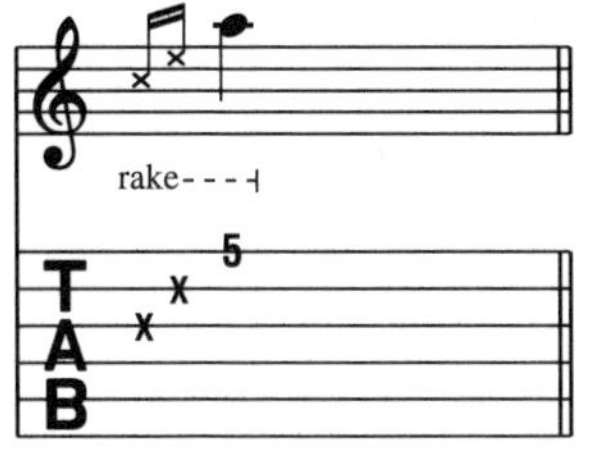

TREMOLO PICKING: The note is picked as rapidly and continuously as possible.

ARPEGGIATE: Play the notes of the chord indicated by quickly rolling them from bottom to top.

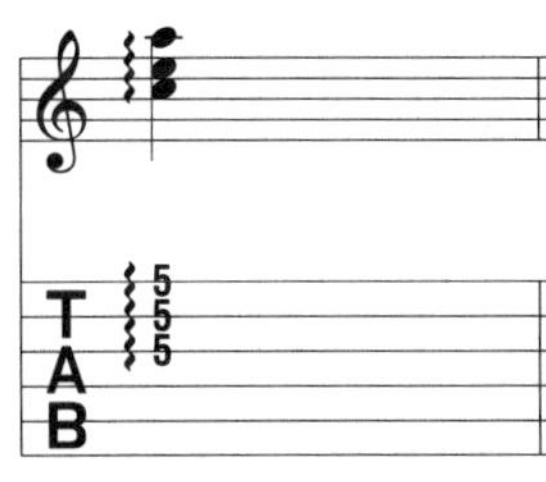

VIBRATO BAR DIVE AND RETURN: The pitch of the note or chord is dropped a specified number of steps (in rhythm) then returned to the original pitch.

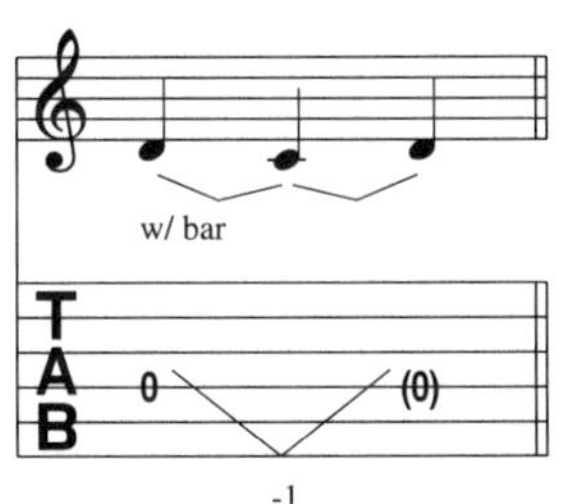

VIBRATO BAR SCOOP: Depress the bar just before striking the note, then quickly release the bar.

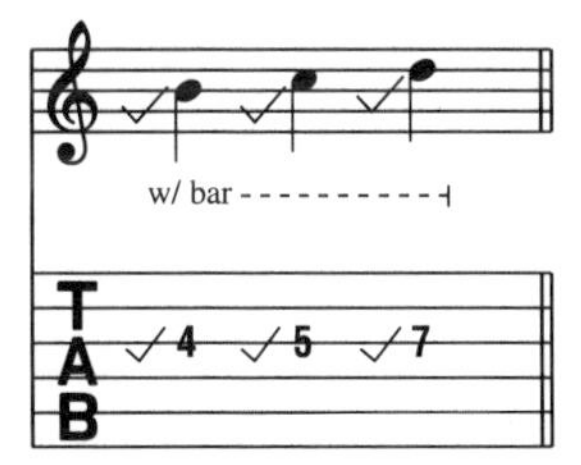

VIBRATO BAR DIP: Strike the note and then immediately drop a specified number of steps, then release back to the original pitch.

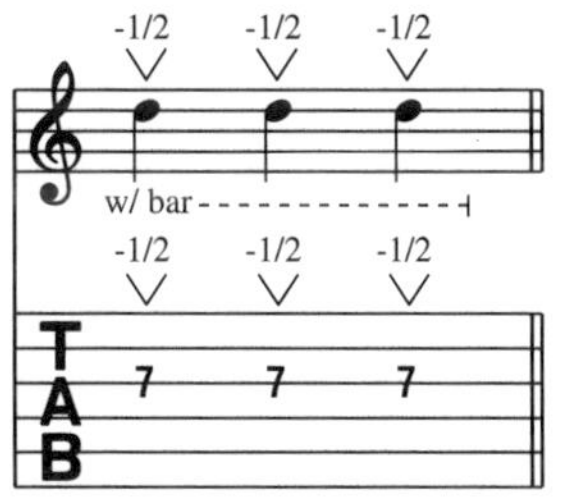

Additional Musical Definitions

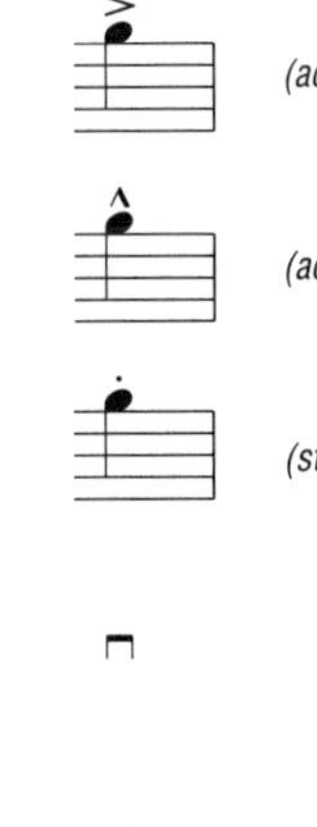

	(accent)	• Accentuate note (play it louder)
	(accent)	• Accentuate note with great intensity
	(staccato)	• Play the note short
⊓		• Downstroke
V		• Upstroke
D.S. al Coda		• Go back to the sign (𝄋), then play until the measure marked "***To Coda***," then skip to the section labelled "**Coda**."
D.C. al Fine		• Go back to the beginning of the song and play until the measure marked "***Fine***" (end).

Rhy. Fig.	• Label used to recall a recurring accompaniment pattern (usually chordal).
Riff	• Label used to recall composed, melodic lines (usually single notes) which recur.
Fill	• Label used to identify a brief melodic figure which is to be inserted into the arrangement.
Rhy. Fill	• A chordal version of a Fill.
tacet	• Instrument is silent (drops out).
	• Repeat measures between signs.
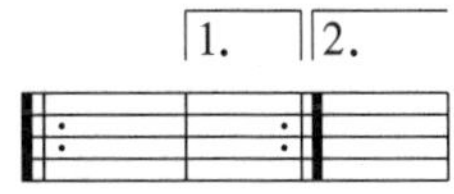	• When a repeated section has different endings, play the first ending only the first time and the second ending only the second time.

NOTE: Tablature numbers in parentheses mean:

1. The note is being sustained over a system (note in standard notation is tied), or
2. The note is sustained, but a new articulation (such as a hammer-on, pull-off, slide or vibrato begins), or
3. The note is a barely audible "ghost" note (note in standard notation is also in parentheses).

Exclusive Distributors
Music Sales Limited.
8/9 Frith Street, London W1D 3JB, England.

Order No. HLE90002242
ISBN 1-84449-583-3
This book © Copyright 2004 by Hal Leonard Europe.

Unauthorised reproduction of any part of this publication by any means including photocopying is an infringement of copyright.

Cover design by Mainartery Design.
Cover photos courtesy of LFI.
Printed in the USA.

Your Guarantee of Quality
As publishers, we strive to produce every book to the highest commercial standards.
The book has been carefully designed to minimise awkward page turns and to make playing from it a real pleasure.
Throughout, the printing and binding have been planned to ensure a sturdy, attractive publication which should give years of enjoyment.
If your copy fails to meet our high standards, please inform us and we will gladly replace it.

www.musicsales.com

All I Wanna Do

Words and Music by Kevin Gilbert, David Baerwald, Sheryl Crow, Wyn Cooper and Bill Bottrell

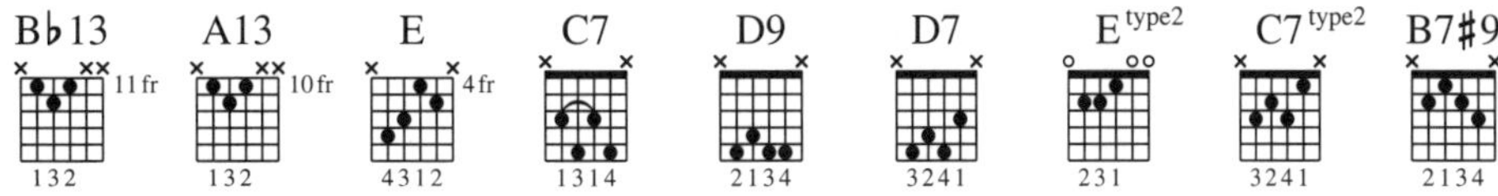

Gtr. 1 tuning:
(low to high) E–A–D–G♯–B–E

Intro

Moderately ♩ = 124

Spoken: Hit it. *This ain't no disco.*

B♭13 A13 B♭13

Rhy. Fig. 1

* Gtr. 1

mf

w/ slide

Gtr. 2 (clean)

mp

let ring

semi-harm.

13⁄14 X X 13⁄14 14 14 X 13⁄14 X 14 | X 14 X 13⁄14 X 14 15 15 15 17 15

* Pedal steel arr. for gtr. Wear slide on pinky throughout.

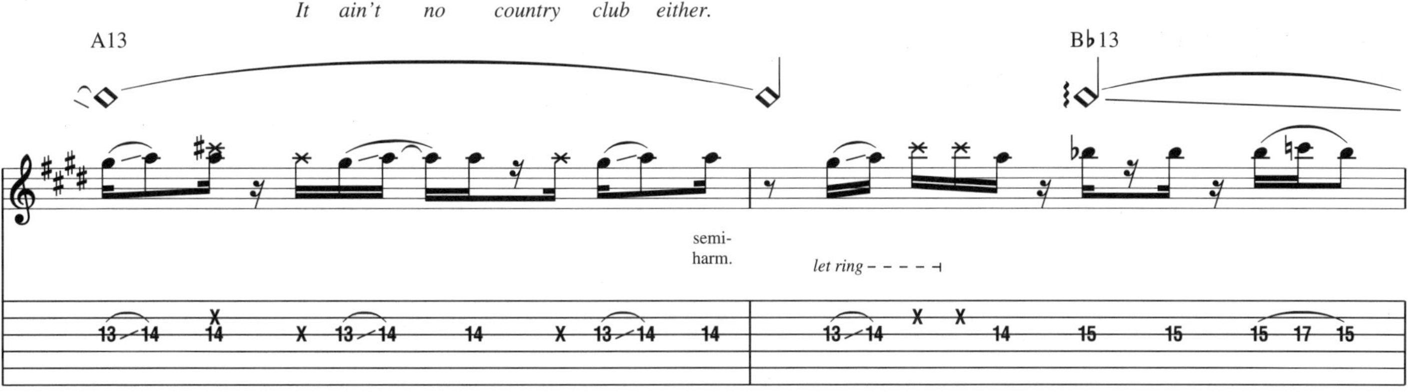

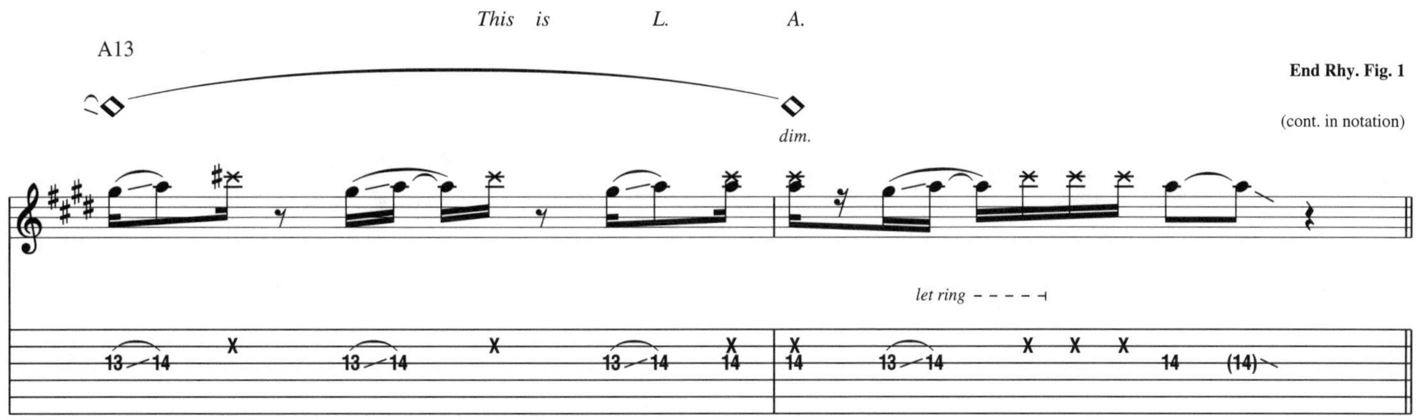

Copyright © 1993 Sony/ATV Tunes LLC, Almo Music Corp., Zen Of Iniquity, Warner-Tamerlane Publishing Corp., Old Crow Music, WB Music Corp., Canvas Mattress Music and Ignorant Music
All Rights on behalf of Sony/ATV Tunes LLC Administered by Sony/ATV Music Publishing, 8 Music Square West, Nashville, TN 37203
All Rights on behalf of Zen Of Iniquity Administered by Almo Music Corp.
International Copyright Secured All Rights Reserved

Verse
Gtr. 2 tacet
E
E
6
open
Rhy. Fig. 2
* Gtr. 3
mf
1. "All I wan - na do is have a lit - tle fun be - fore I die," says the man
Gtr. 1
* Elec. piano arr. for gtr.

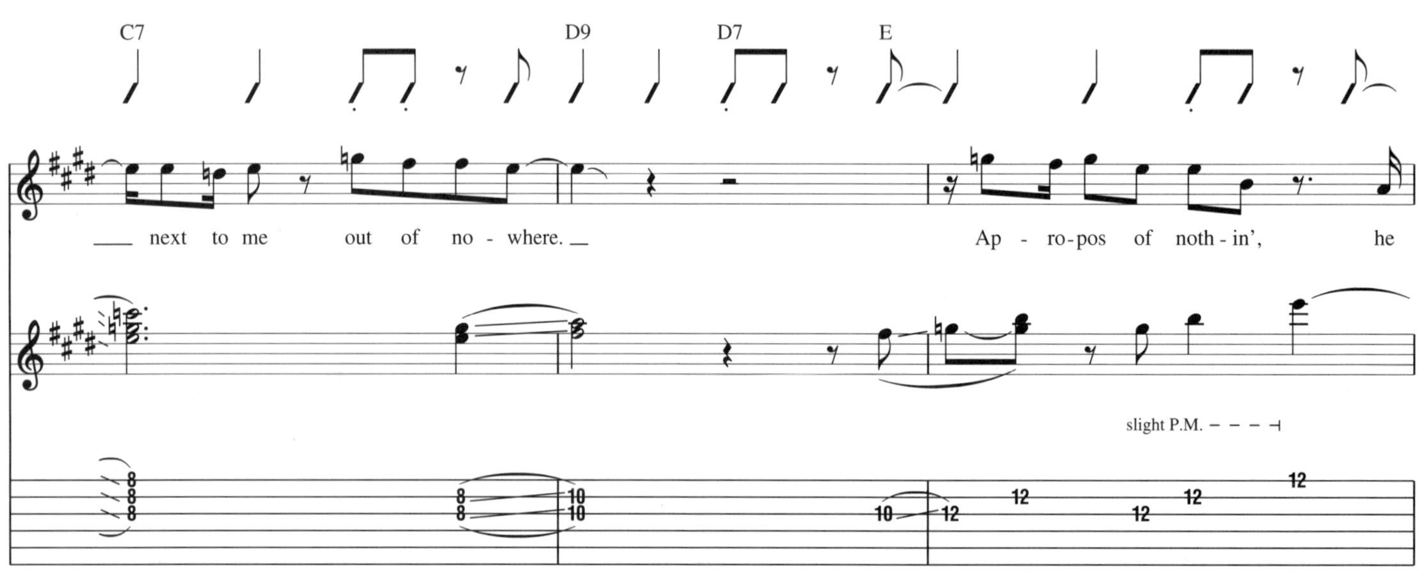
C7
D9
D7
E
next to me out of no - where.
Ap - ro-pos of noth - in', he
slight P.M.

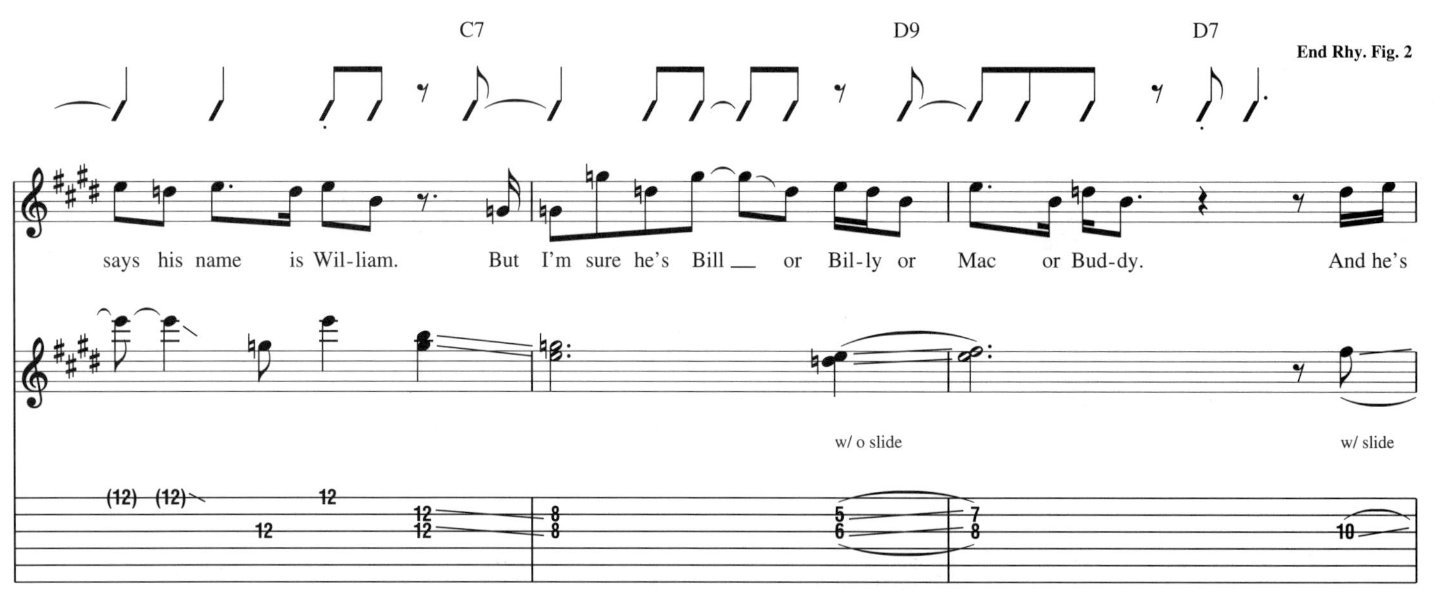
C7
D9
D7
End Rhy. Fig. 2
says his name is Wil - liam. But I'm sure he's Bill or Bil - ly or Mac or Bud - dy. And he's
w/ o slide
w/ slide

Gtr. 3: w/ Rhy. Fig. 2
E
C7
plain ug - ly to me. And I won - der if he's ev - er had a day of fun in his whole
D9
D7
E
C7
life. We are drink - in' beer at noon on Tues - day in a
Gtr. 1
Gtr. 2
divisi
D9
D7
Gtr. 3: w/ Rhy. Fig. 2 (1st 3 meas.)
E
bar that fac - es a gi - ant car wash. And the good peo-ple of the world are wash - in'
C7
D9
Gtr. 3
(cont. in notation)
their cars on their lunch break, hos - in' and scrub-bin' as best they can in skirts and suits.
w/o slide
* let ring
* Refers to Gtr. 1 only.

Pre-Chorus
Gtr. 1: w/ Rhy. Fig. 1
Gtr. 2 tacet
A7
G#7 A7 Bb7
They drive their shin - y Dat - suns and Bu - icks
Gtr. 3
Rhy. Fig. 3
A7
G#7 A7 Bb7
back to the phone com - pa - ny, the re - cord store, too.
A7
N.C.
Well, they're noth - in' like Bil - ly 'n' me. 'Cause all I wan - na
Gtr. 3
End Rhy. Fig. 3
* Gtr. 4 (acous.)
divisi
Fill 1
(Gtr. 4 cont. in slashes)
End Fill 1
* Two gtrs. arr. for one.
Chorus
Gtr. 3 tacet
E
E type2
C7 type2
D7
open
Rhy. Fig. 4
Gtr. 4
do is have some fun. I got a feel - in' I'm not the on -
Gtr. 1
let ring

Gtr. 4: w/ Rhy. Fig. 4 (1 1/2 times)
E
End Rhy. Fig. 4
- ly one. All I wan - na do is have some fun. I got a feel -
let ring
C7 D7 E
- in' I'm not the on - ly one. All I wan - na do is have some fun
let ring
C7 type2 B7#9
Gtr. 4
(cont. in notation)
until the sun comes up o - ver San - ta Mon - i - ca Bou - le - vard.
E E Gtr. 4 tacet C7 D9 E
6 open
Gtr. 3
* Fill 2
End Fill 2
Gtr. 1
Gtr. 1
Gtr. 4 divisi
let ring
let ring
w/o slide
* Refers to Gtr. 4 only.

Verse
Gtr. 3: w/ Rhy. Fig. 2 (last 7 meas.)
C7
2. I like a good beer buzz ear - ly in the morn-in' and Bil-ly likes to peel the la - bels from his
w/ slide
let ring
D9 D7 E C7
bot-tles of Bud. He shreds them on the bar, then he lights ev-'ry match in an o - ver - sized
Gtr. 3: w/ Rhy. Fig. 2 (1st 3 meas.)
D9 D7 E
pack, let-tin' each one burn down to his thick fin - gers be -
Gtr. 1
Gtr. 2
divisi
let ring
C7 D9 D7 B♭7
Gtr. 3
fore blow-in' and curs-in' them out. He's watch-in' the bot-tles of Bud as they spin on the floor.
w/o slide

Pre-Chorus

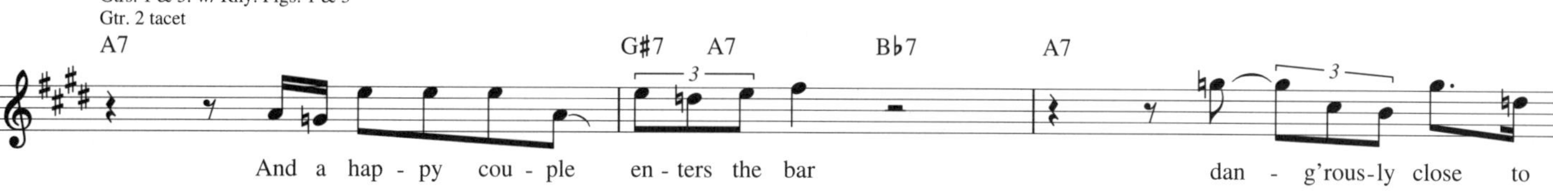
Gtrs. 1 & 3: w/ Rhy. Figs. 1 & 3
Gtr. 2 tacet
A7
G#7 A7
B♭7
A7
And a hap - py cou - ple en - ters the bar
dan - g'rous-ly close to

G#7 A7
B♭7
A7
Gtr. 4: w/ Fill 1
one an - oth - er.
The bar - ten - der looks up from his want ads.
But all I wan - na

Chorus
Gtr. 4: w/ Rhy. Fig. 4 (2 1/2 times)
E
C7
D7
do is have some fun.
I got a feel - in'
I'm not the on -
Gtr. 1
w/ slide
let ring

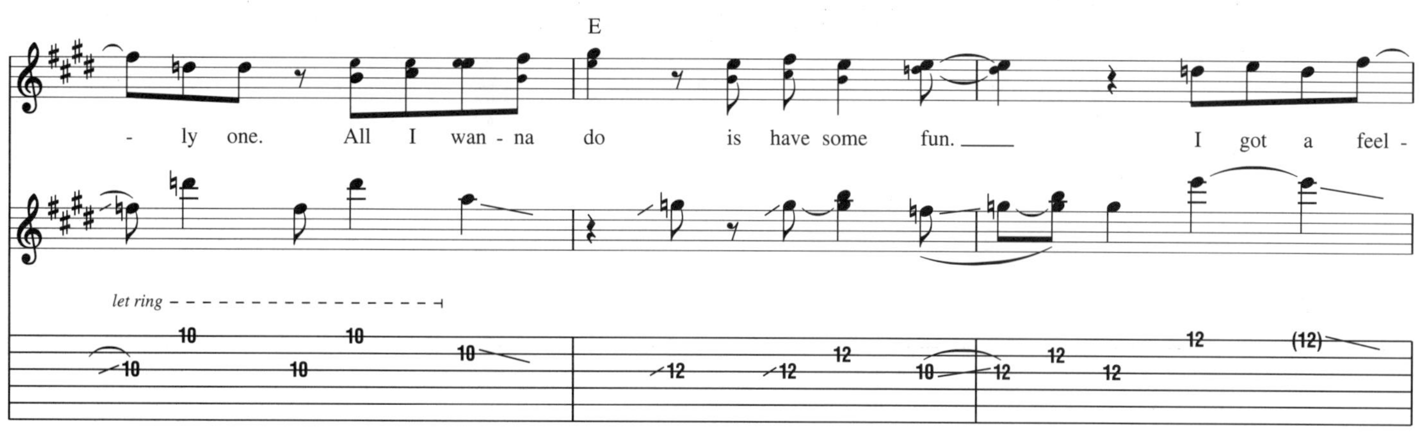
E
- ly one. All I wan - na
do is have some fun.
I got a feel -
let ring

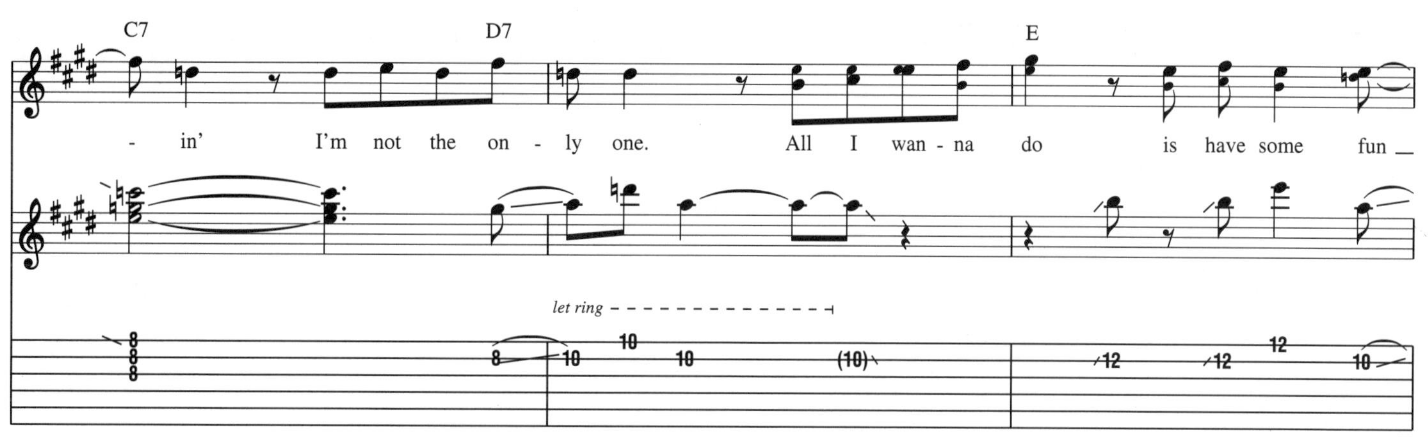
C7
D7
E
- in' I'm not the on - ly one.
All I wan - na
do is have some fun
let ring

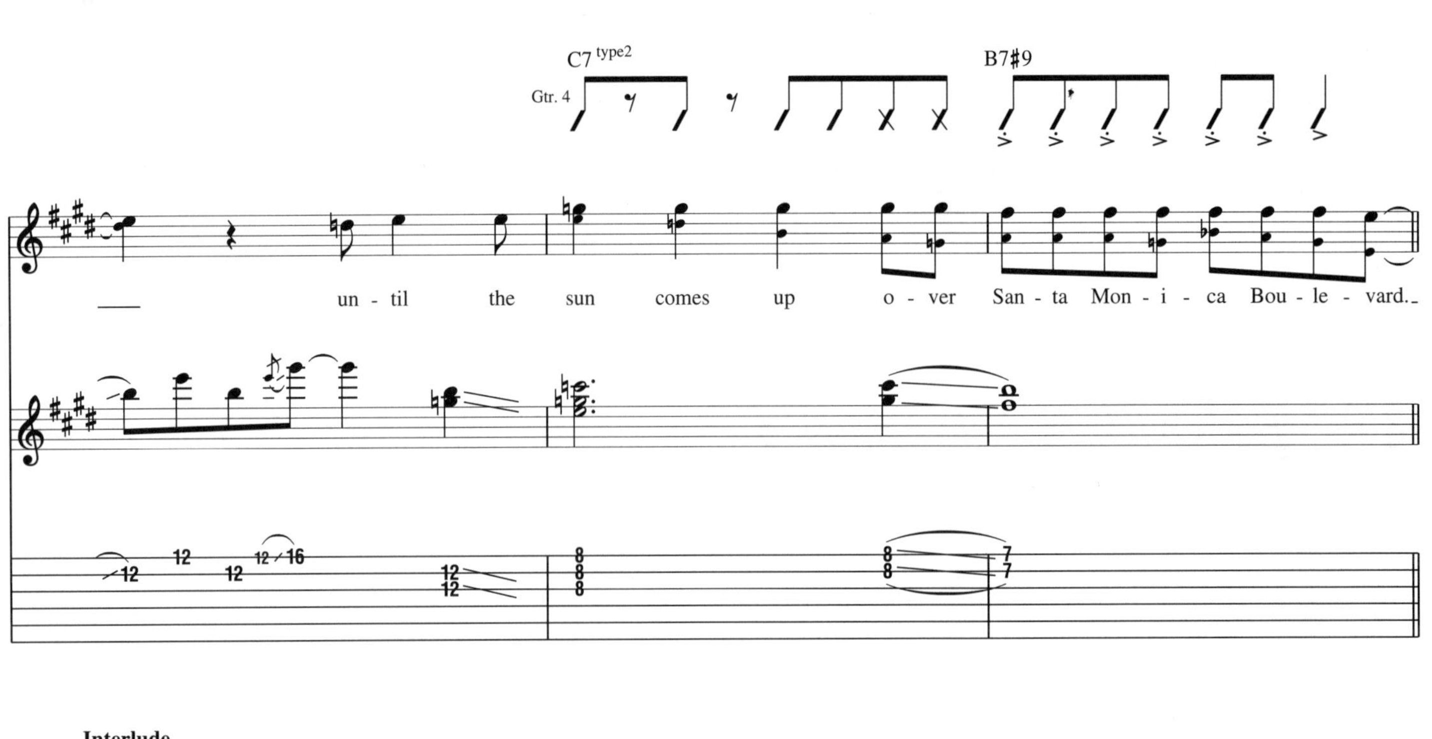

Interlude

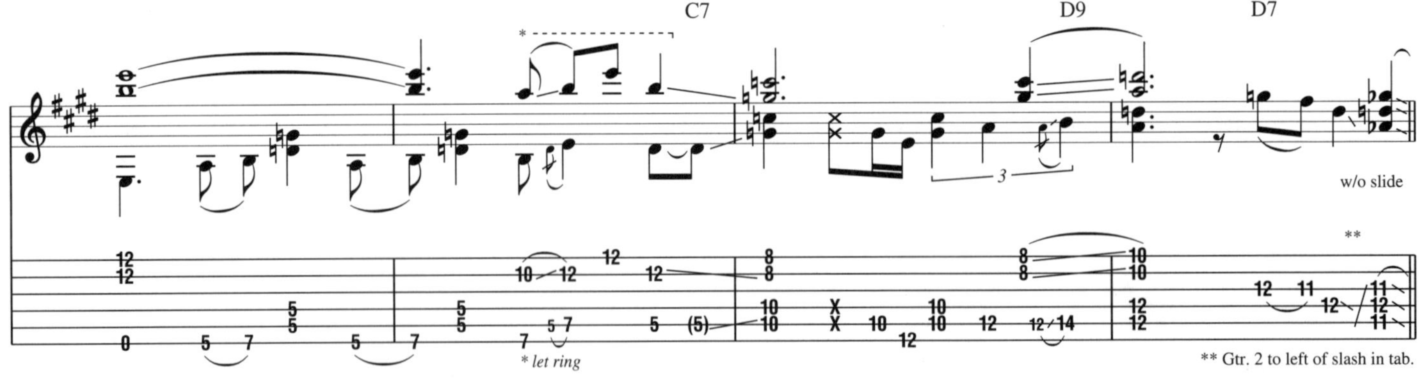

Pre-Chorus

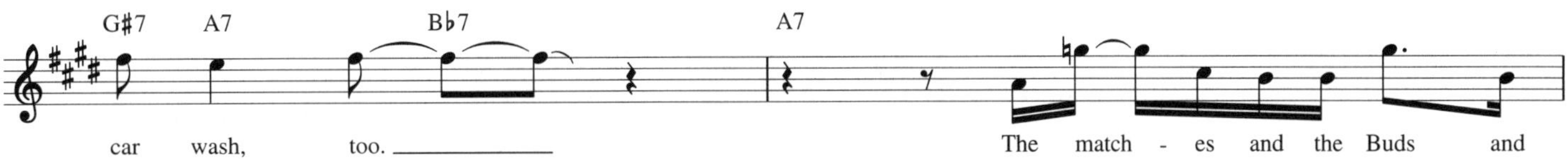

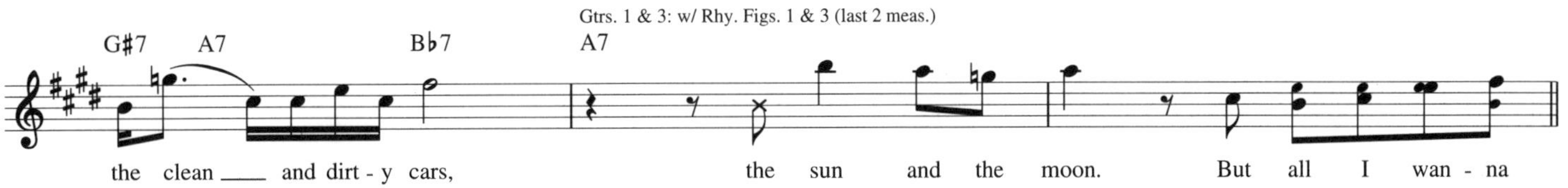

Chorus

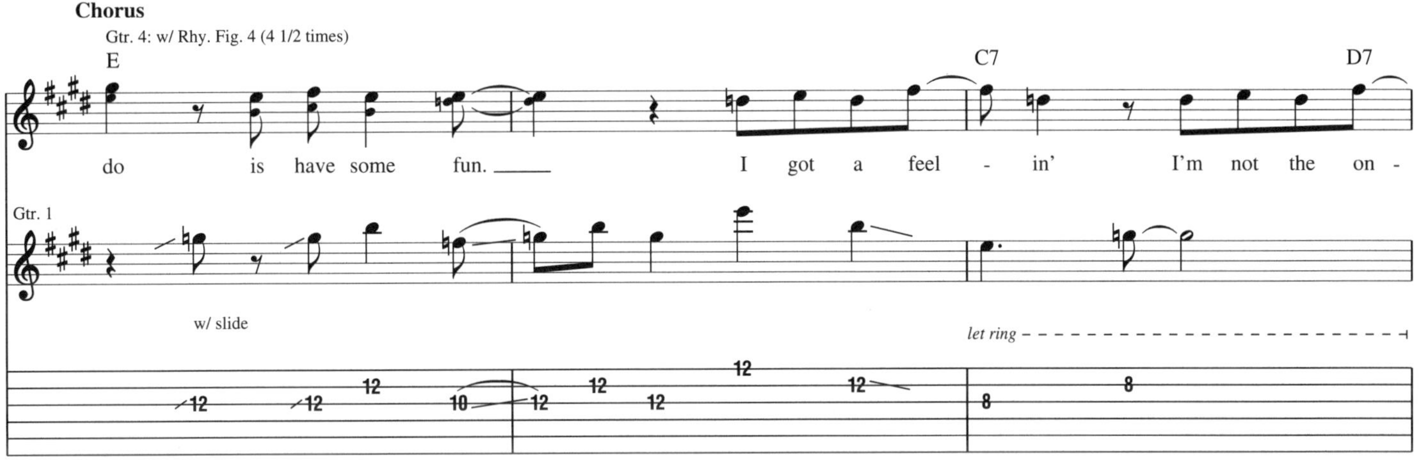

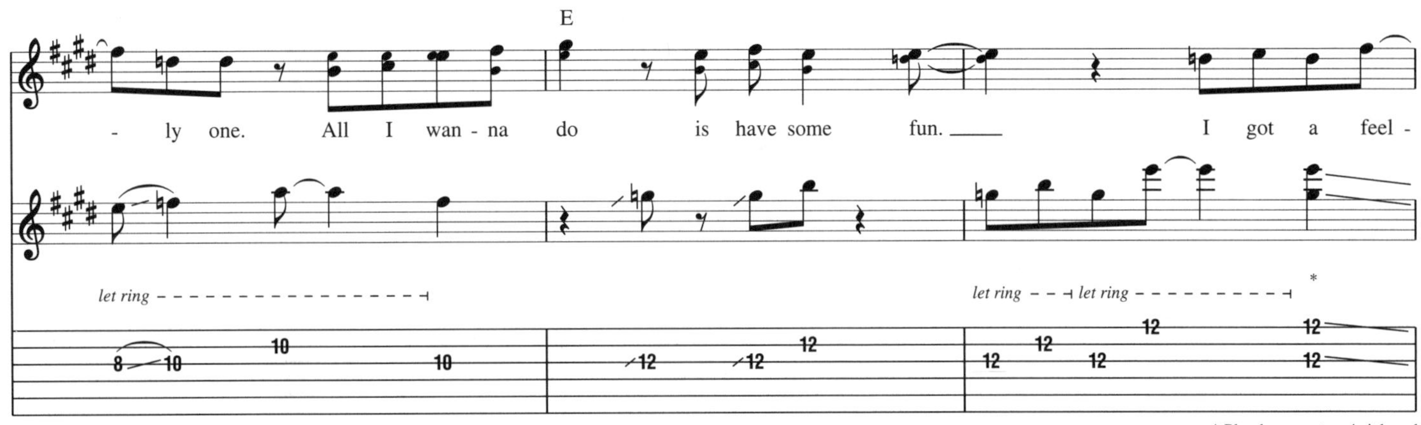

* Play lower note w/ pick and higher note w/ R.H. finger.

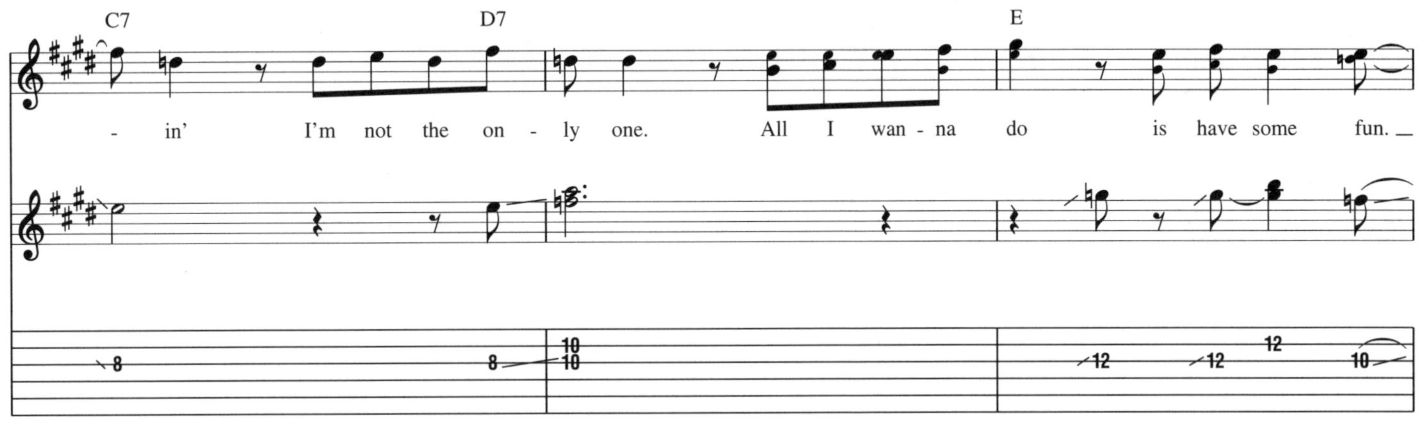

C7
D7
I got a feel - in' the par - ty has just be - gun. All I wan - na
let ring
E
C7
D7
do is have some fun. I won't tell ya that you're the on - ly one. All I wan-na
let ring
let ring
let ring
E
C7 type2
Gtr. 4
do is have some fun un - til the sun comes up o - ver
let ring
let ring
D7
E
6
open
E type2
San - ta Mon - i - ca Bou - le - vard, un - til the
let ring
let ring

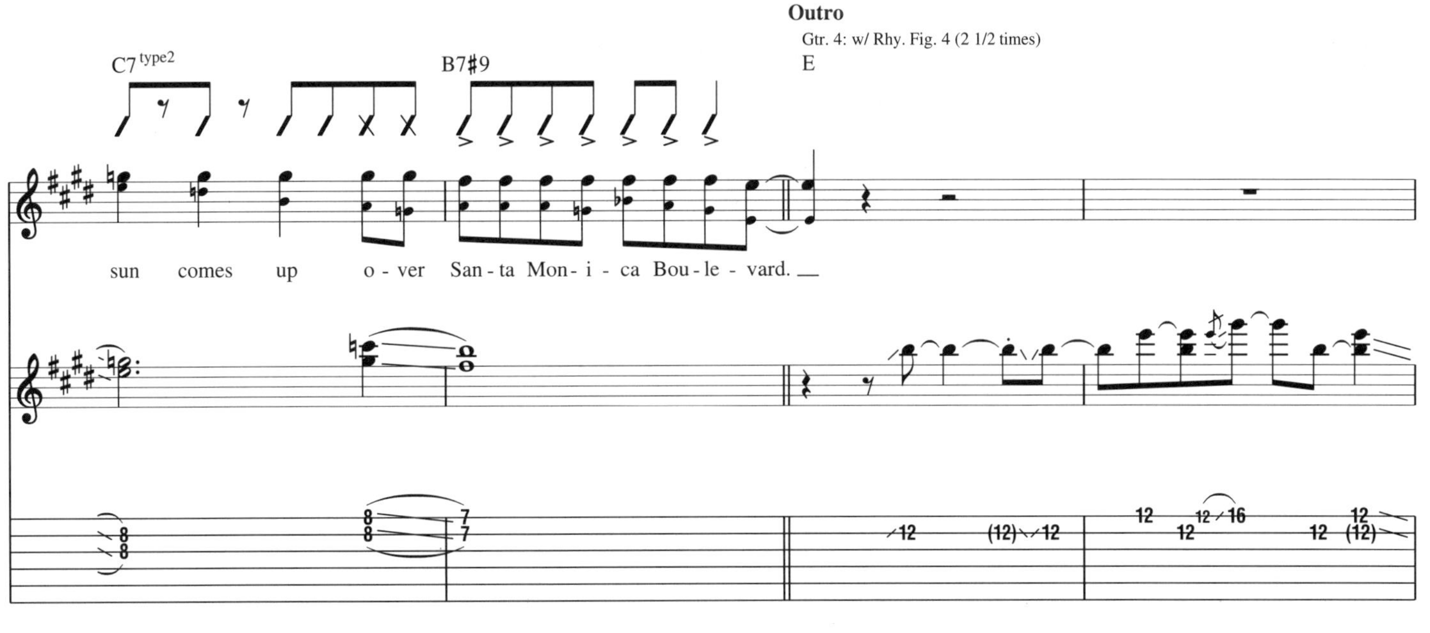
Outro
Gtr. 4: w/ Rhy. Fig. 4 (2 1/2 times)
C7 type2
B7#9
E
sun comes up o - ver San - ta Mon - i - ca Bou - le - vard.

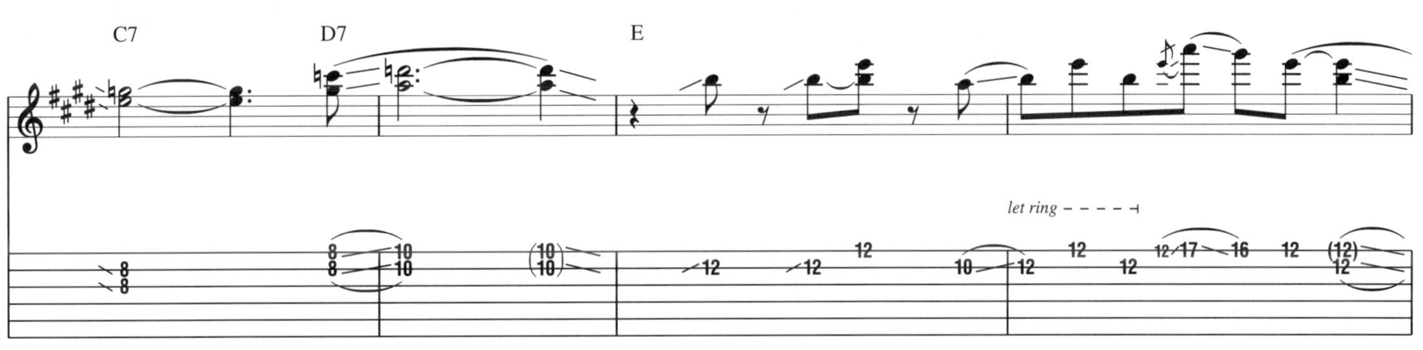
C7
D7
E
let ring

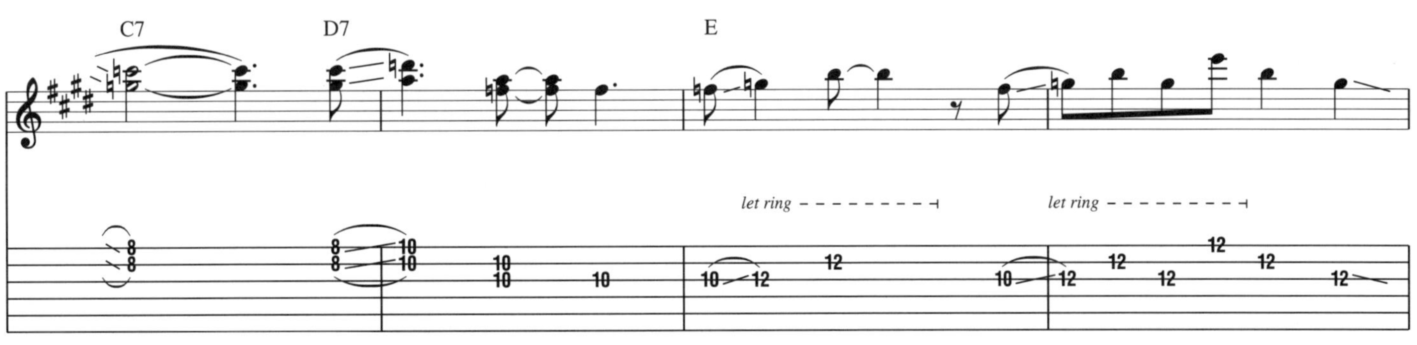
C7
D7
E
let ring
let ring

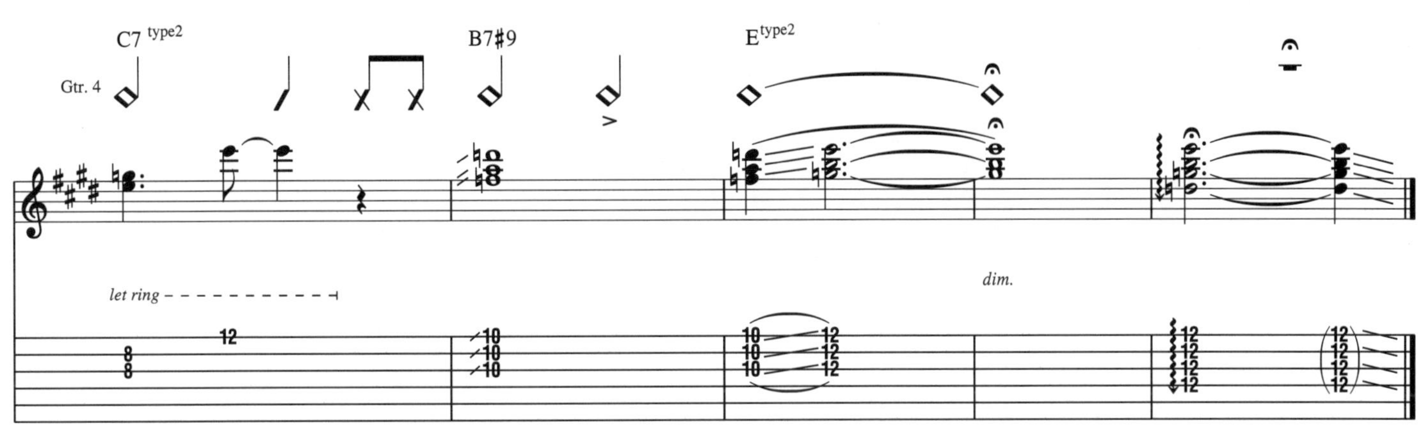
C7 type2
B7#9
E type2
Gtr. 4
let ring
dim.

Barely Breathing

Words and Music by Duncan Sheik

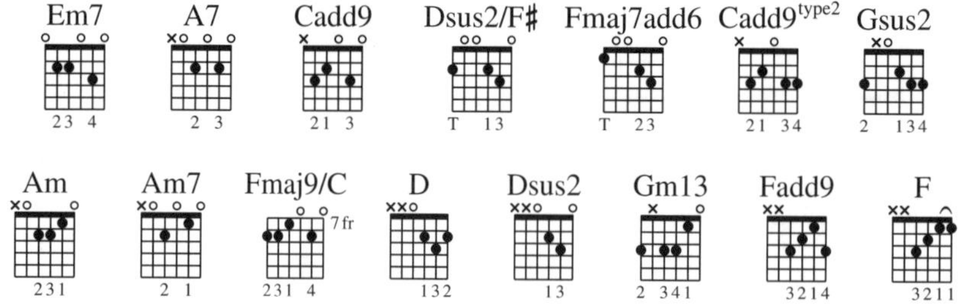

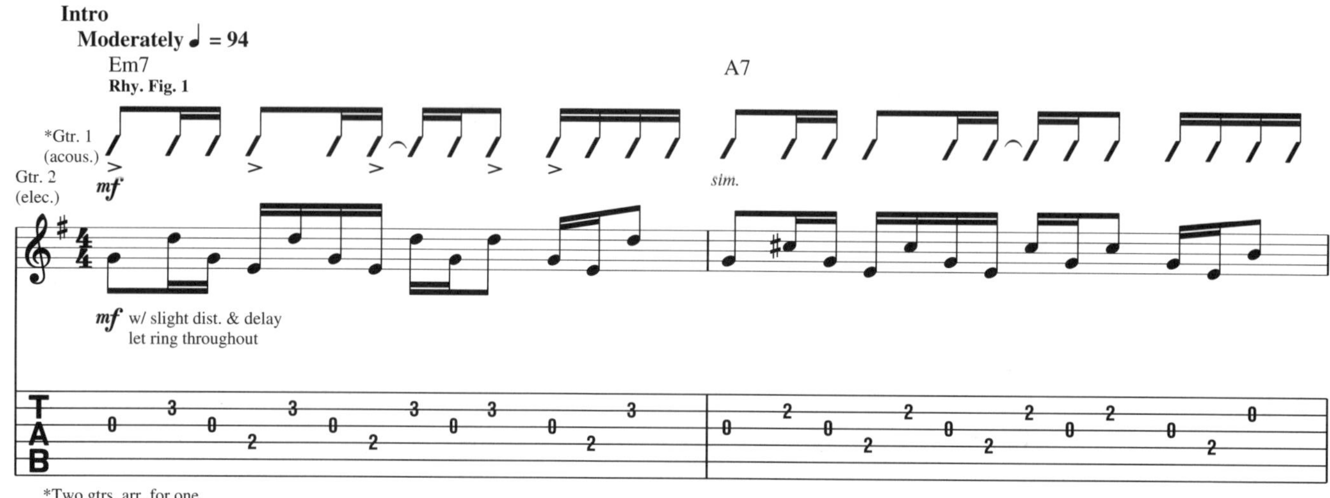

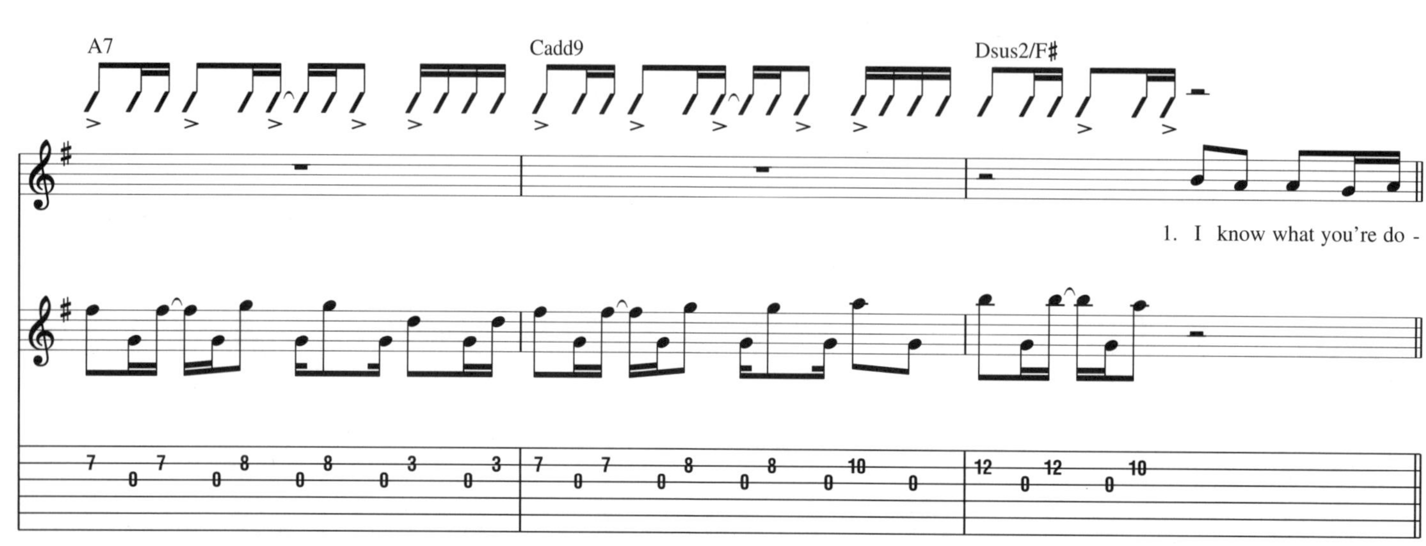

Copyright © 1996 by Careers-BMG Music Publishing, Inc., Duncan Sheik Songs and Happ-Dog Music
All Rights Administered by Careers-BMG Music Publishing, Inc.
International Copyright Secured All Rights Reserved

Verse
Gtr. 1: w/ Rhy. Fig. 1, 2 times, simile
Gtr. 2 tacet
Em7
A7
Cadd9
ing, I see it all too clear. I on - ly taste the sa - line when I kiss a - way your tears.
Dsus2/F#
Em7
A7
You real - ly had me go - ing, wish-ing on a star. But the black holes that sur - round
Cadd9
Dsus2/F#
you are heav - i - er by far. I be - lieved in your con - fu -
Gtr. 1: w/ Rhy. Fig. 1, 2 times, simile
Em7
A7
1. - sion, you were so com - plete - ly torn. (Well) it must have been that yes -
2. - ing, "What's it all a - bout?" I used to be so cer -
Gtr. 2
Cadd9
Dsus2/F#
- ter - day was the day that I was born. There's not much to ex - am -
- tain. Now I can't fig - ure out. What is this at - trac -
Em7
A7
- ine, (there's) noth-ing left to hide. You real - ly can't be se -
- tion? I on - ly feel the pain. And noth - ing left to rea -

Cadd9
Dsus2/F♯
- ri - ous if you have to ask me why. I say
- son, and on - ly you to blame. Will it ev - er

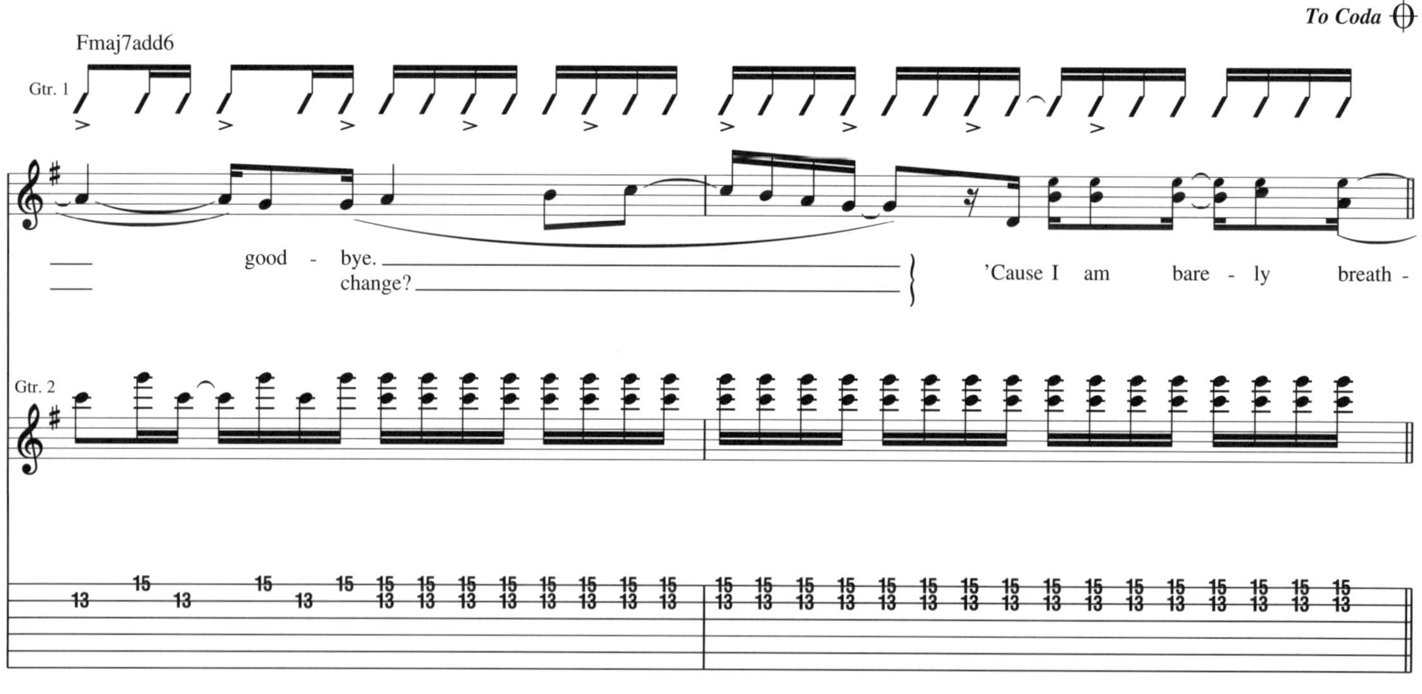
To Coda
Fmaj7add6
Gtr. 1
good - bye.
change?
'Cause I am bare - ly breath -
Gtr. 2

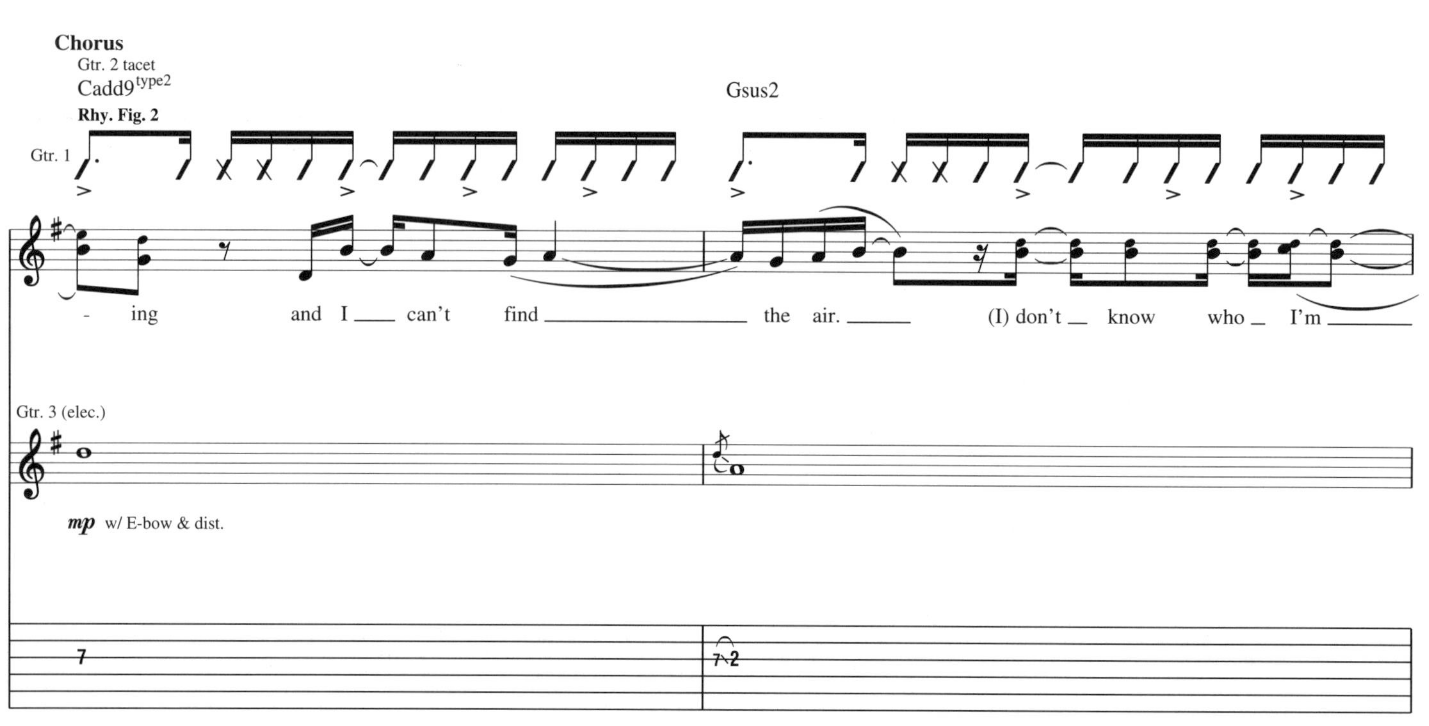
Chorus
Gtr. 2 tacet
Cadd9type2
Rhy. Fig. 2
Gsus2
Gtr. 1
- ing and I can't find the air. (I) don't know who I'm
Gtr. 3 (elec.)
mp w/ E-bow & dist.

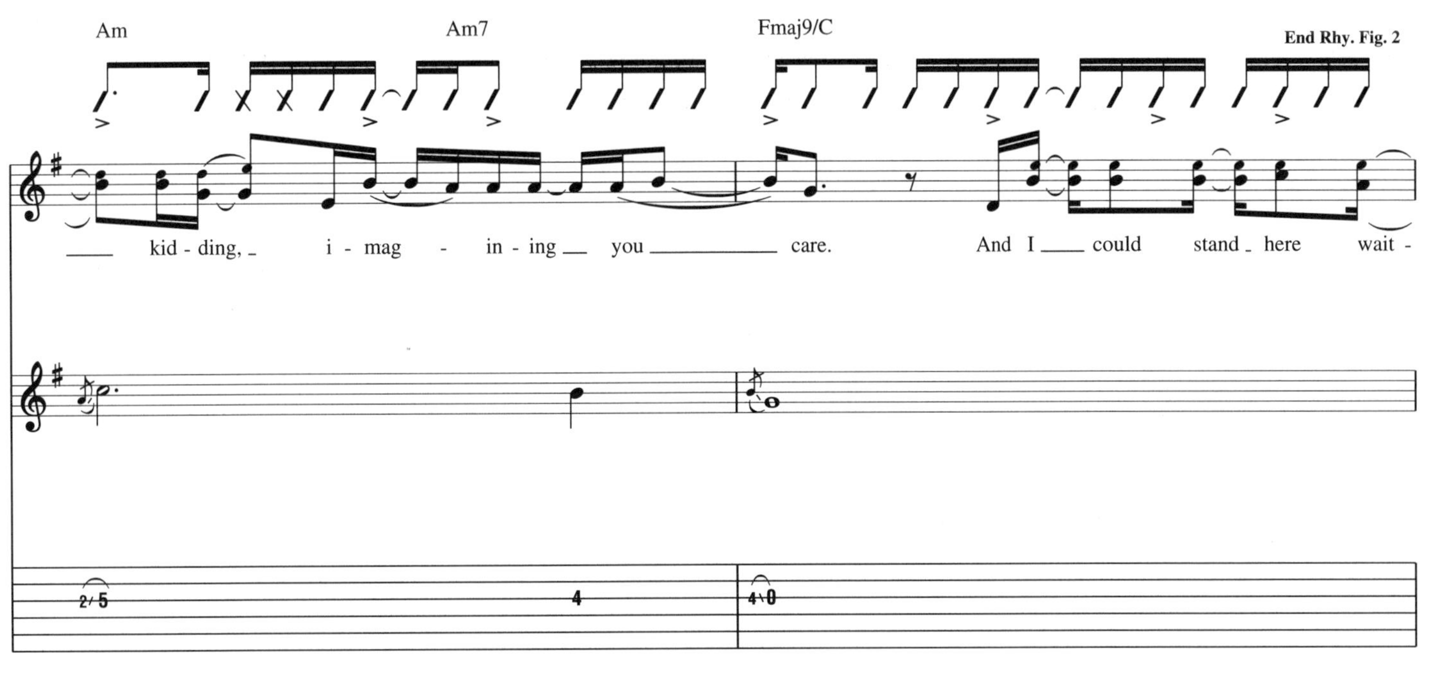

Am
Am7
Fmaj9/C
End Rhy. Fig. 2
kid - ding, i - mag - in - ing you care. And I could stand here wait -

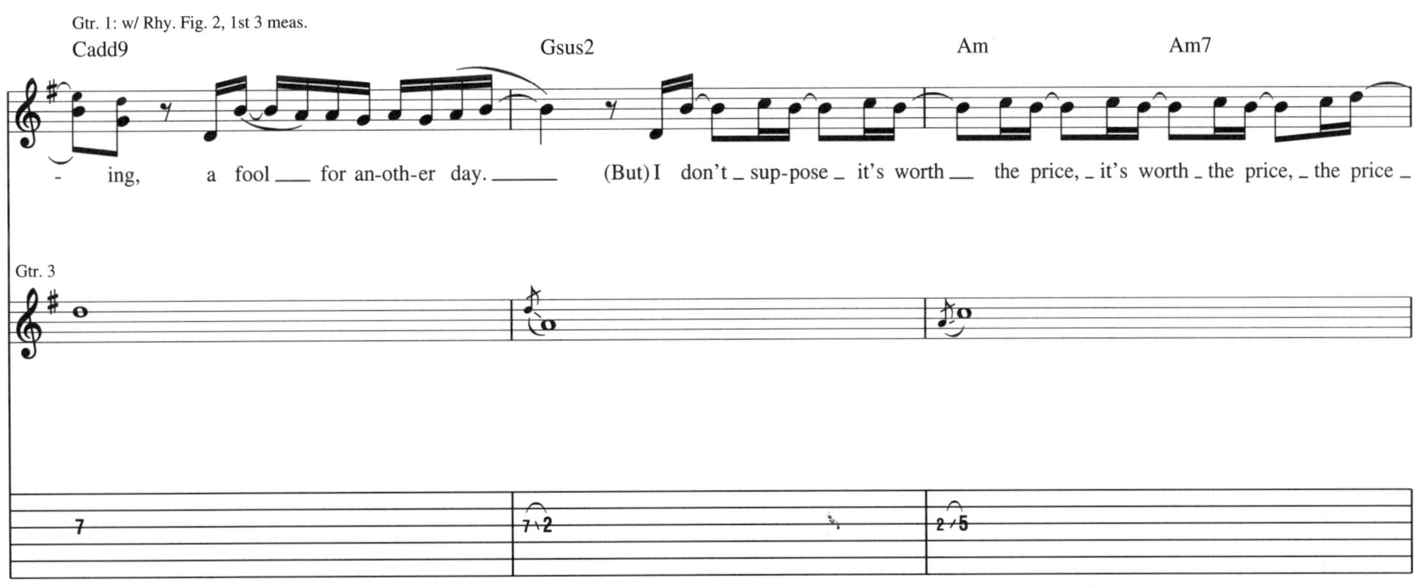

Gtr. 1: w/ Rhy. Fig. 2, 1st 3 meas.
Cadd9
Gsus2
Am
Am7
- ing, a fool for an-oth-er day. (But) I don't sup-pose it's worth the price, it's worth the price, the price
Gtr. 3

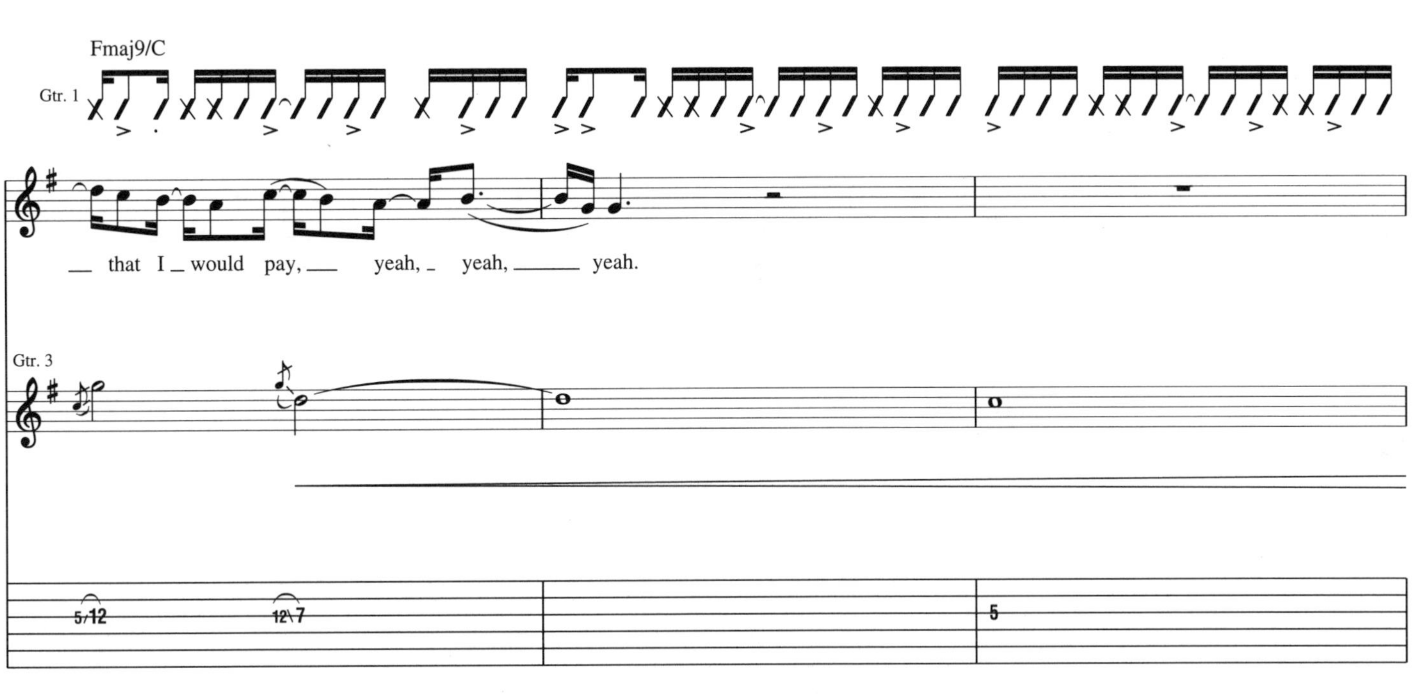

Fmaj9/C
Gtr. 1
that I would pay, yeah, yeah, yeah.
Gtr. 3

Coda

Chorus

Gtr. 1: w/ Rhy. Fig. 2, 3 3/4 times
Gtr. 2 tacet

Cadd9 Gsus2

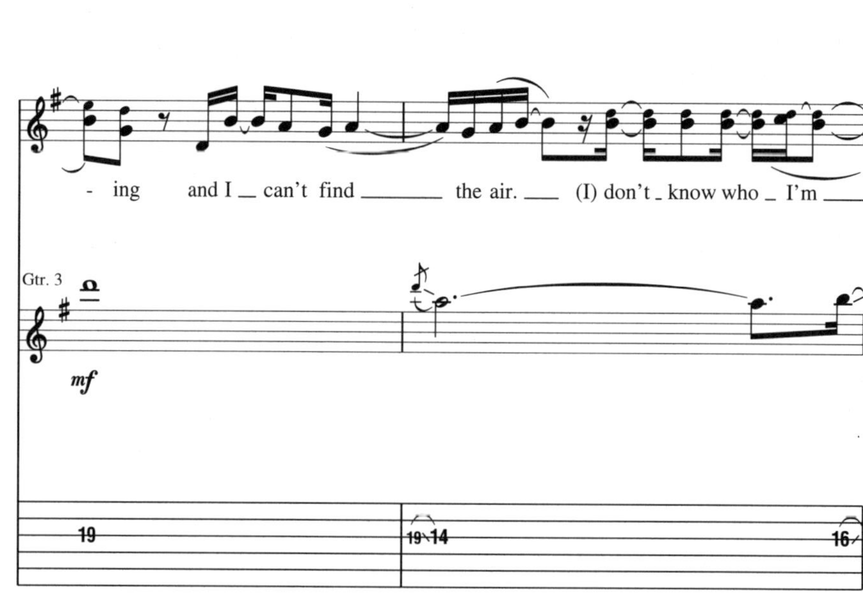

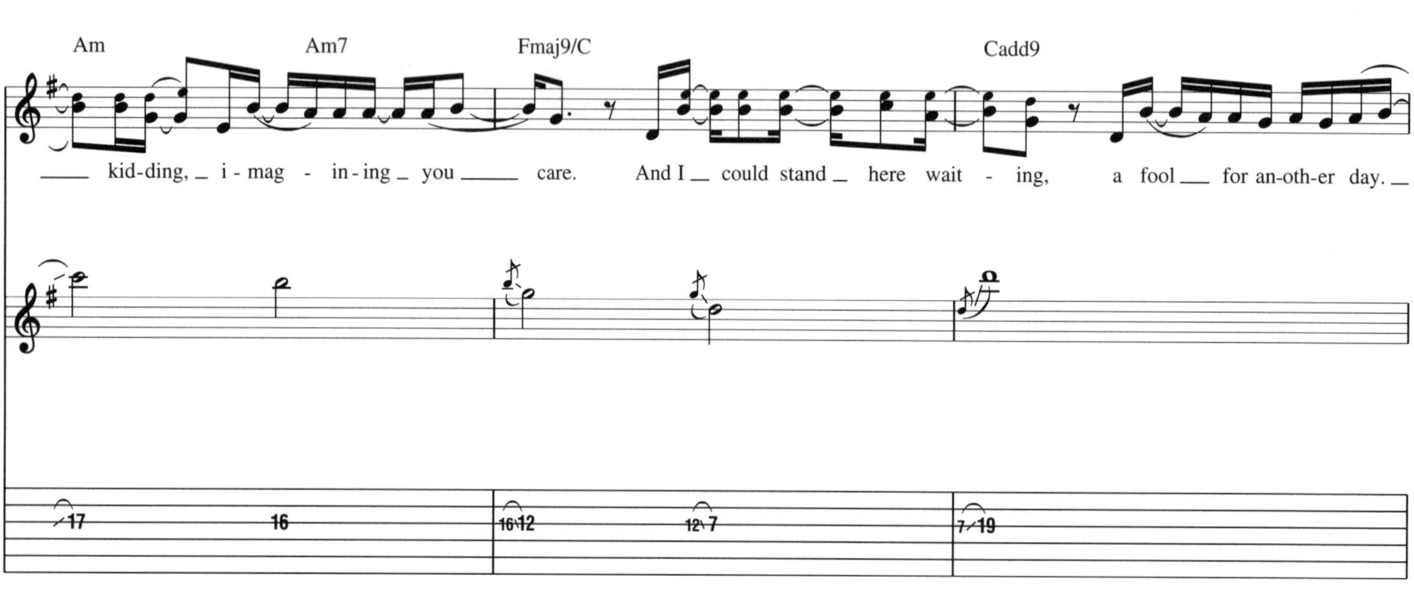

*w/E-bow & dist.

**Gtr. 4 to right of slashes.

I'm think-ing it o - ver an - y - way, yeah, yeah, yeah. Oh.

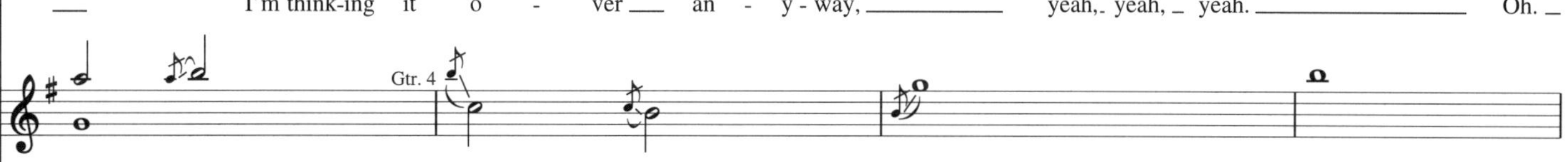

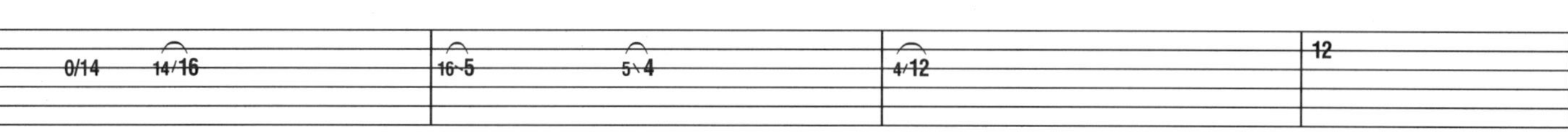

Bridge

Gtr. 2 tacet

D Dsus2 D

Gtr. 4 tacet

Am Am7 Am Am7

Gtr. 1

I've come to find ___ I may. nev-er know

Gtr. 4

Gtr. 5

mf

*Gtr. 5
divisi

Gtr. 6 (elec.)

mf w/ slide & slight dist.

*Piano arr. for gtr.

Cadd9[type2] Gm13 D

your chang-ing mind. ___ Is it friend ___ or foe? ___ I rise - a - bove ___

Am
Am7
Am
Am7
Cadd9
Gm13
or sink be - low
with ev - 'ry time
you come and go.
Fadd9
F
Please, don't
come and go.

Outro-Chorus
Gtr. 1: w/ Rhy. Fig. 2, 4 times
Gtr. 6 tacet
Gtr. 5 tacet
Cadd9
Gsus2
Gtr. 1
'Cause I am bare - ly breath - ing and I can't find the air. (I) don't know who I'm
Gtr. 3
Gtr. 6
divisi
Am
Am7
Fmaj9/C
Cadd9
kid-ding, i - mag - in - ing you care. And I could stand here wait - ing, a fool for an-oth-er day.
Gsus2
Am
Am7
Fmaj9/C
(But) I don't sup-pose it's worth the price, it's worth the price, the price that I would pay, yeah, yeah,
Cadd9
Gsus2
Am
Am7
yeah. But I'm think-ing it o - ver an - y - way.

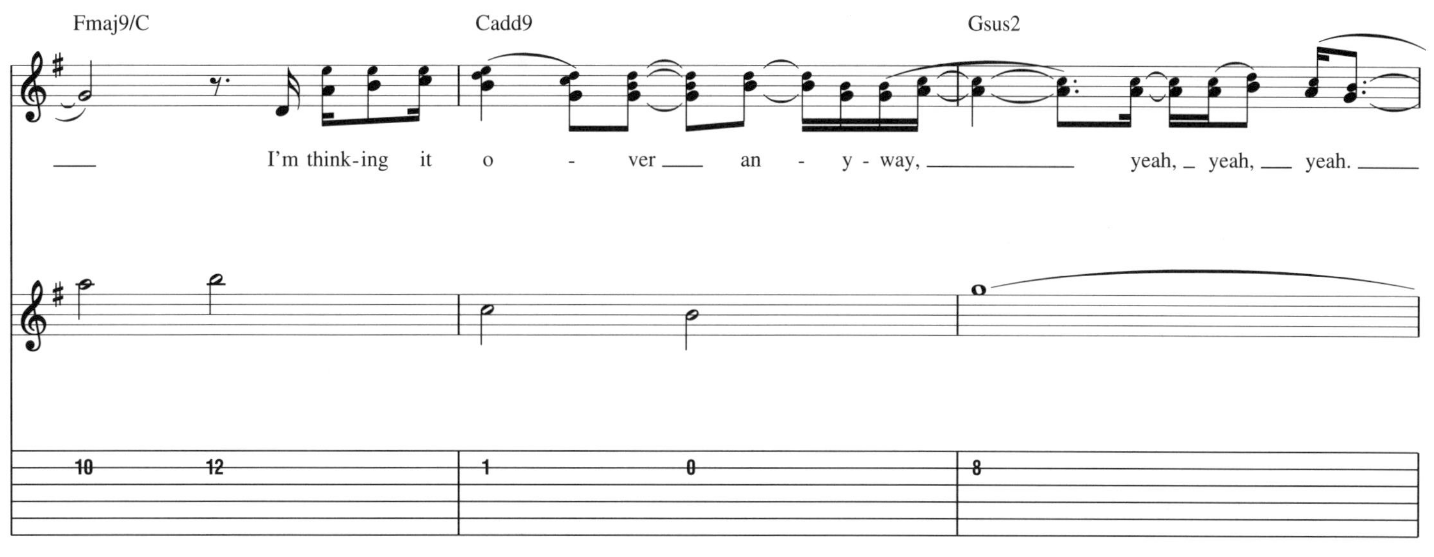
Fmaj9/C
Cadd9
Gsus2
I'm think-ing it o - ver anyway, yeah, yeah, yeah.
10 12
1 0
8

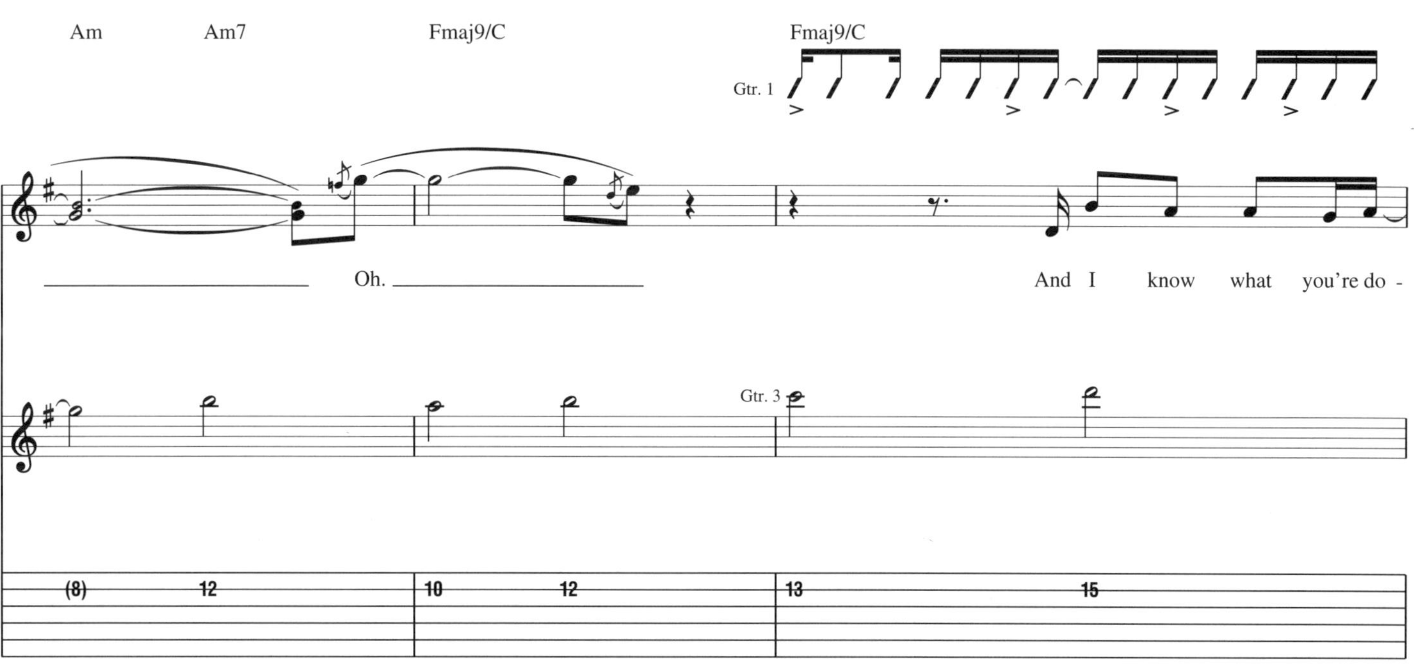
Am
Am7
Fmaj9/C
Fmaj9/C
Gtr. 1
Oh.
And I know what you're do -
Gtr. 3
(8) 12
10 12
13 15

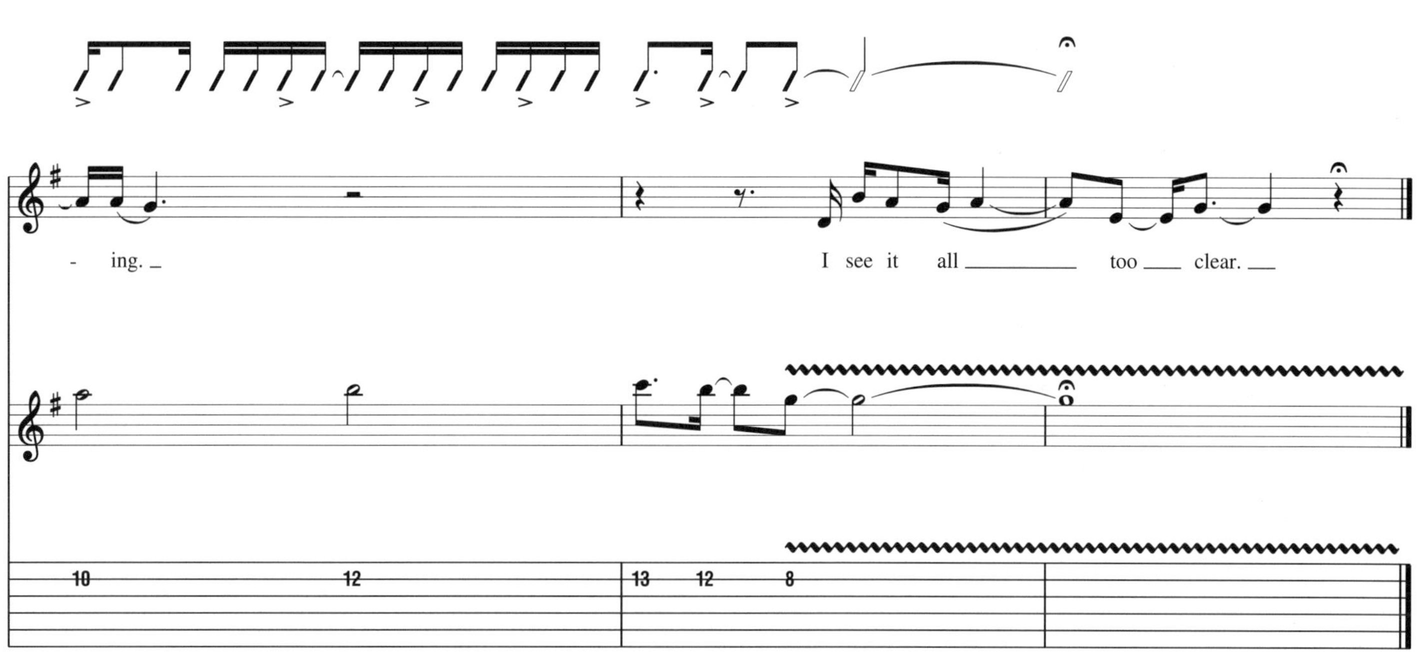
- ing.
I see it all too clear.
10 12
13 12 8

Blaze of Glory

Words and Music by Jon Bon Jovi

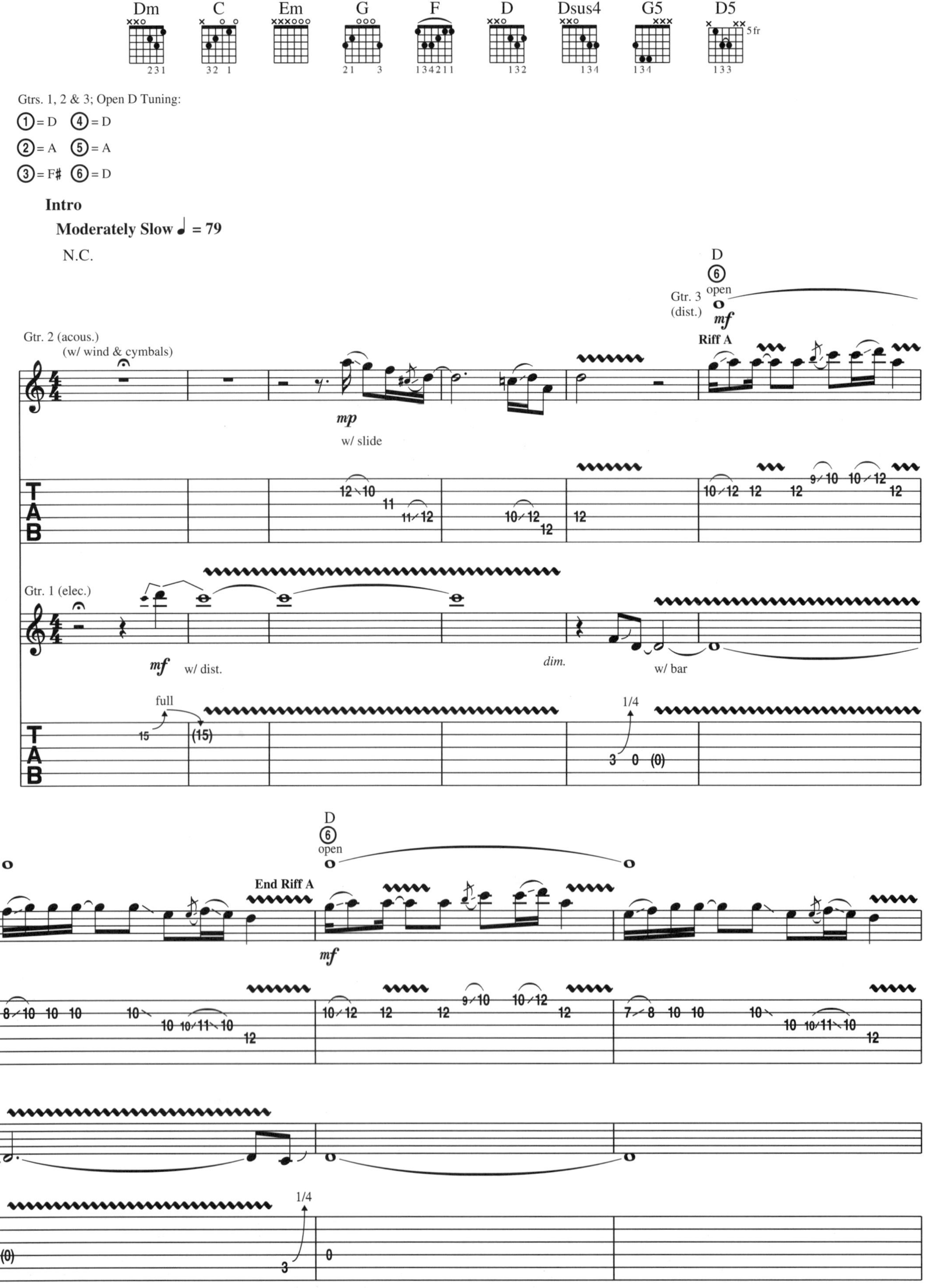

Copyright © 1990 PolyGram International Publishing, Inc. and Bon Jovi Publishing
International Copyright Secured All Rights Reserverd

D
6
open
full
Verse
Gtrs. 1 & 3 tacet
*Dm
C
G
1. Wake up in the morn - ing and I raise my wea-ry head. I've got an old coat for a pil-low, and the
Gtr. 2
pp w/ o slide
Dm
F
C
earth was last night's bed. I don't know where I'm go-ing. On-ly God knows where I've been. I'm a
let ring
let ring
Gtr. 2: w/ Riff A, 2 times
A C D F
5 5 4 4
open 3fr open 3fr
D
4
open
G
Gtr. 1
dev-il on the run, a six-gun lov-er, a can-dle in the wind. Yeah!
let ring
let ring

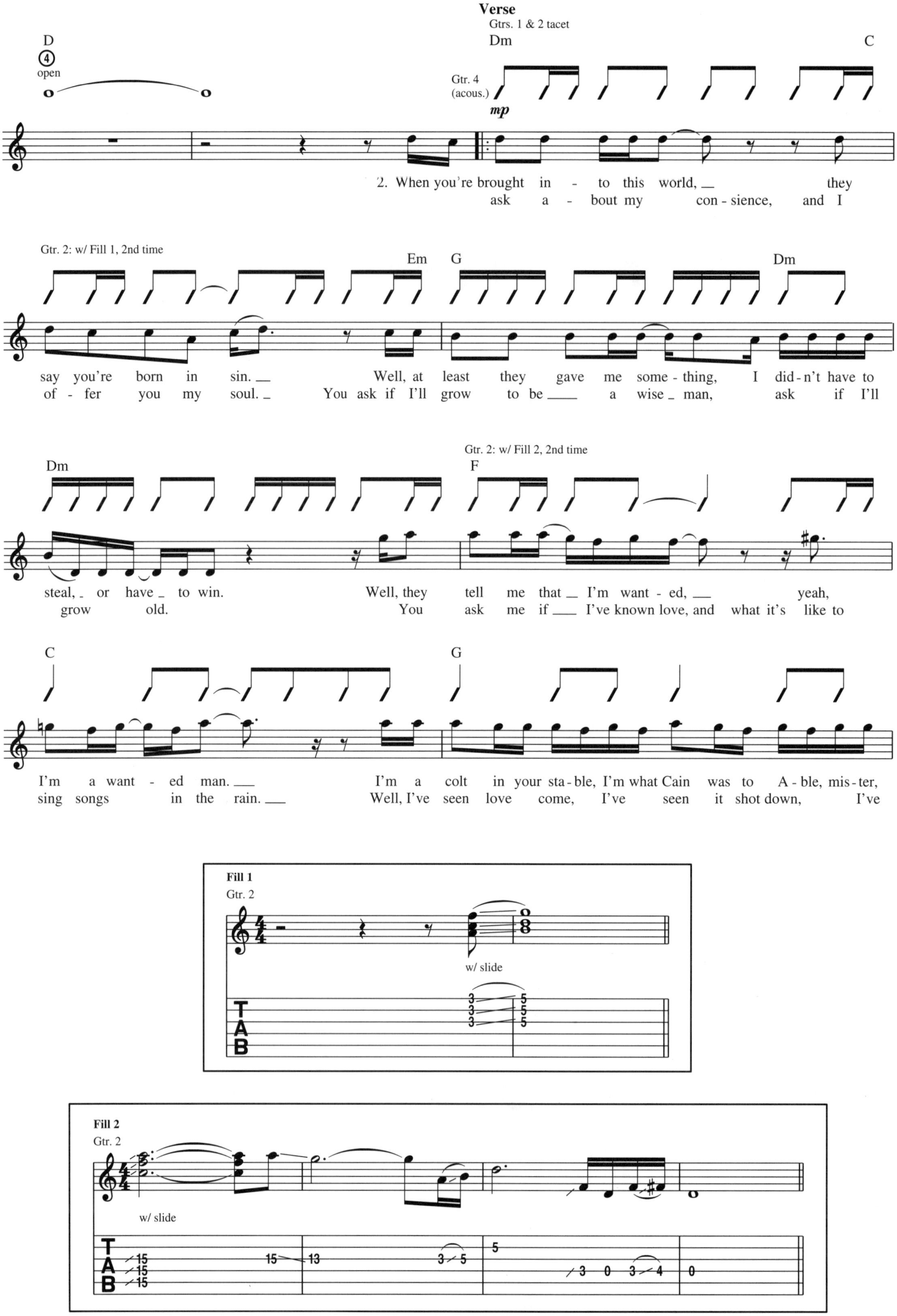

D
④ open

Verse
Gtrs. 1 & 2 tacet

Dm C

Gtr. 4 (acous.)
mp

2. When you're brought in - to this world, __ they
ask a - bout my con - sience, and I

Gtr. 2: w/ Fill 1, 2nd time

Em G Dm

say you're born in sin. __ Well, at least they gave me some - thing, I did - n't have to
of - fer you my soul. _ You ask if I'll grow to be ___ a wise _ man, ask if I'll

Dm

Gtr. 2: w/ Fill 2, 2nd time
F

steal, _ or have _ to win. Well, they tell me that __ I'm want - ed, __ yeah,
grow old. You ask me if ___ I've known love, and what it's like to

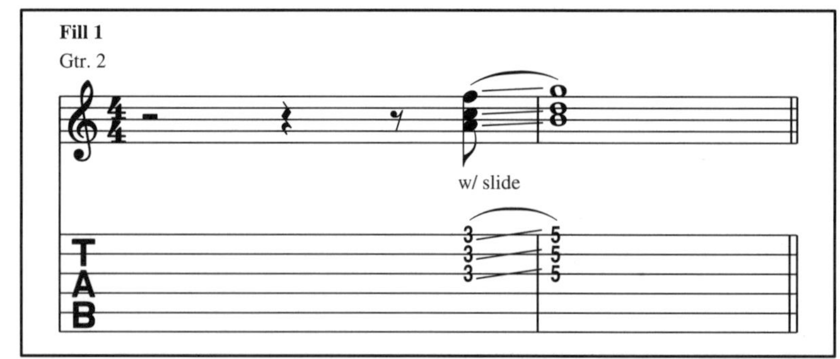

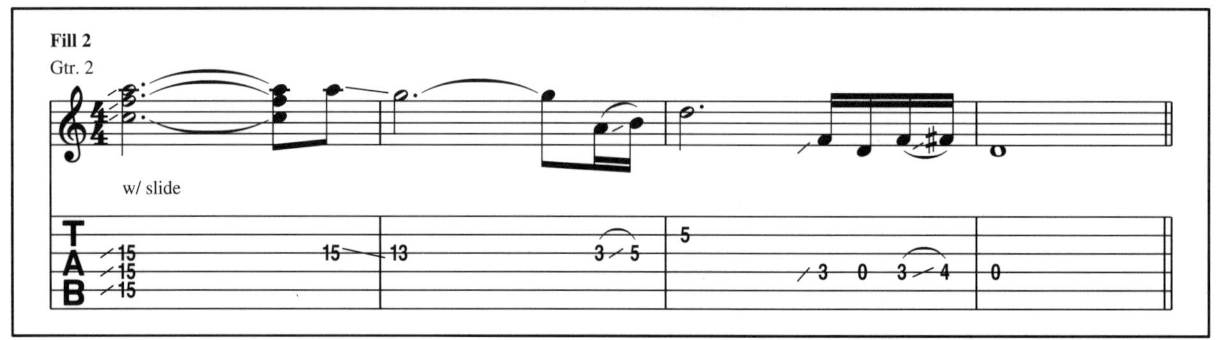

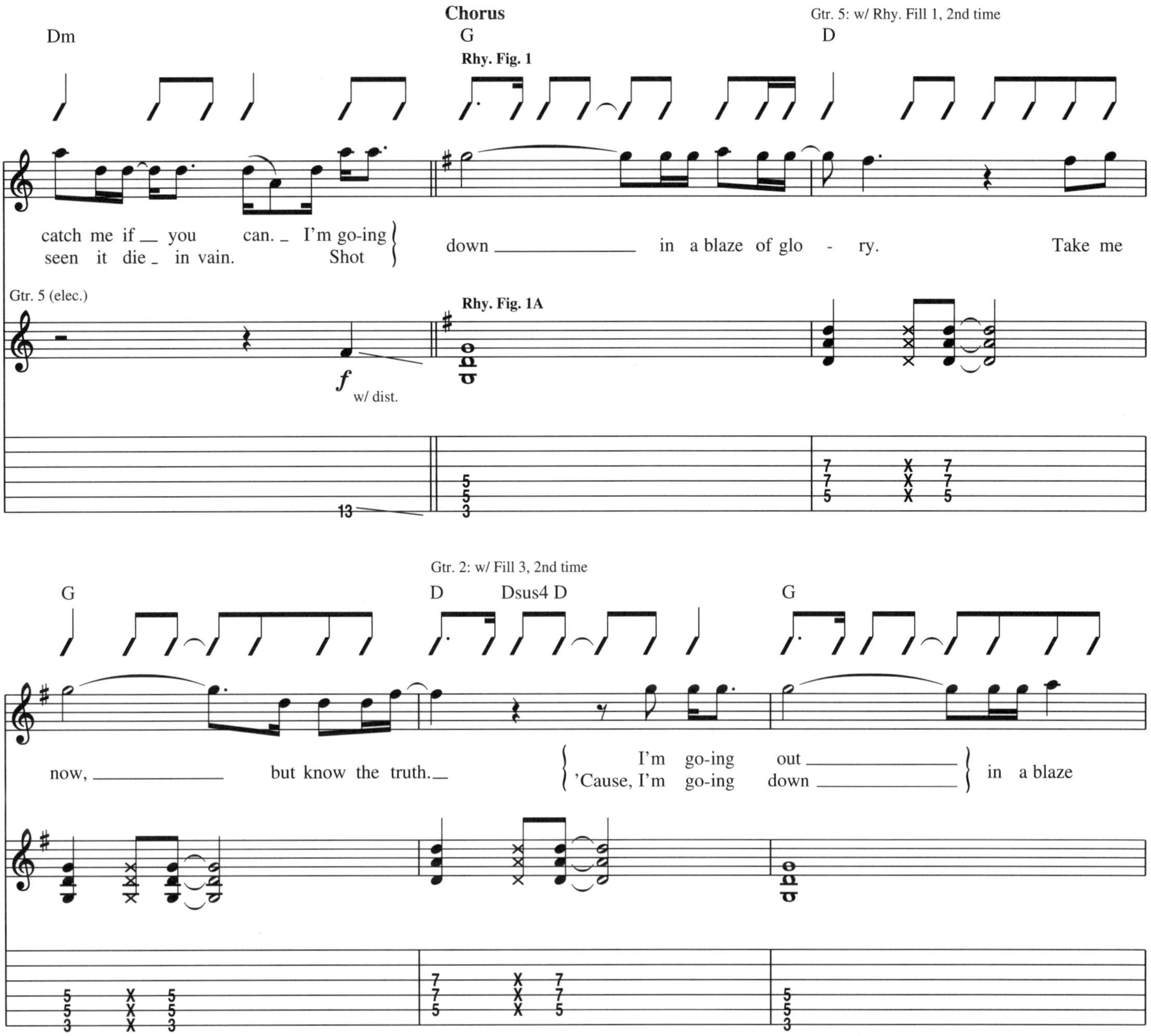

Chorus
Gtr. 5: w/ Rhy. Fill 1, 2nd time
Dm
G
D
Rhy. Fig. 1
catch me if _ you can. _ I'm go-ing
seen it die _ in vain. Shot
down ______ in a blaze of glo - ry. Take me
Gtr. 5 (elec.)
Rhy. Fig. 1A
f
w/ dist.
Gtr. 2: w/ Fill 3, 2nd time
G
D
Dsus4 D
G
now, ______ but know the truth. _
I'm go-ing out ______
'Cause, I'm go-ing down ______
in a blaze

Rhy. Fill 1
Gtr. 5
TAB

Fill 3
Gtr. 2
w/ slide
TAB

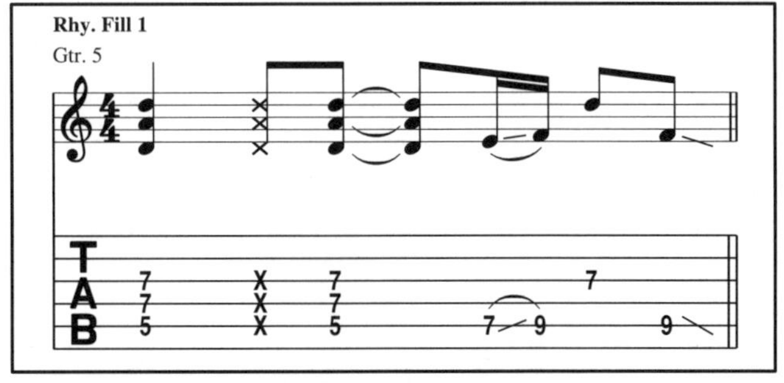

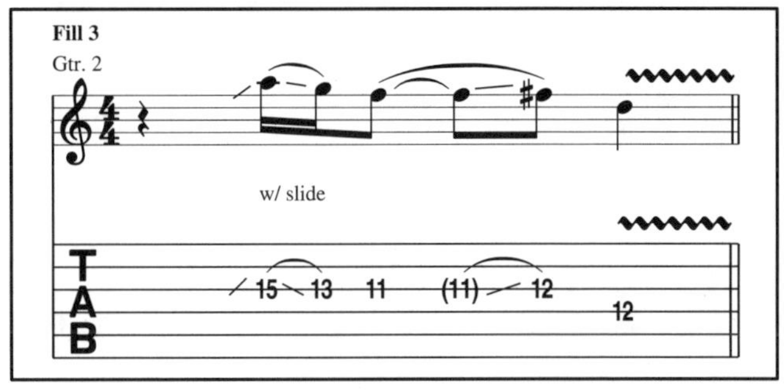

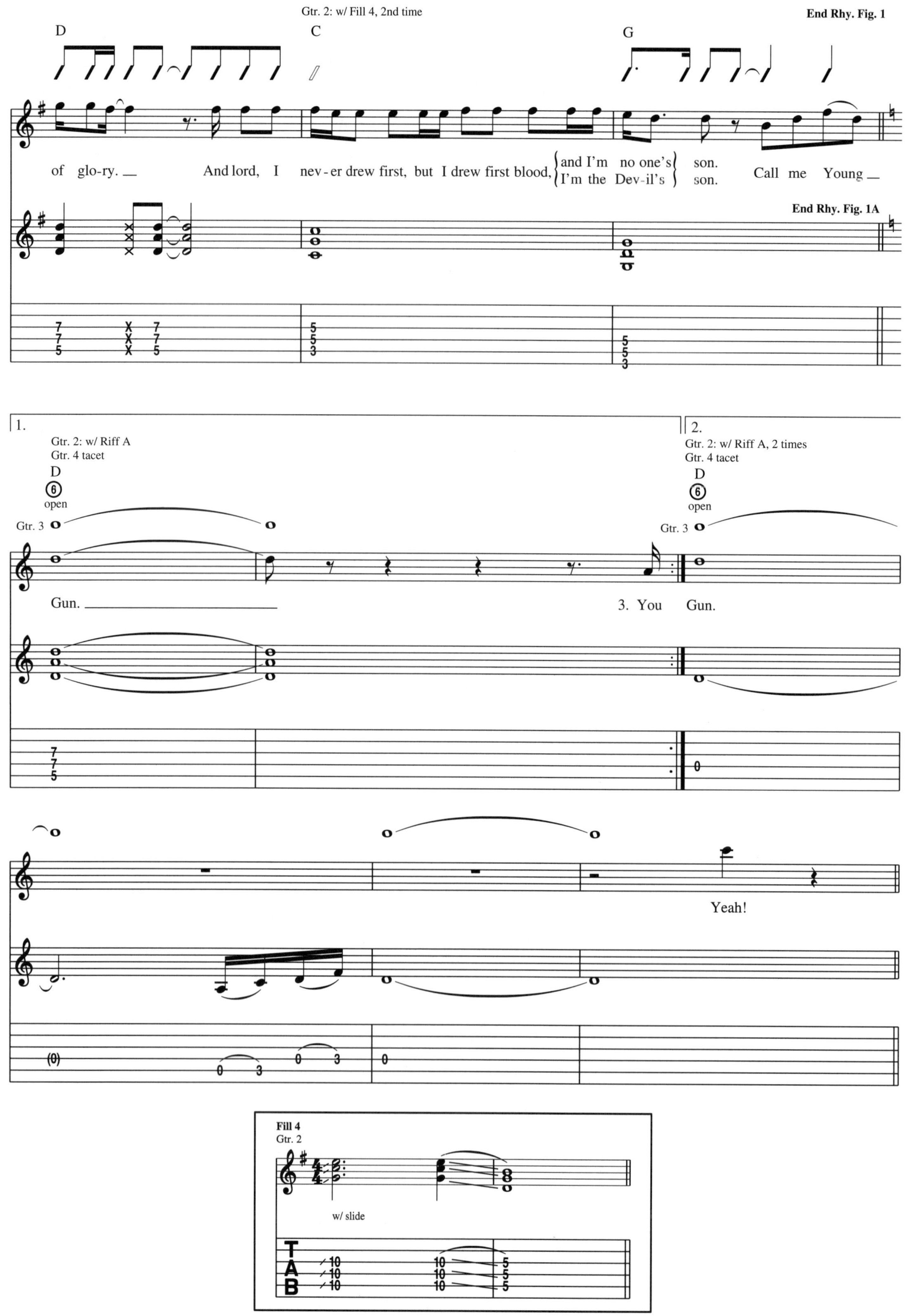
Gtr. 2: w/ Fill 4, 2nd time
End Rhy. Fig. 1
D
C
G
of glo-ry. And lord, I nev-er drew first, but I drew first blood, and I'm no one's son.
I'm the Dev-il's son.
Call me Young
End Rhy. Fig. 1A
1.
Gtr. 2: w/ Riff A
Gtr. 4 tacet
D
6 open
Gtr. 3
Gun.
3. You
2.
Gtr. 2: w/ Riff A, 2 times
Gtr. 4 tacet
D
6 open
Gtr. 3
Gun.
Yeah!
Fill 4
Gtr. 2
w/ slide
TAB

Guitar Solo

Gtr. 5: w/ Rhy. Fig. 2, 3 times
Gtrs. 2 & 3 tacet
G
D
G
Gtr. 4
cont. simile
*Gtr. 6
8va
loco
w/ slide
*clean elec.
D
G
full
full
full
full
full
full
D
Gtr. 5: w/ Rhy. Fig. 3
F
Gtr. 4
*bar flutter
Rhy. Fig. 2
G5
D5
Gtr. 5
Rhy. Fig. 3
Gtr. 5
F5
G5
N.C.

Gtr. 2: w/ Riff A, 2 times
Gtr. 4 tacet
Gtr. 6 tacet
G
N.C.
8va
Verse
Gtrs. 2 & 5 tacet
*Dm
C
G
4. Each night I go to bed, I pray the Lord my soul to keep. No, I ain't look-ing for for-give-ness, but be-
*Chords implied by kybd.
Dm
F
C
fore I'm six feet deep. Lord, I got to ask a fa - vor, and I hope you'll un-der-stand. 'Cause, I've
G
Dm
G
Dm
lived life to the ful-lest, let this boy die like a man. Star-ing down a bul-let, let me make my fi - nal stand.
Chorus
Gtr. 4 & 5: w/ Rhy. Figs. 1 & 1A
N.C.
G
D
G
D
Shot down in a blaze of glo - ry. Take me now, but know the truth. I'm go-ing
Gtr. 2
w/ slide
G
D
C
G
out in a blaze of glo-ry. Lord, I nev-er drew first, but I drew first blood, and I'm no one's son. Call me Young

Gtr. 2 tacet
D
C
G
D
Rhy. Fig. 4
End Rhy. Fig. 4
Gtr. 4
Gun.
I'm a young gun.
Yeah.
Young
Gtr. 6
w/ slide
Rhy. Fig. 4A
End Rhy. Fig. 4A
Gtr. 5
Outro
Gtrs. 4 & 5: w/ Rhy. Figs. 4 & 4A
Gtrs. 4, 5 & 6 tacet
open
Gtr. 3
gun.
Yeah, yeah, yeah. Young
Gun.
Ah.
Gtr. 2
Free Time
dim.
rit.
let ring

Blue on Black

Words and Music by Tia Sillers, Mark Selby and Kenny Wayne Shepherd

Gtrs. 3 & 4; Drop D Tuning:
(low to high) D-A-D-G-B-E

Intro

Moderately Slow ♩ = 78

D5 Csus2 D5 Csus2 D5 N.C. Cadd9 G/B G

Gtr. 1 (acous.) Rhy. Fig. 1 *mf* End Rhy. Fig. 1

Gtr. 2 (elec.) Riff A *mp* w/ clean tone End Riff A

* Key signature denotes G Mixolydian.

Verse

Gtr. 1: w/ Rhy. Fig.1, 8 times
Gtr. 2: w/ Riff A, 8 times

1. Night falls and I'm a - lone.
Skin, yeah, chilled to their bone.
You turned and you ran, oh, yeah, oh,
slipped right from my hand.
Hey,

Copyright © 1997 by I Know Jack Music, Ensign Music Corporation, Bro 'N Sis Music Inc.,
Estes Park Music, A Division of Moraine Music Group, Songs Of Universal, Inc. and Only Hit Music
All Rights for Estes Park Music, A Division of Moraine Music Group Administered by Bro 'N Sis Music Inc.
All Rights for Only Hit Music Controlled and Administered by Songs Of Universal, Inc.
All Rights Reserved International Copyright Secured Used by Permission

Chorus
Gtr. 1: w/ Rhy. Fig. 1, 2 times
Gtr. 4: w/ Fill 1, 3rd time
D5 Csus2 D5 Csus2 D5 N.C. Cadd9 G/B G
blue on black, tears on a riv - er, push on a shove, it don't mean much.
* Gtr. 3 (elec.)
Riff A1
End Riff A1
mf
w/ dist. & tremolo effect
P.M.
let ring
1/4
* Two gtrs. arr. for one.

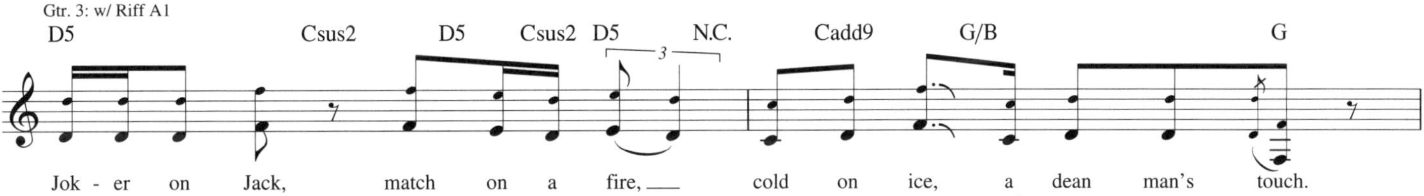
Gtr. 3: w/ Riff A1
D5 Csus2 D5 Csus2 D5 N.C. Cadd9 G/B G
Jok - er on Jack, match on a fire, cold on ice, a dean man's touch.

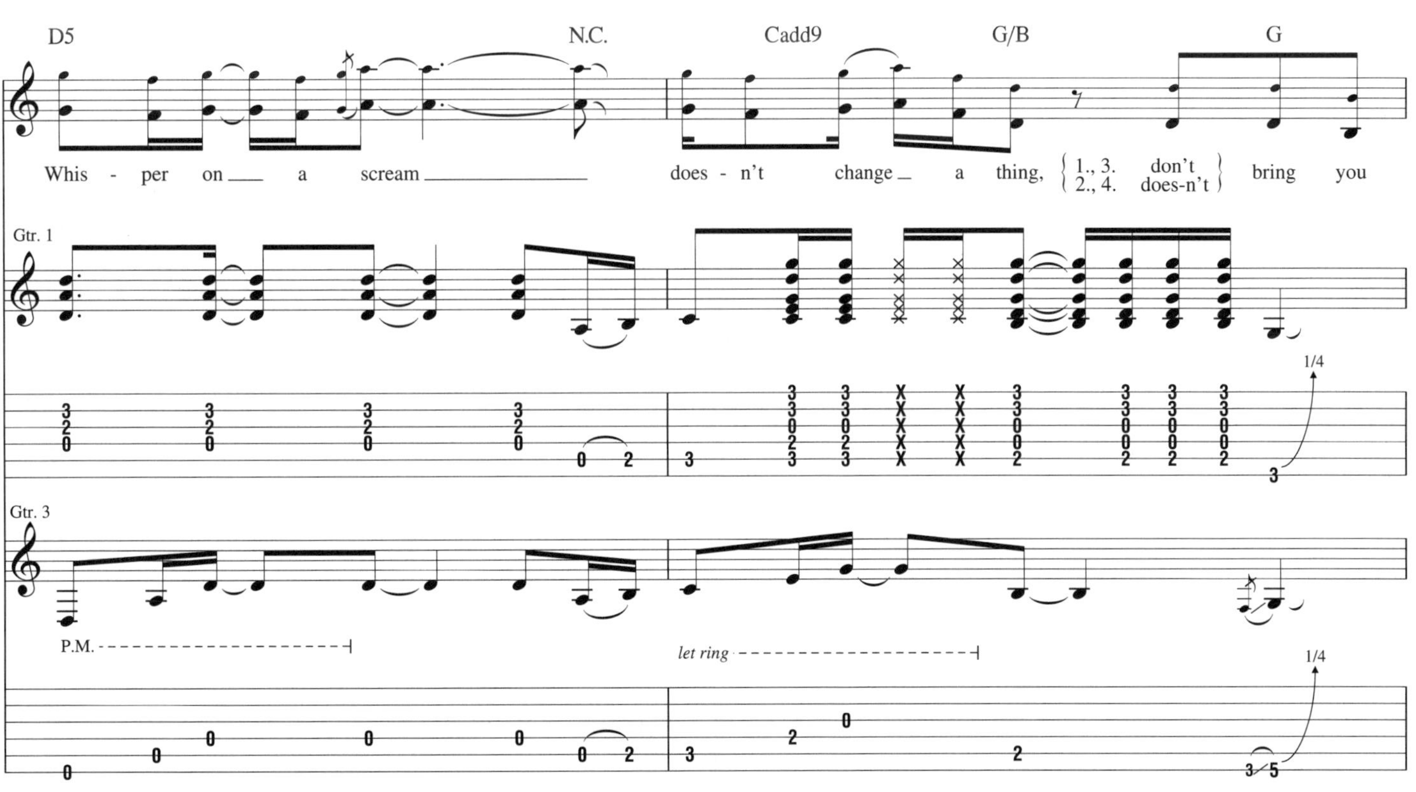
D5 N.C. Cadd9 G/B G
Whis - per on a scream does - n't change a thing, 1., 3. don't 2., 4. does-n't bring you
Gtr. 1
1/4
Gtr. 3
P.M.
let ring
1/4

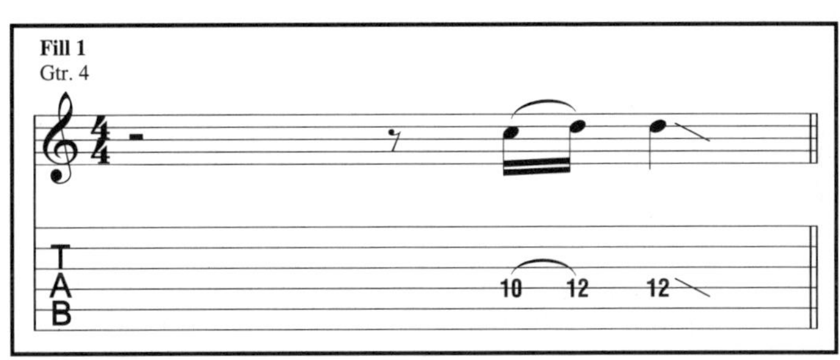
Fill 1
Gtr. 4
T
A
B

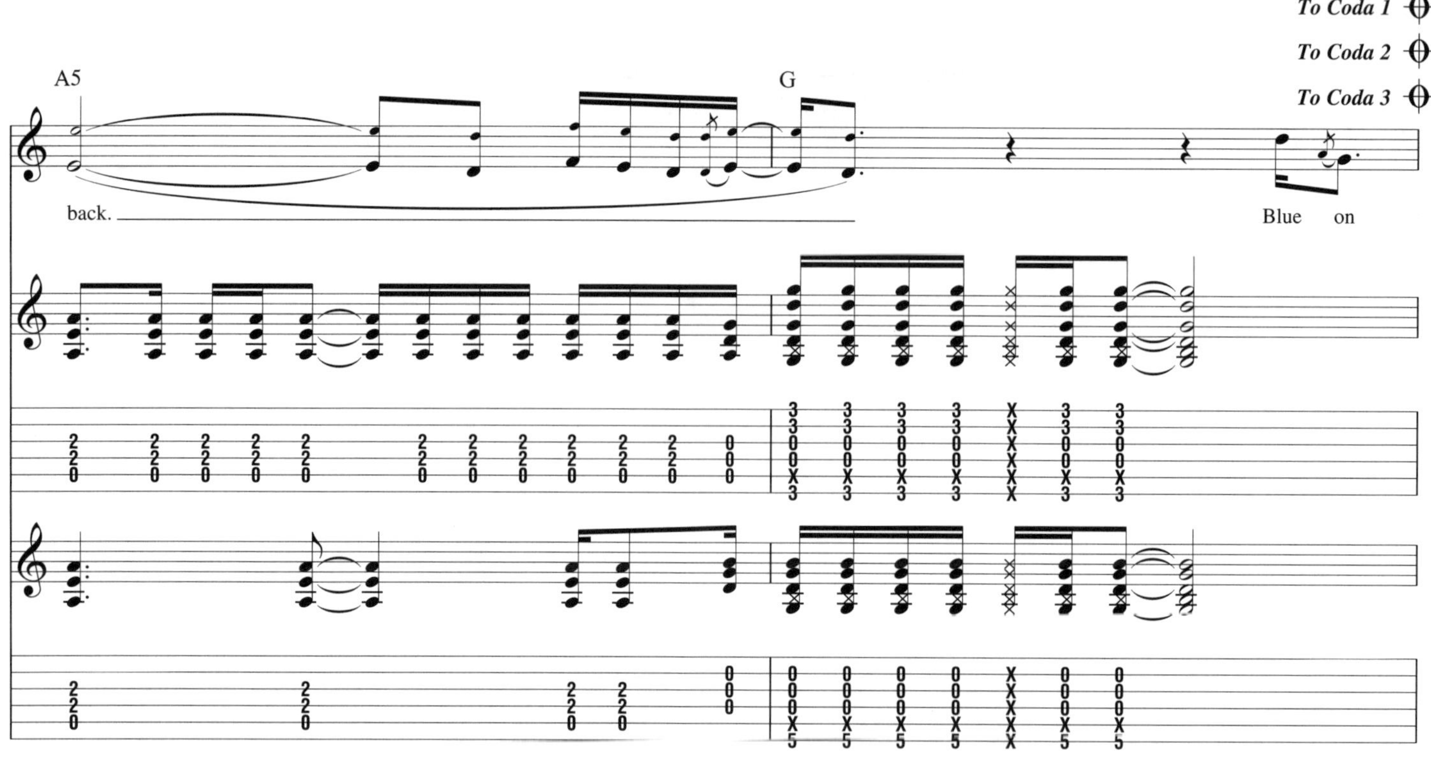

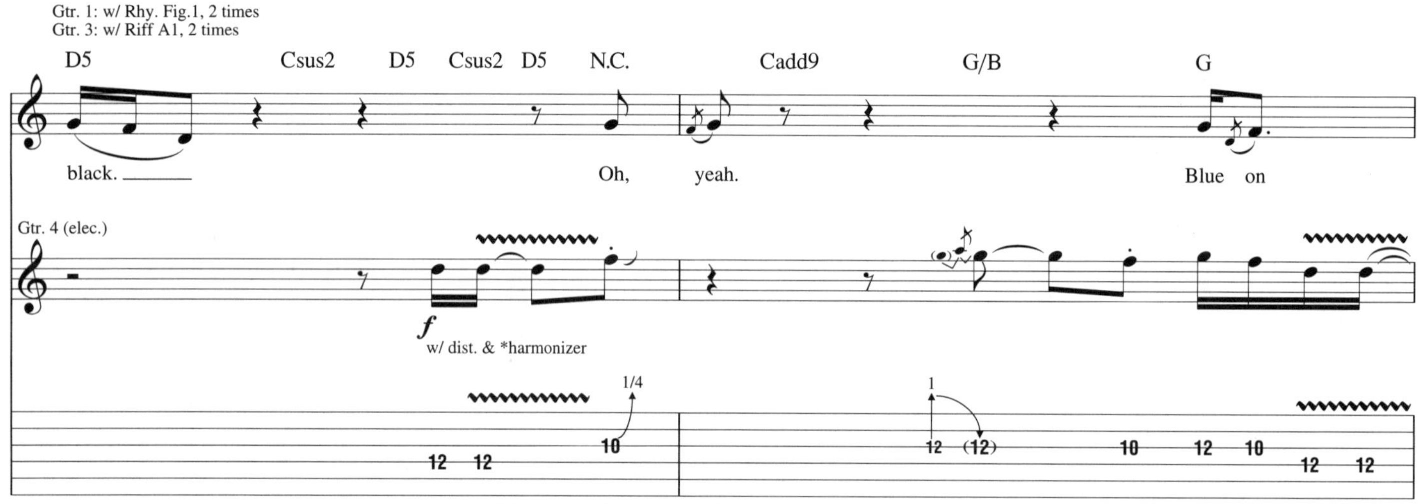

* Set to harmonize one octave above.

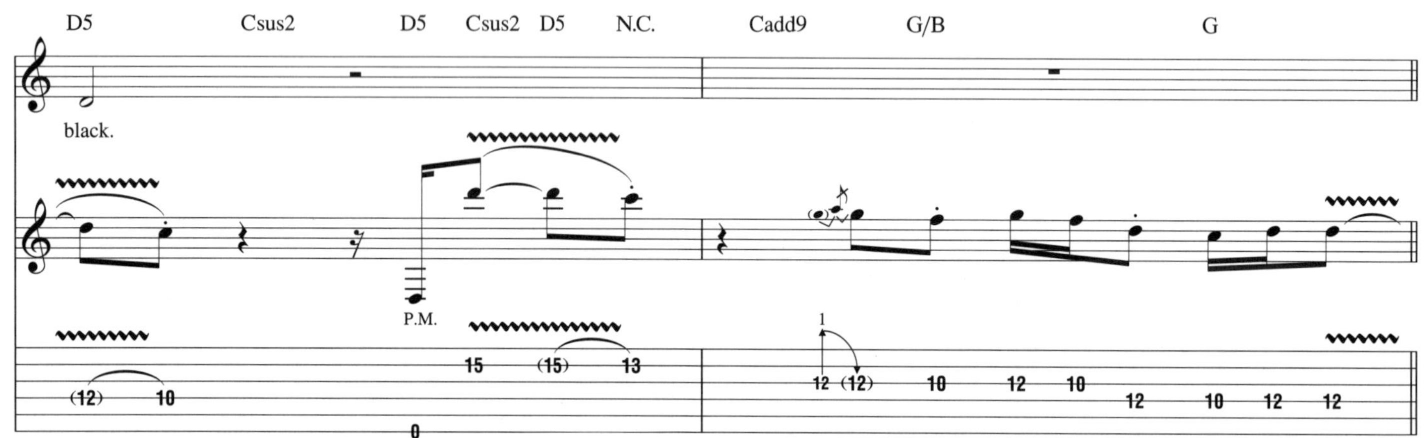

Verse

Gtr. 1: w/ Rhy. Fig. 1, 8 times
Gtr. 3: w/ Riff A1, 8 times

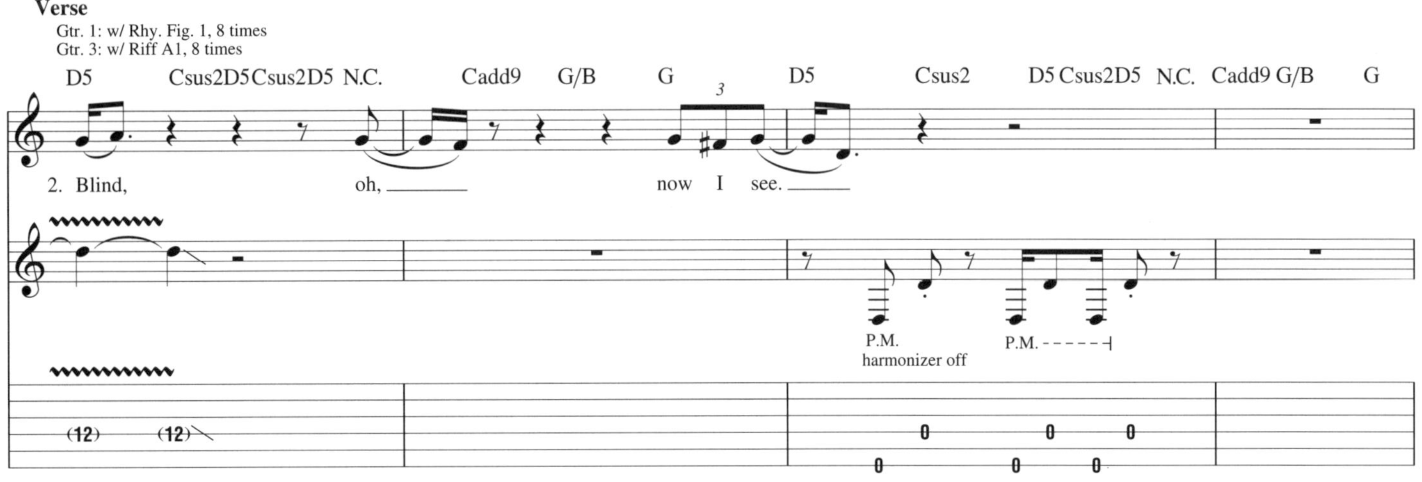

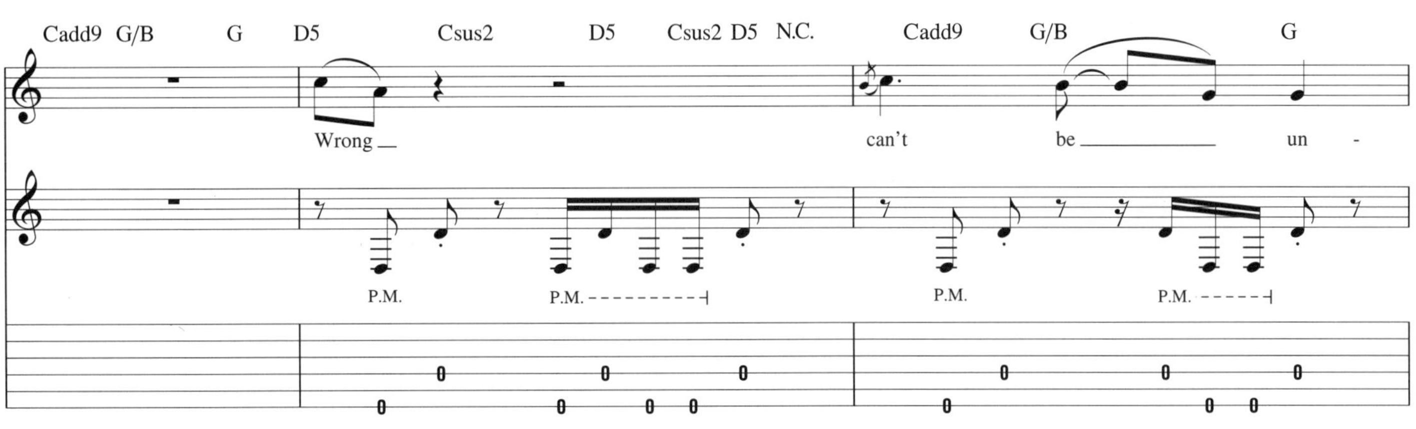

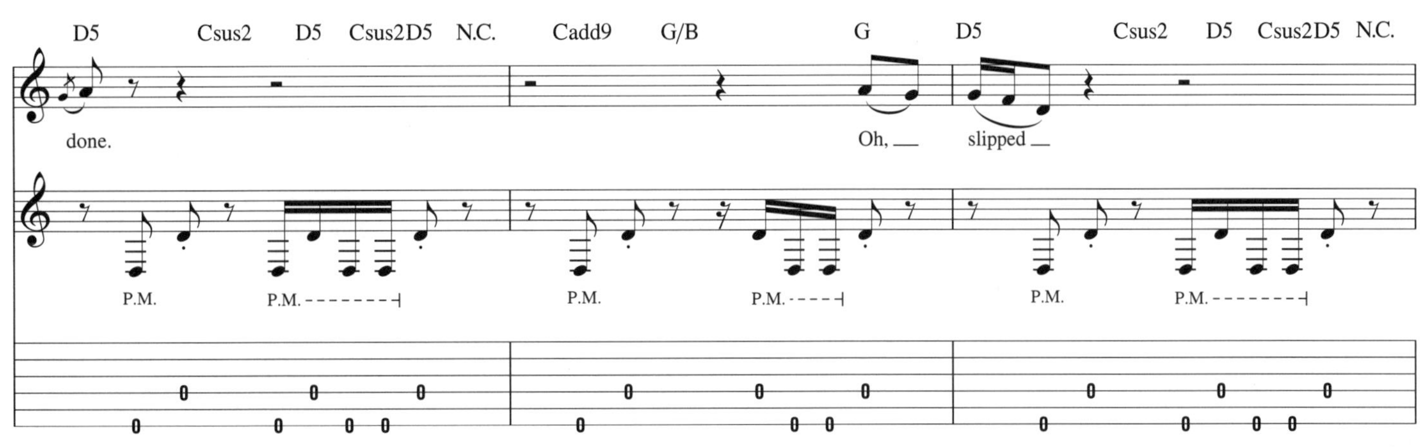

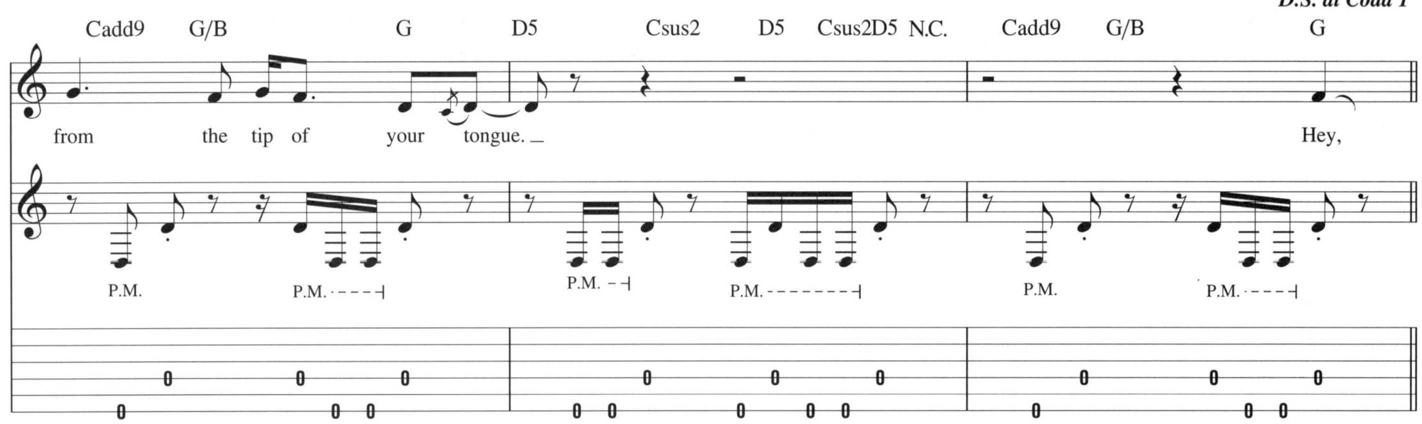
D.S. al Coda 1
Cadd9 G/B G D5 Csus2 D5 Csus2D5 N.C. Cadd9 G/B G
from the tip of your tongue. Hey,
P.M. P.M. P.M. P.M. P.M. P.M.

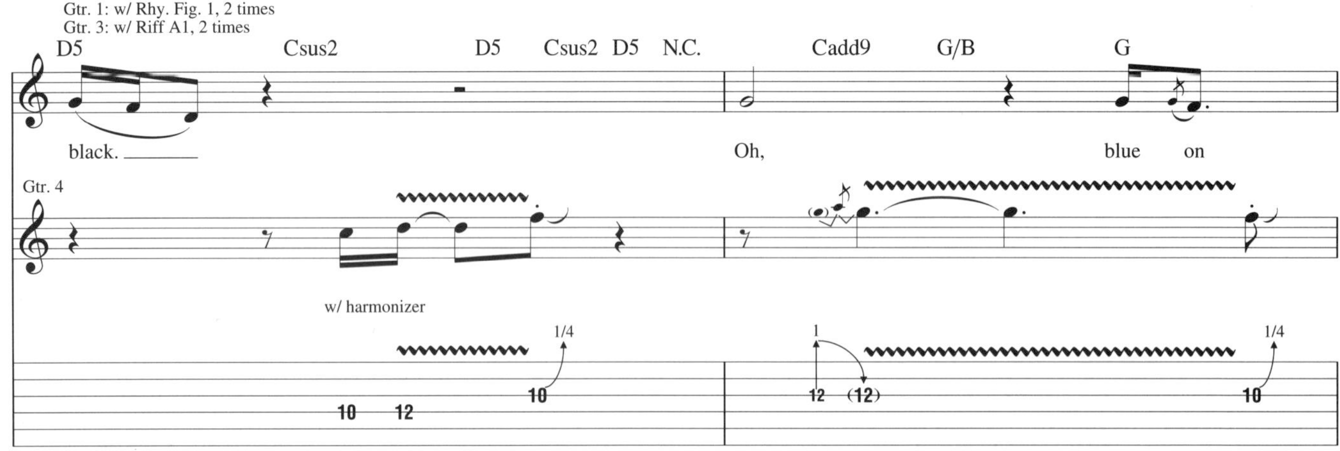
Coda 1
Gtr. 1: w/ Rhy. Fig. 1, 2 times
Gtr. 3: w/ Riff A1, 2 times
D5 Csus2 D5 Csus2 D5 N.C. Cadd9 G/B G
black. Oh, blue on
Gtr. 4
w/ harmonizer

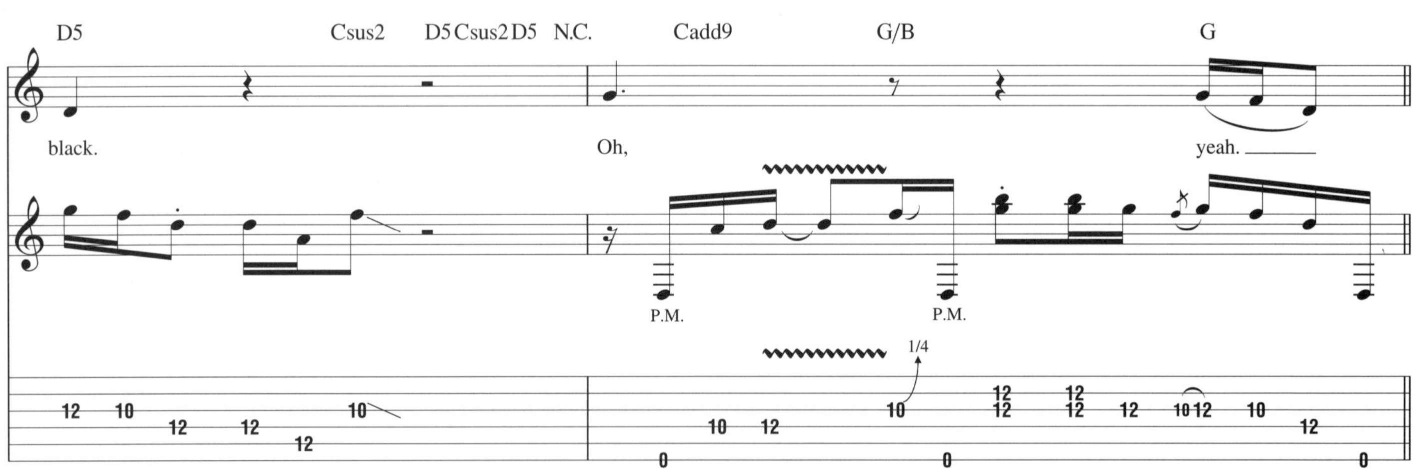
D5 Csus2 D5 Csus2 D5 N.C. Cadd9 G/B G
black. Oh, yeah.
P.M. P.M.

Guitar Solo

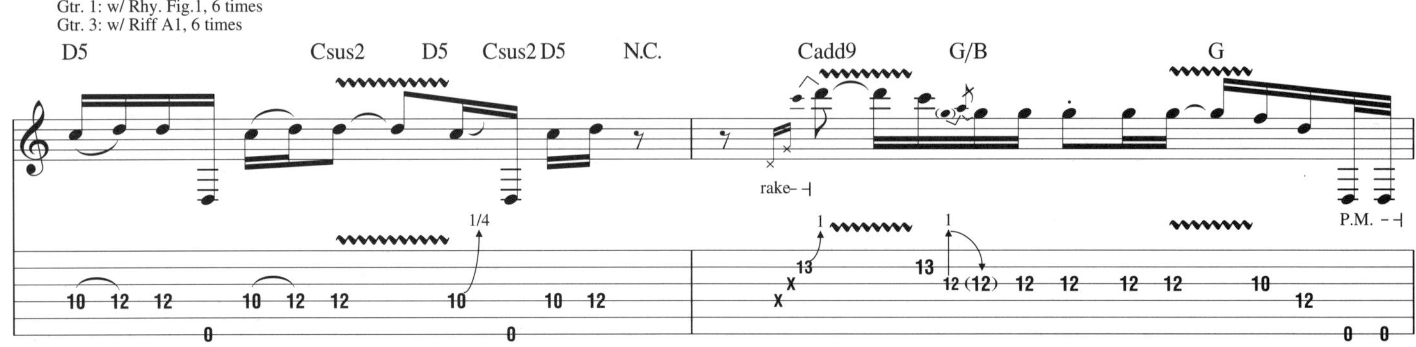
Gtr. 1: w/ Rhy. Fig.1, 6 times
Gtr. 3: w/ Riff A1, 6 times
D5 Csus2 D5 Csus2 D5 N.C. Cadd9 G/B G
rake
P.M.

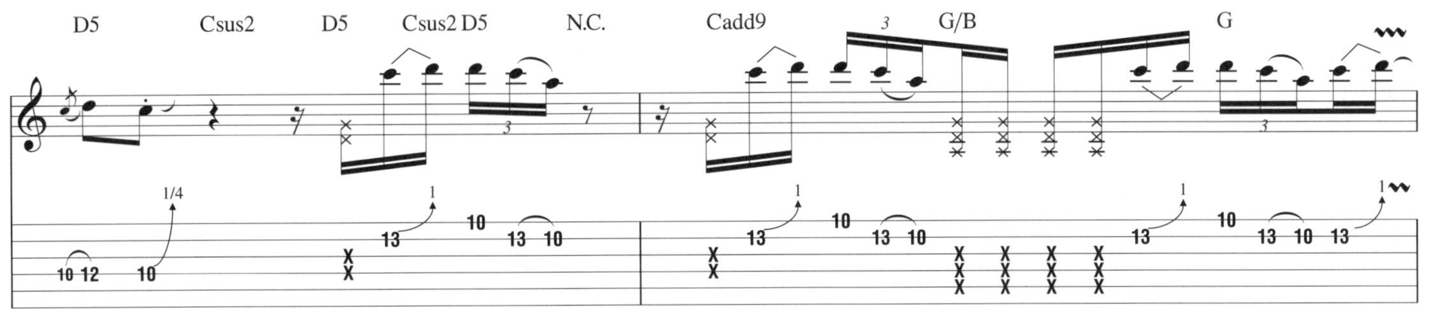
D5 Csus2 D5 Csus2 D5 N.C. Cadd9 G/B G

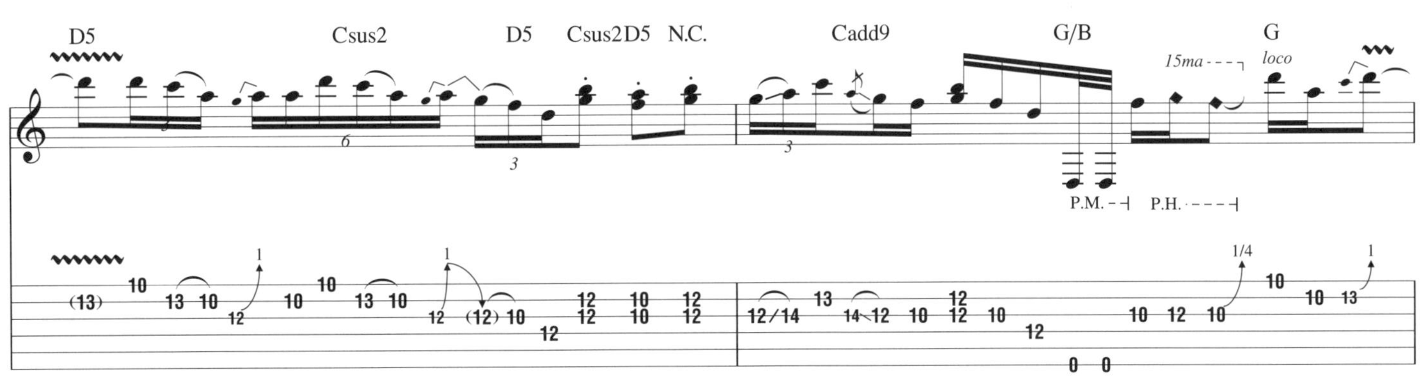
D5 Csus2 D5 Csus2 D5 N.C. Cadd9 G/B G
15ma
loco
P.M.
P.H.

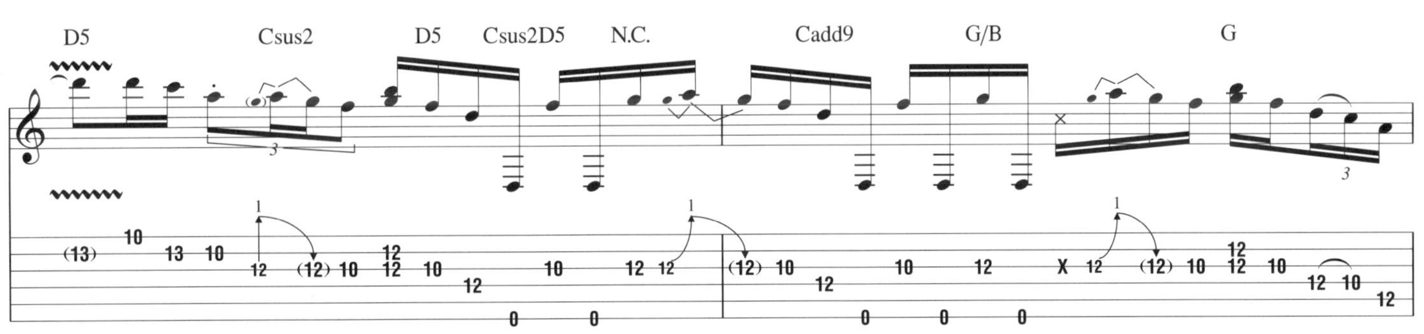
D5 Csus2 D5 Csus2 D5 N.C. Cadd9 G/B G

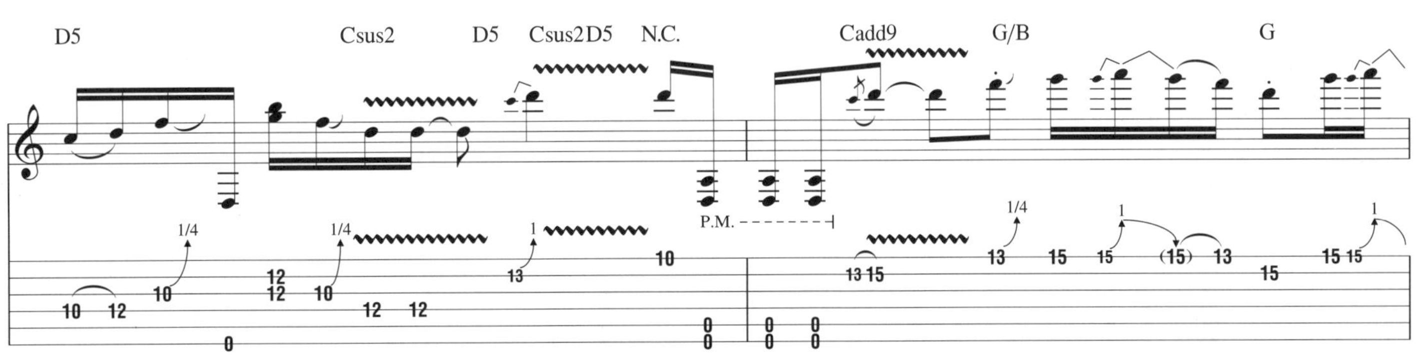
D5 Csus2 D5 Csus2 D5 N.C. Cadd9 G/B G
P.M.

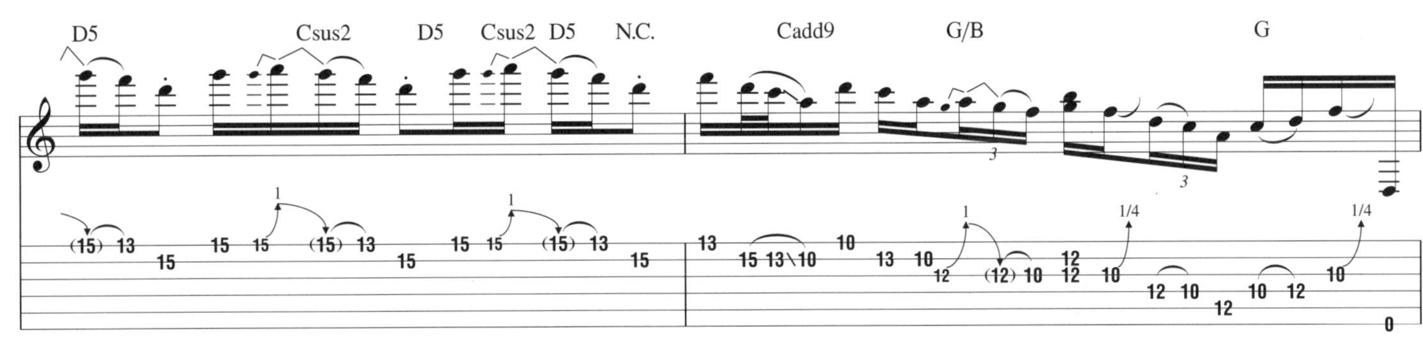
D5 Csus2 D5 Csus2 D5 N.C. Cadd9 G/B G

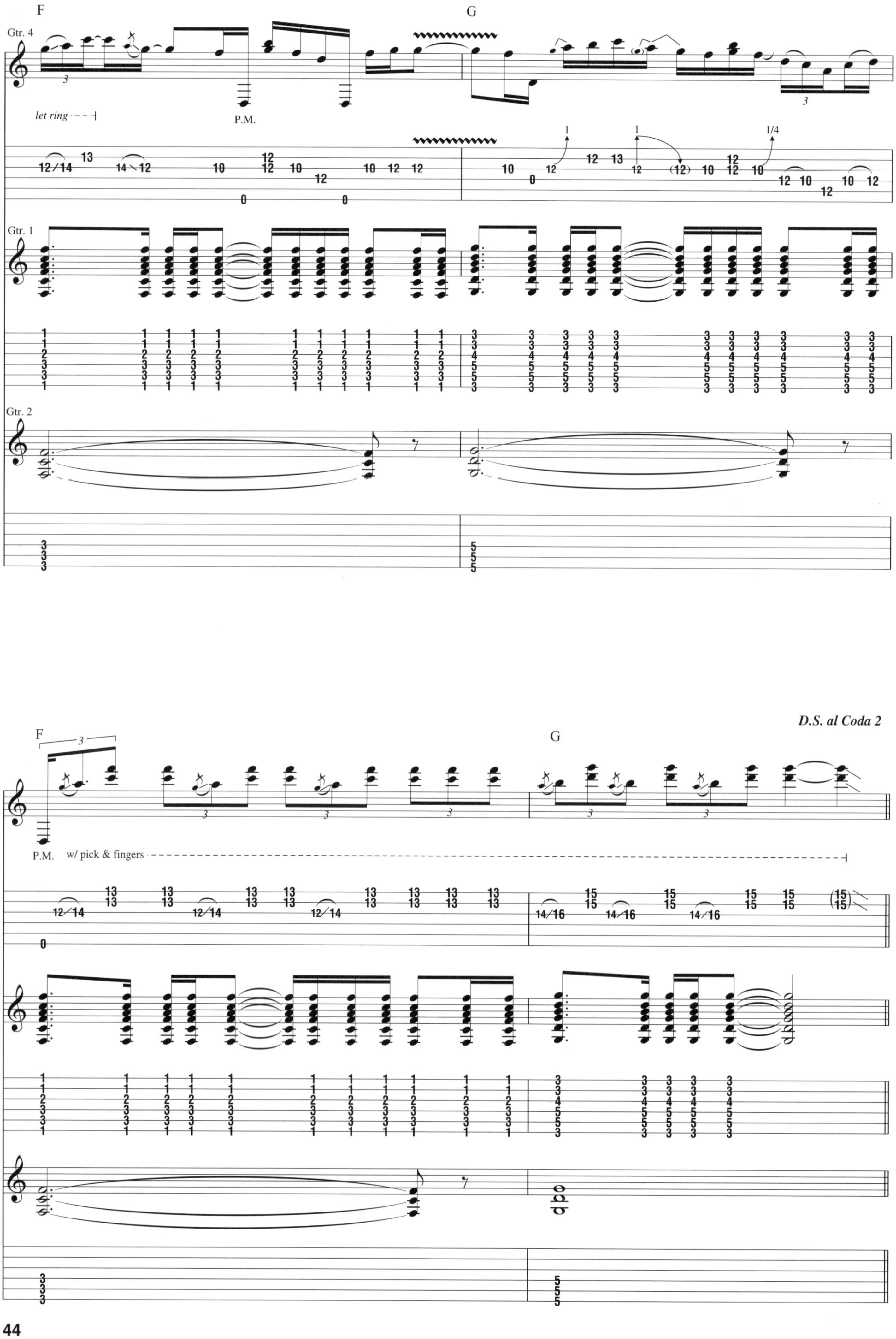

F G

Gtr. 4

let ring

P.M.

Gtr. 1

Gtr. 2

D.S. al Coda 2

F G

P.M. w/ pick & fingers

Coda 2

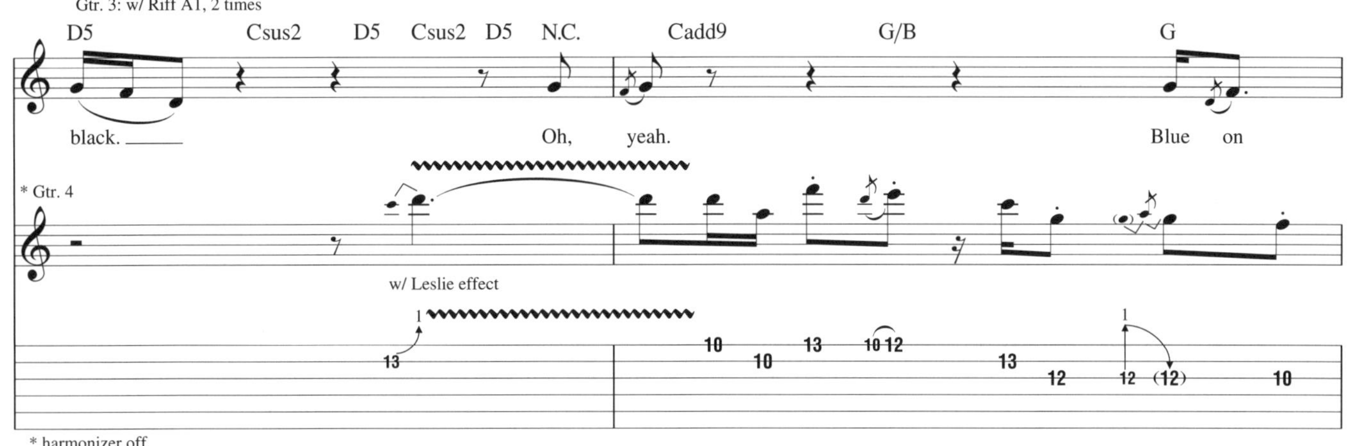
Gtr. 1: w/ Rhy. Fig. 1, 2 times
Gtr. 3: w/ Riff A1, 2 times
D5
Csus2
D5
Csus2
D5
N.C.
Cadd9
G/B
G
black.
Oh,
yeah.
Blue
on
* Gtr. 4
w/ Leslie effect
* harmonizer off

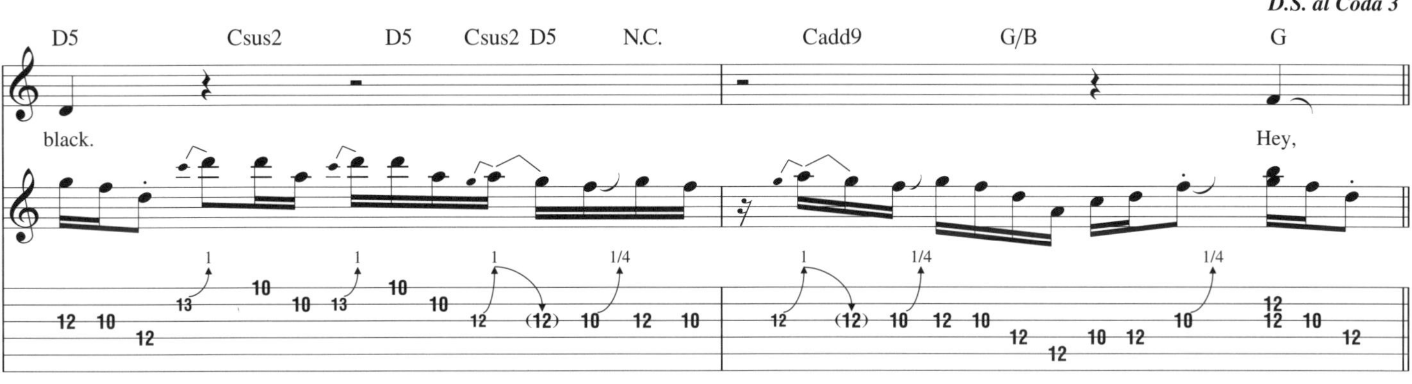
D.S. al Coda 3
D5
Csus2
D5
Csus2
D5
N.C.
Cadd9
G/B
G
black.
Hey,

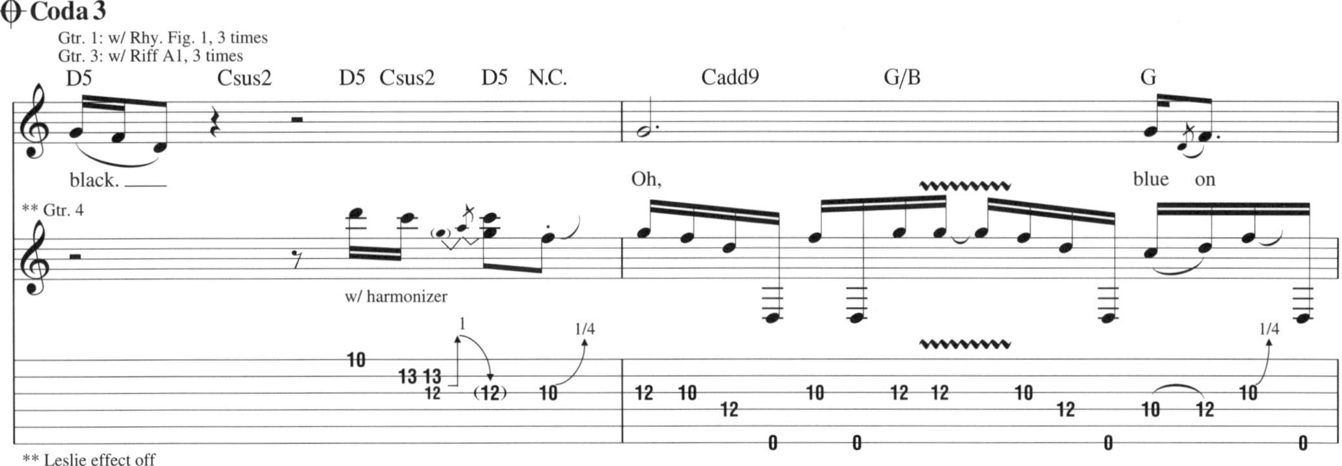
Coda 3
Gtr. 1: w/ Rhy. Fig. 1, 3 times
Gtr. 3: w/ Riff A1, 3 times
D5
Csus2
D5
Csus2
D5
N.C.
Cadd9
G/B
G
black.
Oh,
blue
on
** Gtr. 4
w/ harmonizer
** Leslie effect off

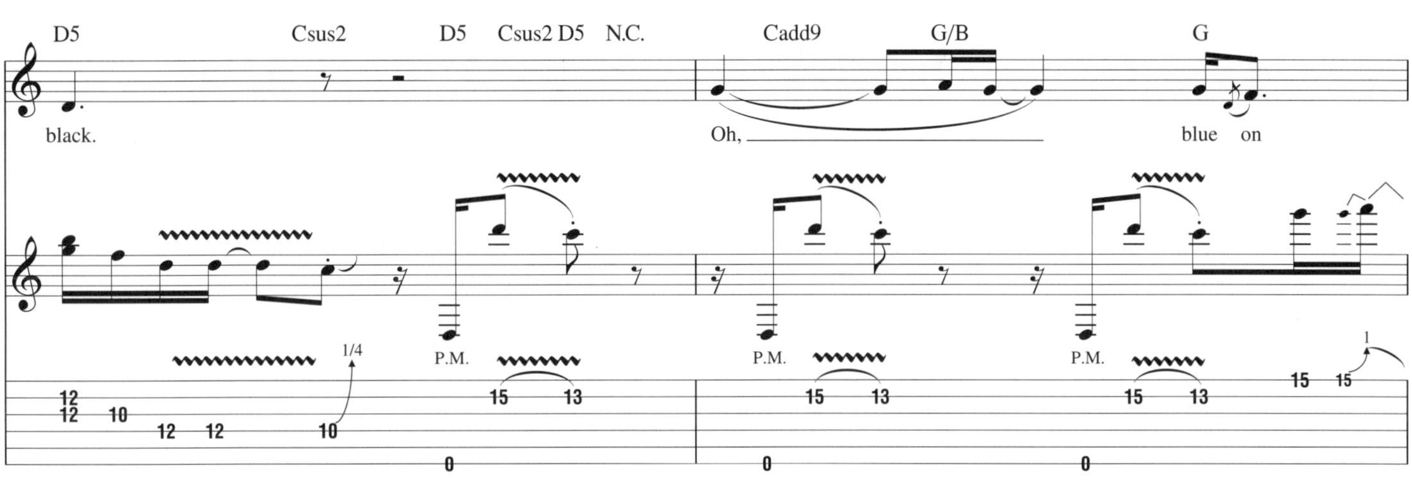
D5
Csus2
D5
Csus2
D5
N.C.
Cadd9
G/B
G
black.
Oh,
blue
on
P.M.
P.M.
P.M.

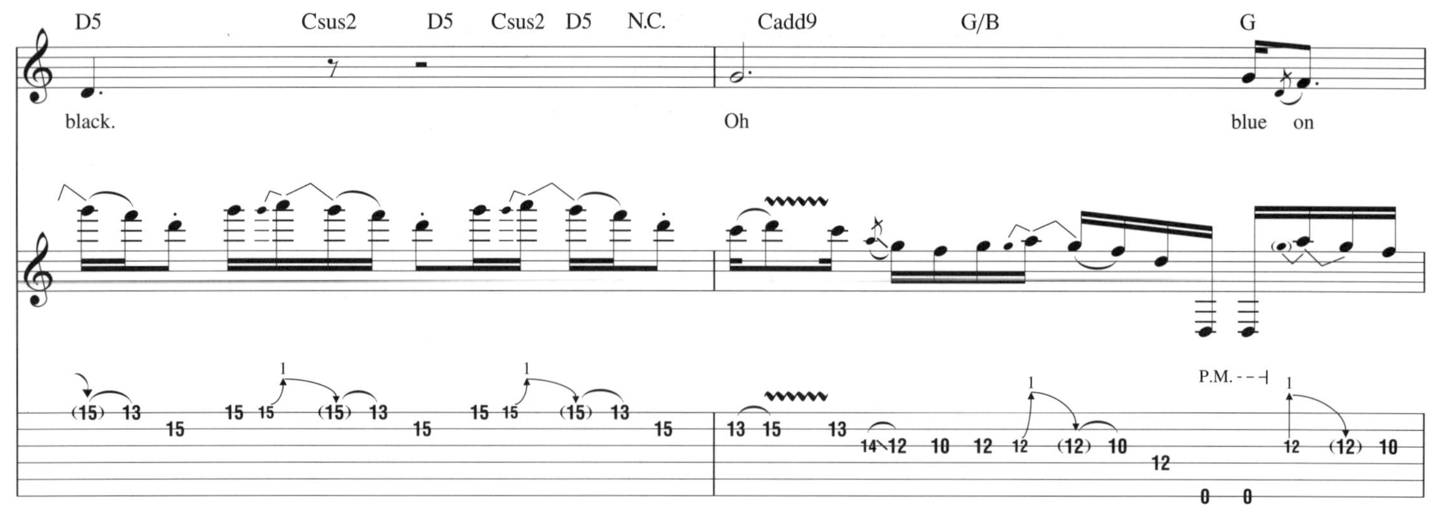

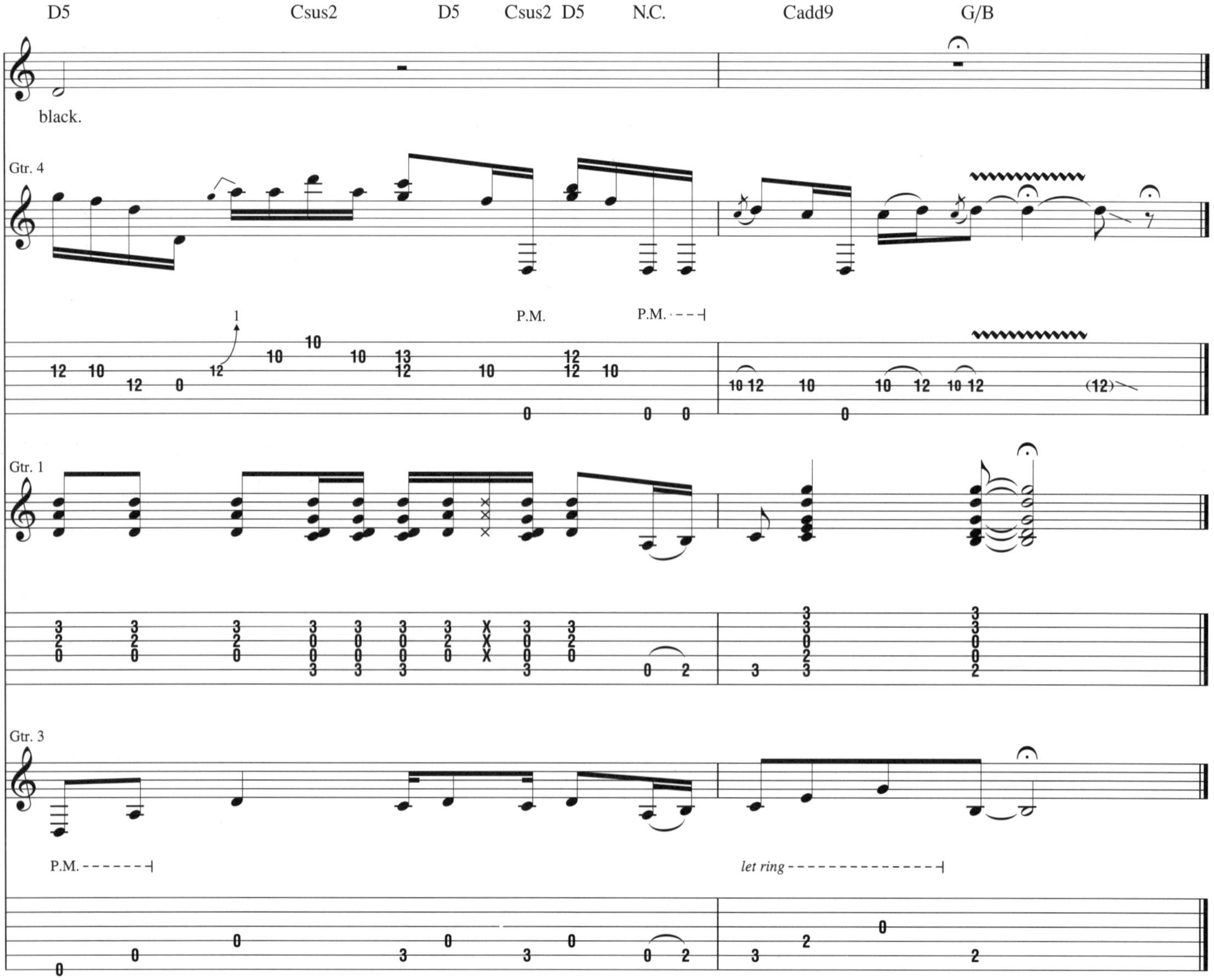

D5 Csus2 D5 Csus2 D5 N.C.
Cadd9 G/B G
black.
Oh
blue on
P.M.

D5 Csus2 D5 Csus2 D5 N.C.
Cadd9 G/B
black.
Gtr. 4
P.M.
P.M.
Gtr. 1
Gtr. 3
P.M.
let ring

Boot Scootin' Boogie

Words and Music by Ronnie Dunn

Copyright © 1991 Sony/ATV Songs LLC
All Rights Administered by Sony/ATV Music Publishing, 8 Music Square West, Nashville, TN 37203
International Copyright Secured All Rights Reserved

A

hon - ky tonk near the coun - ty line. The joint starts jump - in' ev - 'ry
quit - tin' time, I hit the door run - nin'. I fire up my pick - up truck

shot at that red - head yon - der look - in' at me. The dance floor's hop - pin' and it's

4th time only

E B

night when the sun goes down. They got whis - key, wom - en,
and let the hors - es run. I go fly - in' down that high way

Fiddle Solo

hot - ter than the Fourth of Ju - ly. I see out - laws, in - laws,

4th time only

3rd time, omit these 2 measures

mu - sic and smoke. It's where all the cow - boy folk go to
to that hide - a - way stuck out in the woods to do the boot scoot - in'
crooks and straights, all out mak - in' it shake, do - in' the

4th time only

1., 3. | 2., 4.

Gtr. 1 as in 1st verse

Chorus

E A

boo - gie. 2. I've Yeah, heel to toe, do - sa do,
4. The

2nd ending (1st chorus)

Gtr. 2 (Slide)

Gtr. 1

1/2

4th time

4th ending (2nd chorus)

E A

come on ba-by, let's go boot scoot-in'! Whoa, Cad-il-lac, Black-jack,

1st chorus

2nd chorus

E

ba-by meet me out back. We're gon-na boo-gie. Oh,

1st chorus

2nd chorus

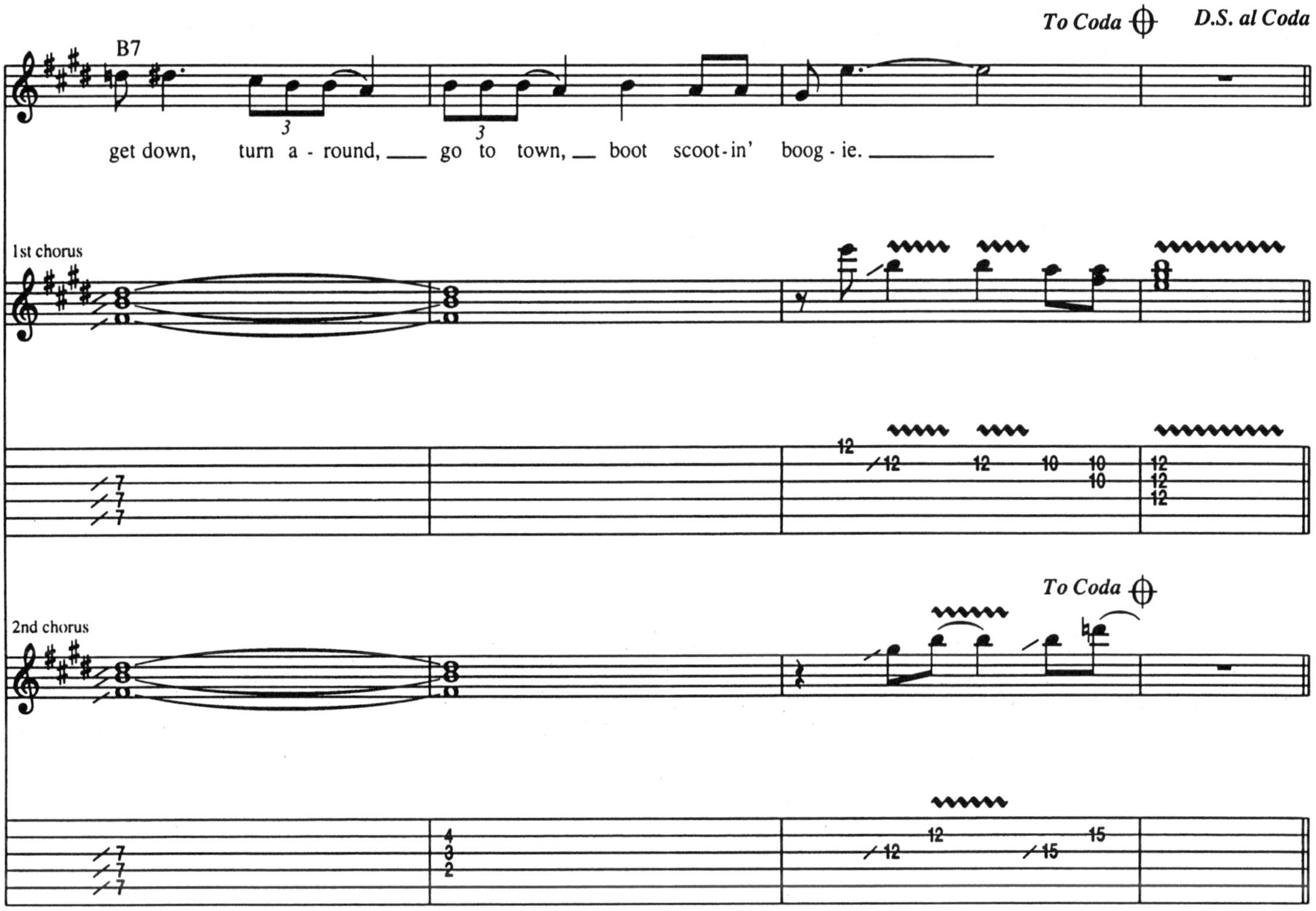

To Coda ⊕ D.S. al Coda

B7

get down, turn a - round, go to town, boot scoot-in' boog - ie.

1st chorus

2nd chorus

To Coda ⊕

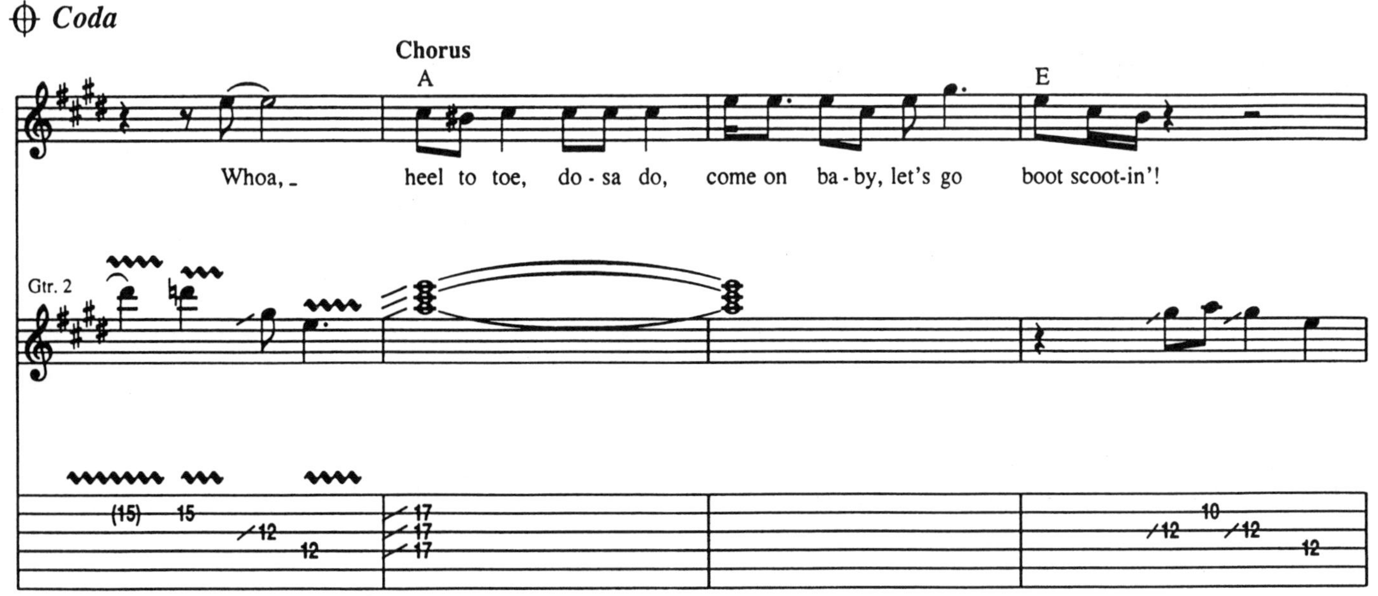
⊕ Coda
Chorus
A
E
Whoa, heel to toe, do - sa do, come on ba - by, let's go boot scoot-in'!
Gtr. 2

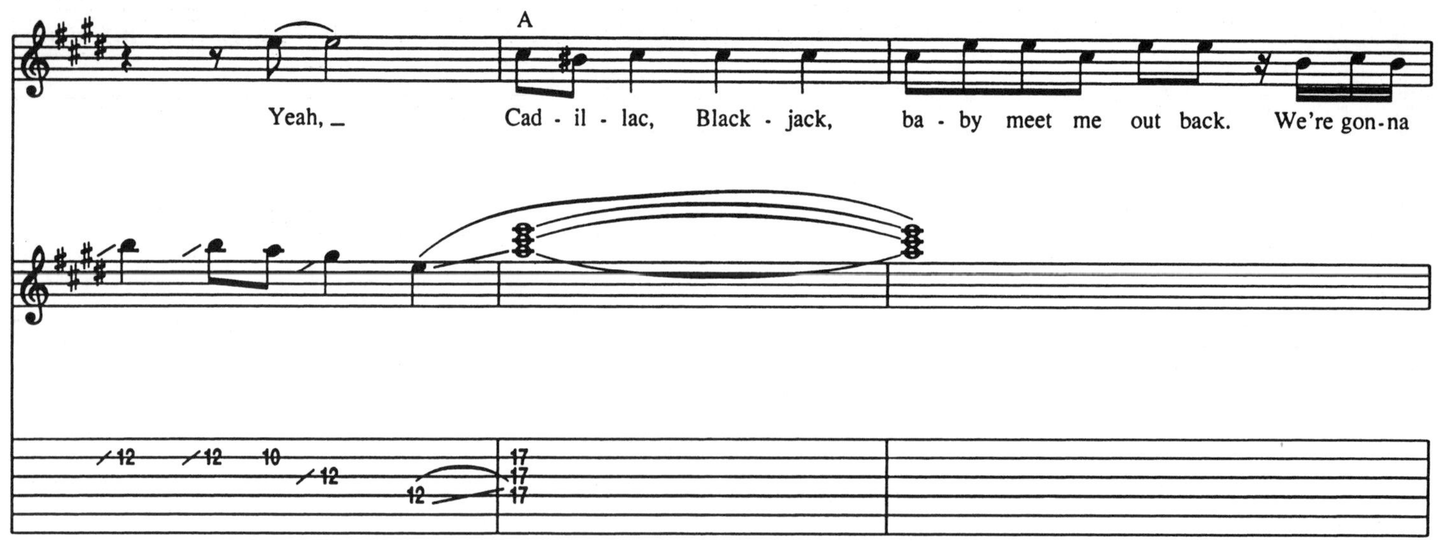
A
Yeah, _ Cad - il - lac, Black - jack, ba - by meet me out back. We're gon-na
12 12 10 12 12 17 17 17

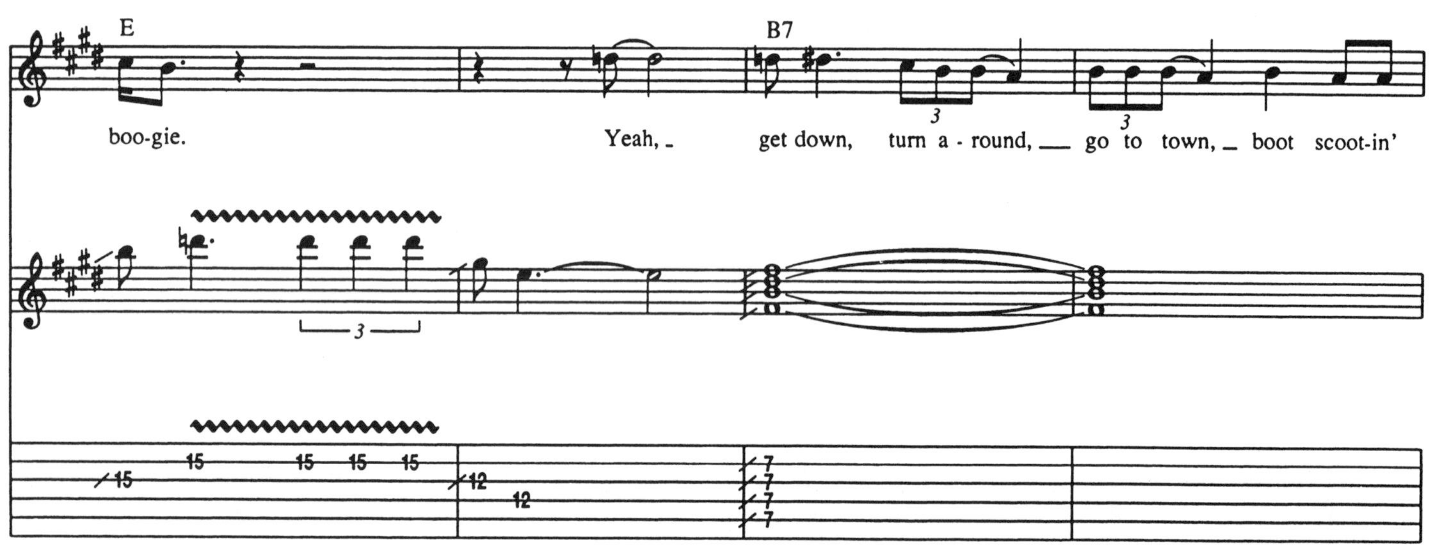
E
B7
boo-gie. Yeah, _ get down, turn a - round, __ go to town, _ boot scoot-in'
15 15 15 15 15 12 12 7 7 7 7

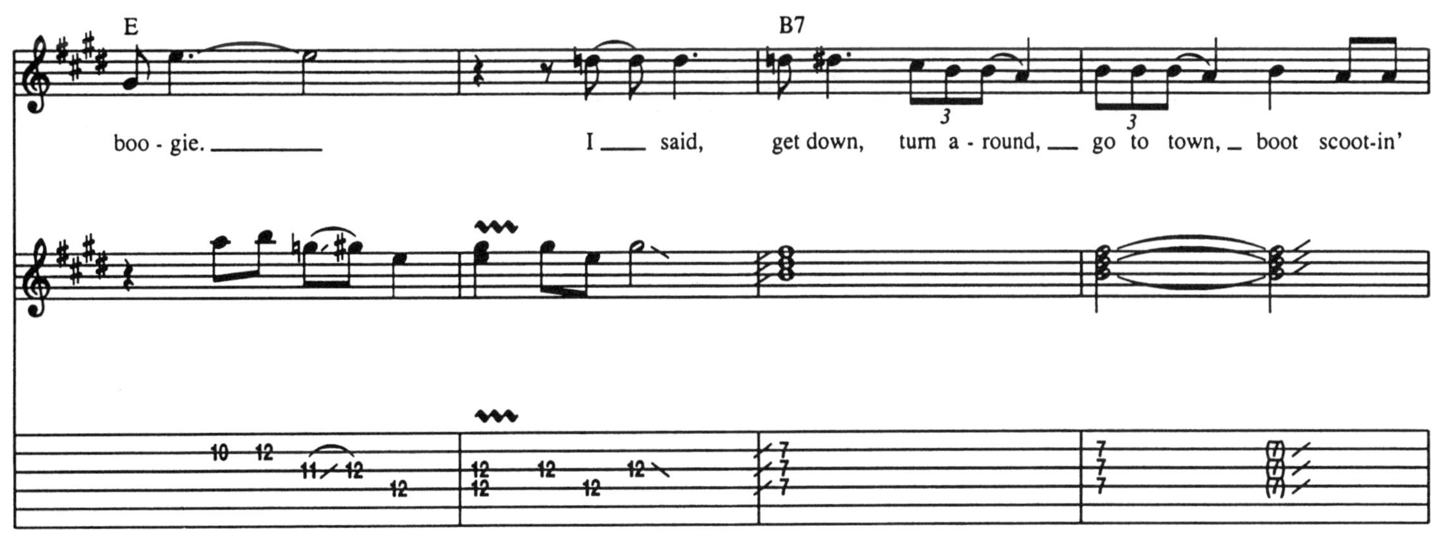
E
B7
boo - gie.
I said, get down, turn a - round, go to town, boot scoot-in'

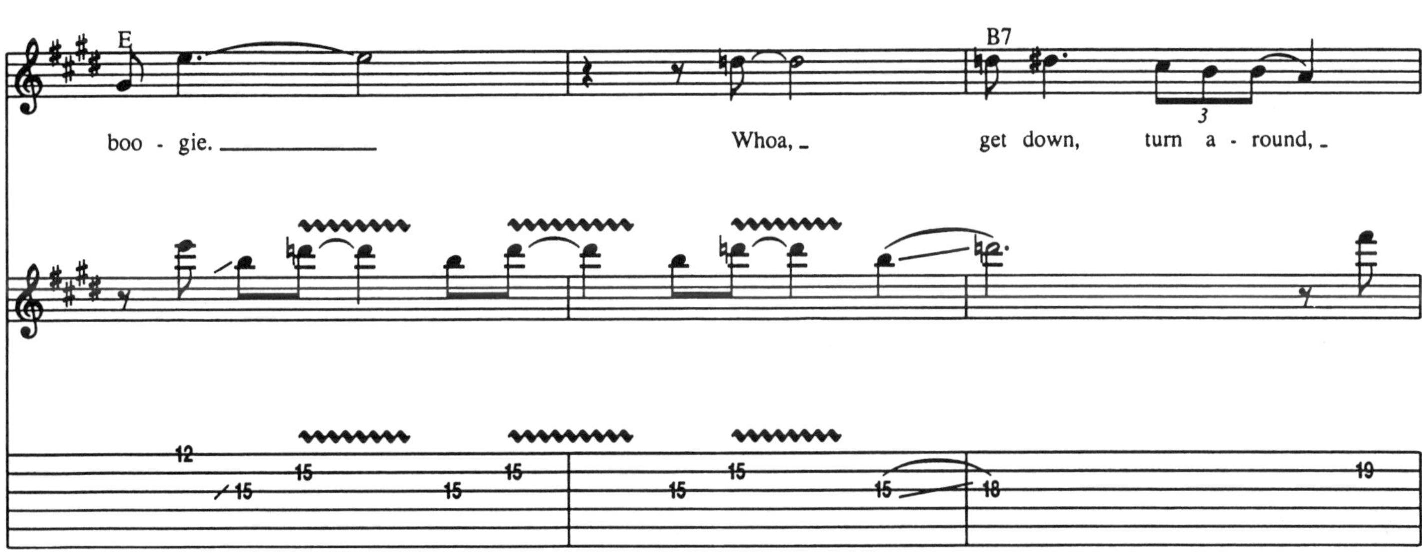
E
B7
boo - gie.
Whoa, get down, turn a - round,

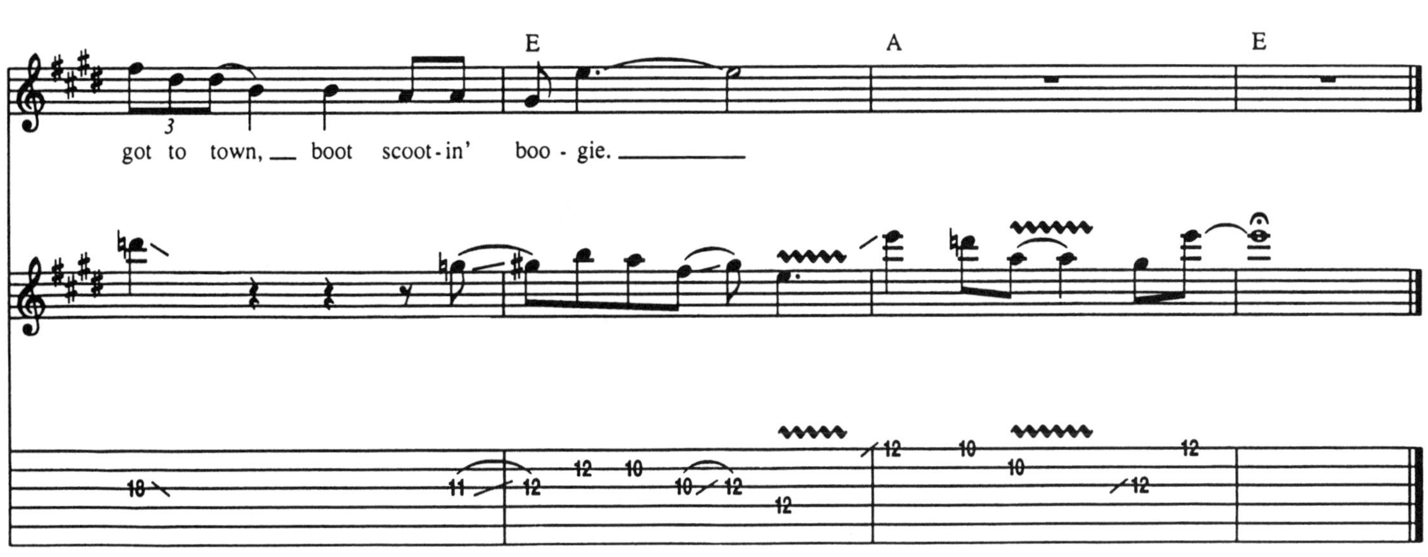
E
A
E
got to town, boot scoot - in' boo - gie.

Building a Mystery

Words and Music by Sarah McLachlan and Pierre Marchand

Copyright © 1997 Sony/ATV Songs LLC, Tyde Music and Pierre J. Marchand
All Rights on behalf of Sony/ATV Songs LLC and Tyde Music Administered by Sony/ATV Music Publishing,
8 Music Square West, Nashville, TN 37203
International Copyright Secured All Rights Reserved

Verse
Gtr. 1: w/ Rhy. Fig. 1, 3 times, simile
Gtr. 3 tacet
Bm (Em) ((Am))
G (C/G) ((F))
D (G) ((C))
A (D/A) ((G))
come out at night,
that's when the en - er - gy comes _ and the dark side's _ light ___ and the
Gtr. 3
Gtr. 2
slight P.M.
vam - pires roam. ___
You strut your ras - ta wear _ and your
Gtr. 1: w/ Rhy. Fig. 2
su - i - cide _ po - em and a cross from a faith _ that died _____ be - fore Je - sus came. _

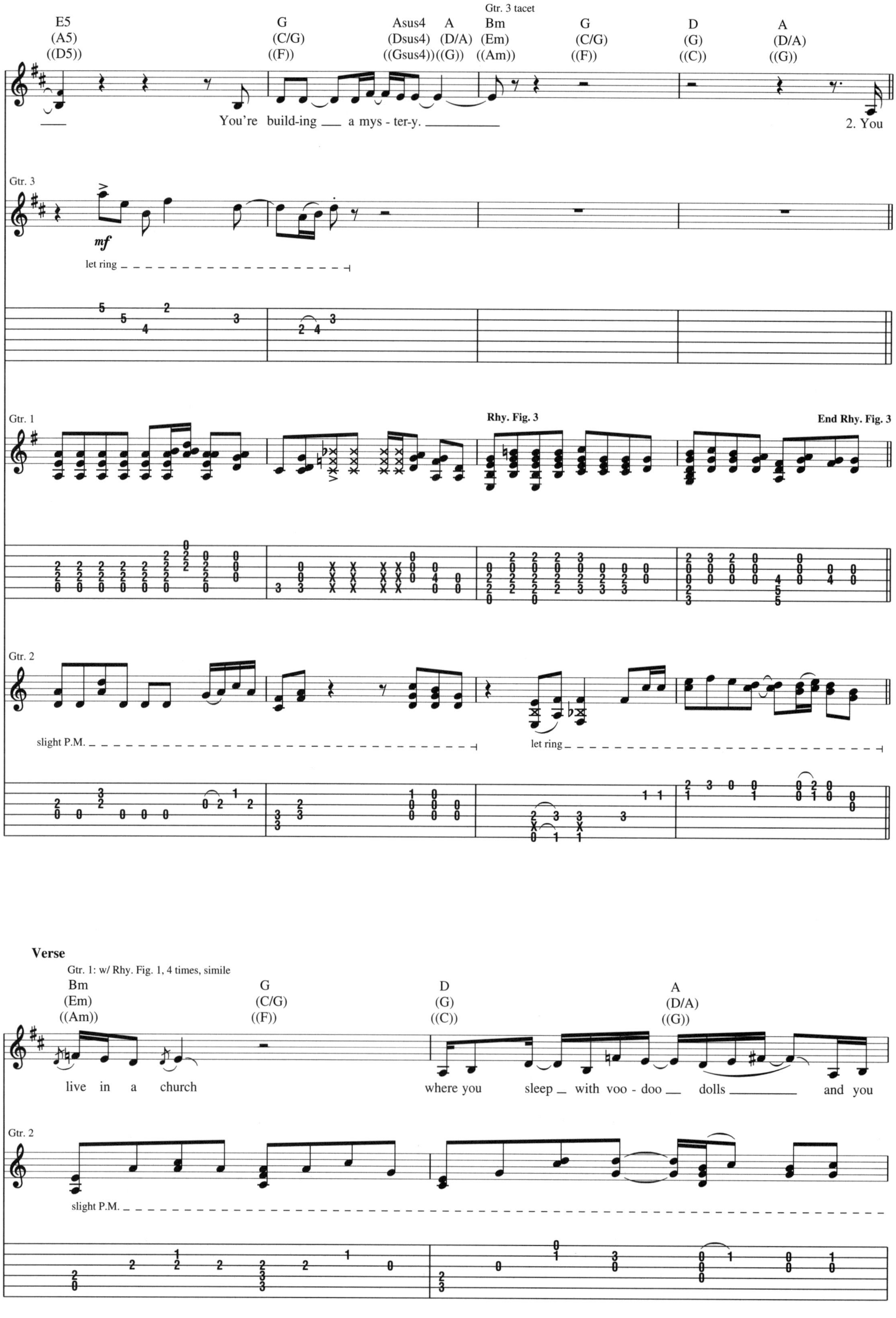

Gtr. 3 tacet

E5 (A5) ((D5)) G (C/G) ((F)) Asus4 (Dsus4) ((Gsus4)) A (D/A) ((G)) Bm (Em) ((Am)) G (C/G) ((F)) D (G) ((C)) A (D/A) ((G))

You're build-ing a mys - ter-y. 2. You

Gtr. 3

mf

let ring

Gtr. 1

Rhy. Fig. 3

End Rhy. Fig. 3

Gtr. 2

slight P.M.

let ring

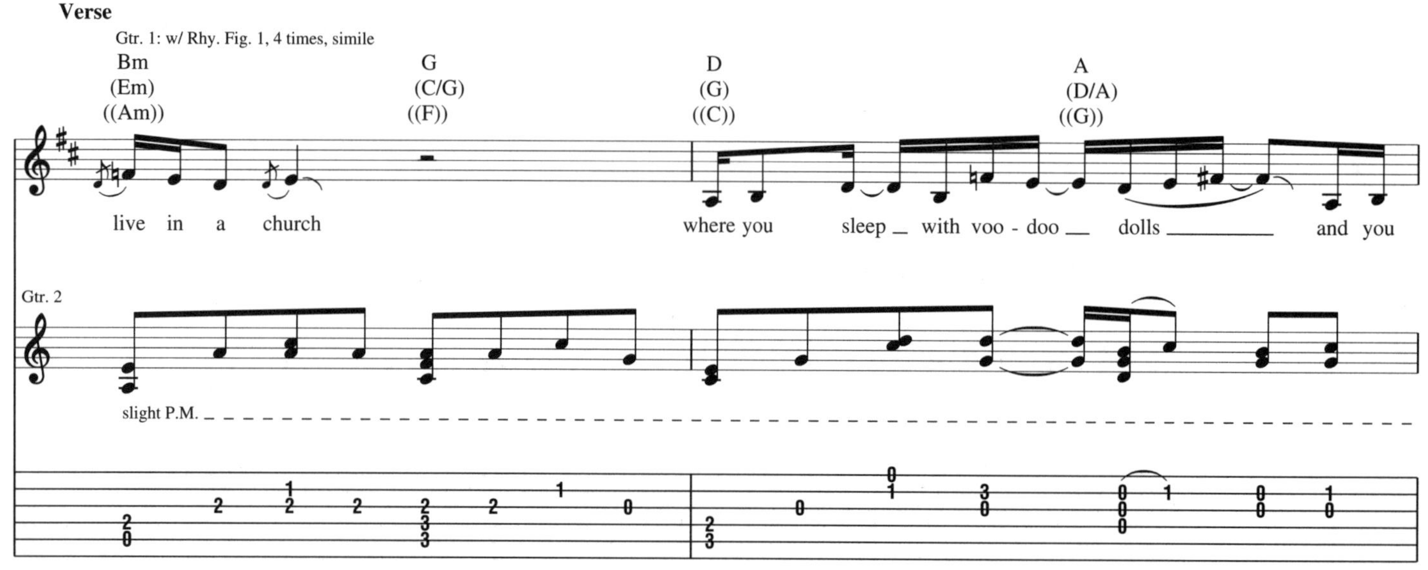

Bm (Em) ((Am))
G (C/G) ((F))
D (G) ((C))
A (D/A) ((G))
won't give up the search for the ghosts in the halls.
slight P.M.
You wear sandals in the snow and a smile that won't wash away.
(Smile that won't wash away.
Can you look out the window without your shadow getting in the way?
)

Pre-Chorus
E5
(A5)
((Dsus4))
((D))
G
(C/G)
((Fsus2))
Voc. Fig. 1
You're so beau - ti - ful, with an edge and charm - ing.
(Oh, oh, la, la.
Gtr. 3
w/ chorus effect
let ring throughout
Gtr. 1
Rhy. Fig. 4
mp
Gtr. 2
let ring
E5
(A5)
((D5))
((D))
G
(C/G)
((F))
A
(D/A)
((G))
End Voc. Fig. 1
You're so care - ful when I'm in your arms
Oo, la, la, ah.)
End Rhy. Fig. 4
let ring

Chorus

Gtr. 1: w/ Rhy. Fig. 3, 3 times, simile

Bm (Em) ((Am)) G (C/G) ((F)) D (G) ((C)) D (D/A) ((G)) Bm (Em) ((Am)) G (C/G) ((F))

'cause you're work-ing, build-ing a mys-ter-y. Hold-ing on

Gtr. 3 Riff A

mf w/ dist. & chorus effect

let ring

Gtr. 2

pp mf P.H. vol. swell

pitch: D

D (G) ((C)) A (D/A) ((G)) Bm (Em) ((Am)) G (C/G) ((F)) D (G) ((C)) A (D/A) ((G))

and hold-ing it in. Yeah, you're work-ing, build-ing a mys-ter-y

let ring mp mf let ring

slight P.M.

Bm (Em) ((Am))
G (C/G) ((F))
D (G) ((C))
A (D/A) ((Gsus4)) ((G))
((Gsus4)) ((G))
((Gsus4)) ((G))
and choos - ing so care - ful - ly.
3. You woke up
Gtr. 3
End Riff A
mp
mf
let ring
Gtr. 1
Gtr. 2
slight P.M.
Verse
Gtr. 1: w/ Rhy. Fig. 1, 4 times, simile
Bm (Em) ((Am))
G (C/G) ((F))
D (G) ((C))
A (D/A) ((G))
Bm (Em) ((Am))
G (C/G) ((F))
scream-ing a - loud, a prayer from your se-cret god to feed off our fears and
Gtr. 3
let ring throughout
Gtr. 2
slight P.M.
let ring
slight P.M.

D
(G)
((C))
A
(D/A)
((G))
Bm
(Em)
((Am))
G
(C/G)
((F))
D
(G)
((C))
A
(D/A)
((G))
hold back your tears, oh. You give us a tan-trum and a know-it-all grin
slight P.M.
Bm
(Em)
((Am))
G
(C/G)
((F))
D
(G)
((C))
A
(D/A)
((G))
Pre-Chorus
Bkgd. Voc.: w/ Voc. Fig. 1
Gtr. 1: w/ Rhy. Fig. 4, simile
E5
(A5)
((Dsus4))
((D))
just when you need one when the eve-ning stayed. You're a beau-ti-ful,
slight P.M.

G (C/G) ((Fsus2))
E5 (A5) ((Dsus4)) ((D))
G (C/G) ((Fsus2))
A (D/A) ((G))
a beau-ti-ful fucked up man.
You set-ting up your ra - zor wire shrine
Chorus
Gtr. 1: w/ Rhy. Fig. 3, 4 times, simile
Gtr. 3: w/ Riff A, simile
Bm (Em) ((Am))
G (C/G) ((F))
D (G) ((C))
A (D/A) ((G))
'cause you're work - ing, build - ing a mys - ter - y.
Gtr. 2
Rhy. Fig. 3A
End Rhy. Fig. 3A
Gtr. 2: w/ Rhy. Fig. 3A, 3 times, simile
Bm (Em) ((Am))
G (C/G) ((F))
D (G) ((C))
A (D/A) ((G))
Bm (Em) ((Am))
G (C/G) ((F))
Hold - ing on and hold - ing it in. Yeah, you're work - ing,
D (G) ((C))
A (D/A) ((G))
Bm (Em) ((Am))
G (C/G) ((F))
D (G) ((C))
A (D/A) ((G))
build - ing a mys - ter - y and choos - ing so care - ful - ly.

Guitar Solo
G (C/G)
A (D/A)
G (C/G)
E5 (A5)
G (C/G)
A (D/A)
(Oo, oh, oo.
Gtr. 2
* pp < mf
Gtr. 1
mf
*quick vol. swell
G (C/G)
A (D/A)
G (C/G)
E5 (A5)
G (C/G)
Oo. Ah, Ah.)
Oo, you're work-ing, build-ing a mys - ter - y.
Gtr. 3
Gtr. 2
Gtr. 1
*vol. swells, backwards guitar arranged for guitar next 4 meas.

Outro-Chorus

Bm
(Em)
((Am))
G
(C/G)
((F))
D
(G)
((C))
A
(D/A)
((G))
Oh, yeah, you're work - ing, build - ing a mys - ter - y and choos - ing so
8va
care - ful - ly.
You're build-ing a mys-ter - y.
Gtr. 3
loco
rit.
Harm.
Gtr. 1
Gtr. 2
let ring

Cryin'

Words and Music by Steven Tyler, Joe Perry and Taylor Rhodes

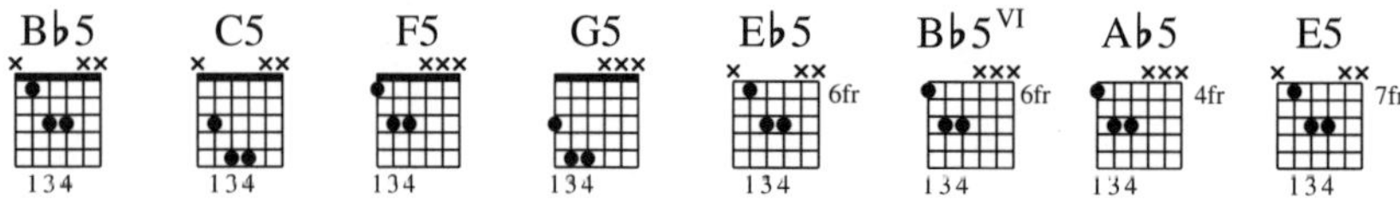

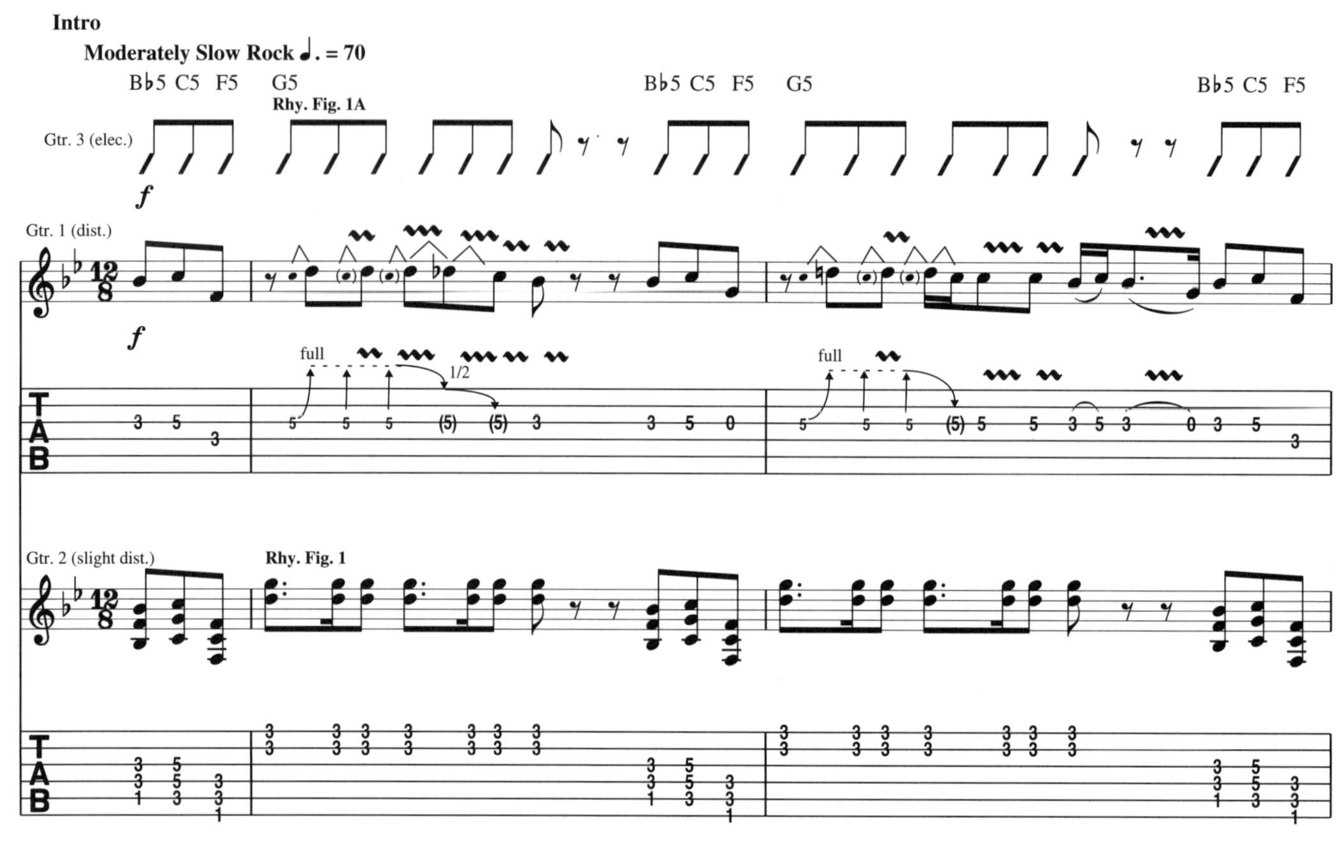

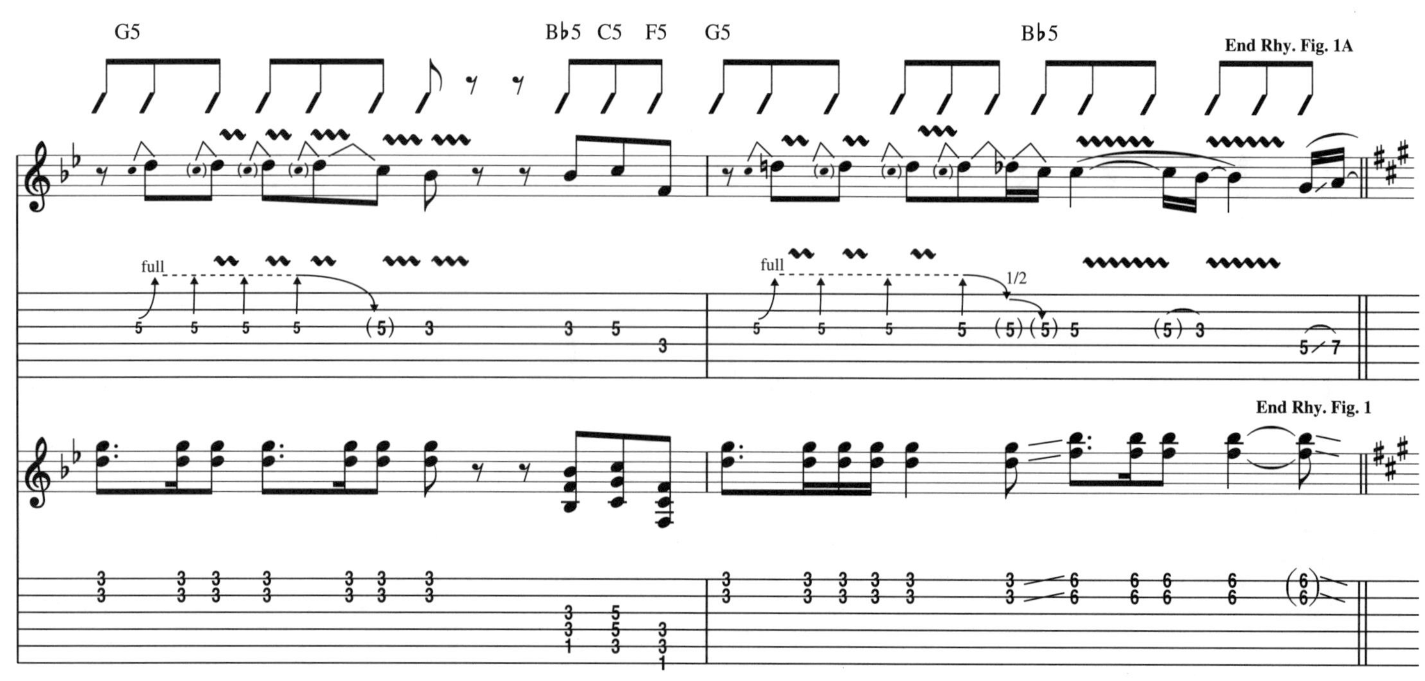

© 1992 EMI APRIL MUSIC INC., SWAG SONG MUSIC, INC., UNIVERSAL - MCA MUSIC PUBLISHING,
A Division of UNIVERSAL STUDIOS, INC. and TAYLOR RHODES SONGS
All Rights for SWAG SONG MUSIC, INC. Controlled and Administered by EMI APRIL MUSIC INC.
All Rights for TAYLOR RHODES SONGS Controlled and Administered by
UNIVERSAL - MCA MUSIC PUBLISHING, A Division of UNIVERSAL STUDIOS, INC.
All Rights Reserved International Copyright Secured Used by Permission

Verse
Gtr. 3 tacet
A
E
Gtr. 1 tacet
F♯m
C♯m
D
A
1. There was a time
when I was so bro - ken - heart - ed.
Love was-n't much
of a
Gtr. 1
Gtr. 2
Gtr. 2
divisi
mf
let ring throughout
Gtr. 4 (elec. 12-str.)
mf
let ring throughout
E
A
E
F♯m
C♯m
friend of mine.
The ta - bles have turned,
yeah,
'cause me and them ways
have part - ed.
D
A
E
Pre-Chorus
Gtr. 4 tacet
G
D
That kind of love
was the kill - in' kind.
Lis - ten!
All I want
is some -
Rhy. Fig. 2
Gtr. 3

G D C G E
one I can't re - sist. I know all I need to know by the way that I got kissed. I was
End Rhy. Fig. 2
Chorus
A E F♯m D A E
cry - in' when I met you. Now I'm try - in' to for-get you. Love is sweet mis-er -
Rhy. Fig. 3
D A E C♯m D
y. I was cry - in' just to get you. Now I'm dy - in' cause I let you

A
E
D
B♭5 C5 F5
do what you do
down on
me.
Yeah!
Gtr. 2
End Rhy. Fig. 3
Gtr. 1
Gtr. 3
Bridge
Gtrs. 2 & 3: w/ Rhy. Figs. 1 & 1A
G5
B♭5 C5 F5
G5
B♭5 C5 F5
Now there's not e - ven breath - in' room
be - tween plea - sure and pain.
Gtr. 1
full
full
1/2
full
1/2
G5
B♭5 C5 F5
G5
B♭5
Yeah, you cry when we're mak - in' love.
Must be one and the same.
full
1/2
full
full
full
1/2
full

Verse
A
E
F♯m
C♯m
D
A
2. It's down on me, yeah, I got to tell you one thing. It's been on my mind, girl, I
Gtr. 2
mf
Gtr. 1
mf
E
Gtrs. 3 & 5: w/ Fill 1
A
E
F♯m
C♯m
got-ta say. We're part-ners in crime. You got that cer-tain some-thing.
full
full
Fill 1
Gtr. 3
Gtr. 5
Gtr. 5 (elec.)
divisi.
full
1/2
1/2
full
full
1/2
T
A
B

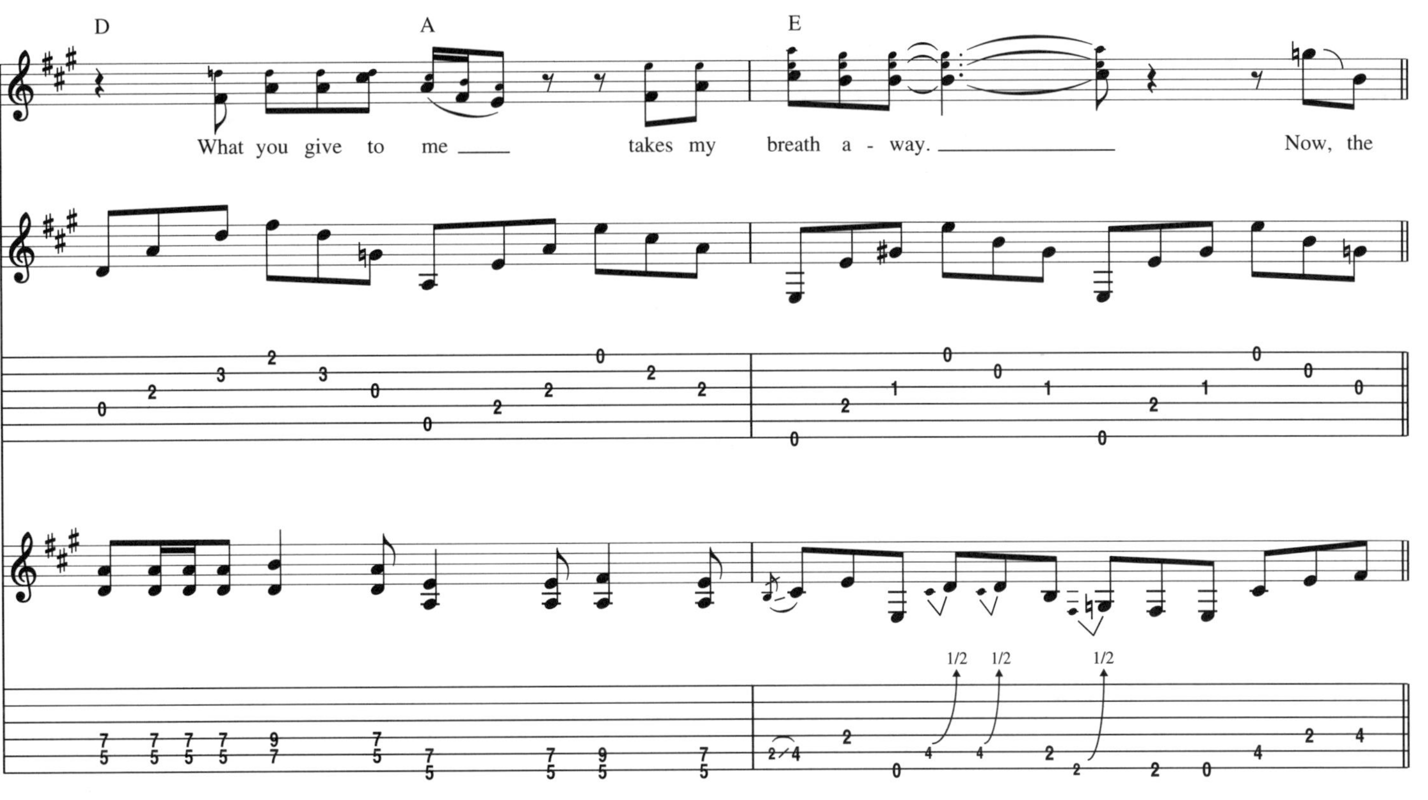
D
A
E
What you give to me takes my breath a - way. Now, the
1/2
1/2
1/2

Pre-Chorus
Gtr. 2: w/ Rhy. Fig. 2
Gtr. 1 tacet
G
D
G
D
C
G
word out on the street is the dev - il's in your kiss. If our love goes up in flames, it's a
Gtr. 1
Gtr. 3
Gtr. 3
divisi
full

Chorus
Gtr. 2: w/ Rhy. Fig. 3, simile
E
A
E
F#m7
D
fire I can't re - sist. I was cry - in' when I met you. Now I'm try - in' to for-get you.

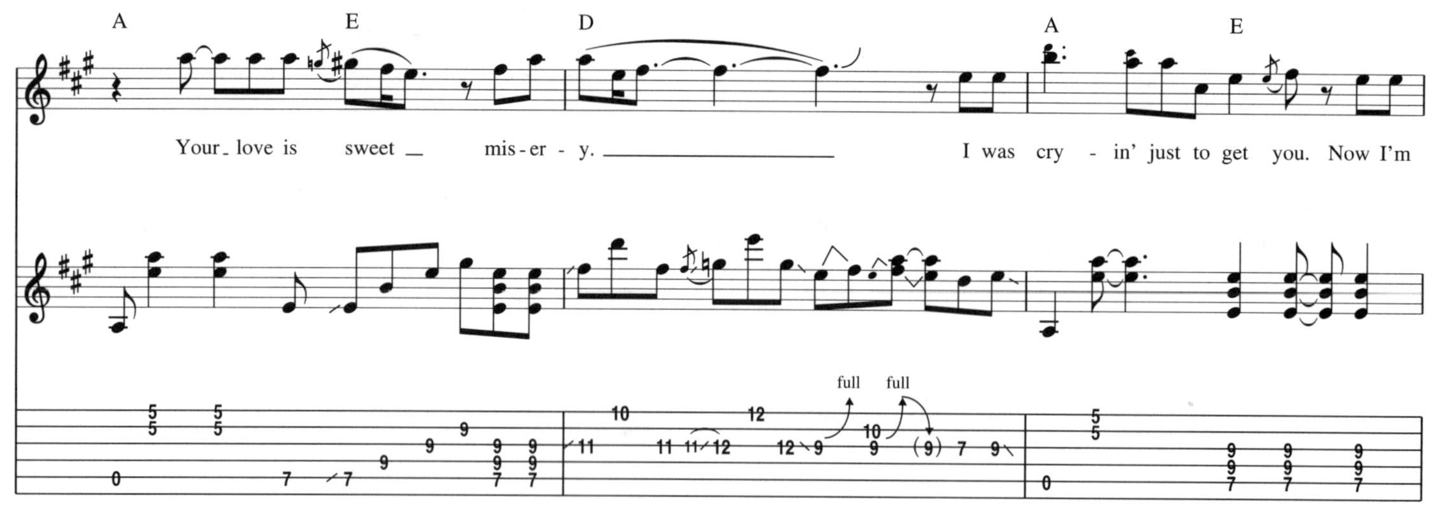

Guitar Solo

Gtrs. 2 & 3: w/ Rhy. Figs. 1 & 1A, 1st 3 meas. only

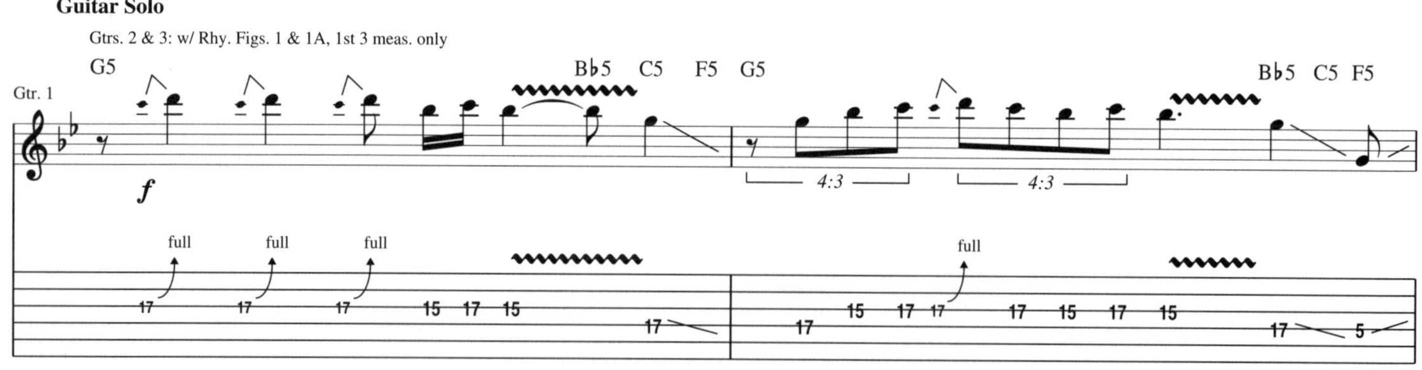

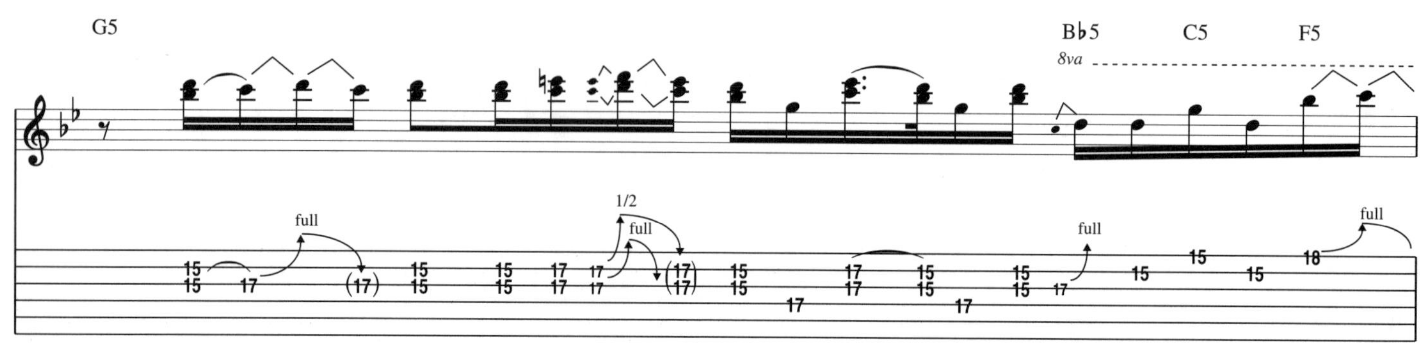

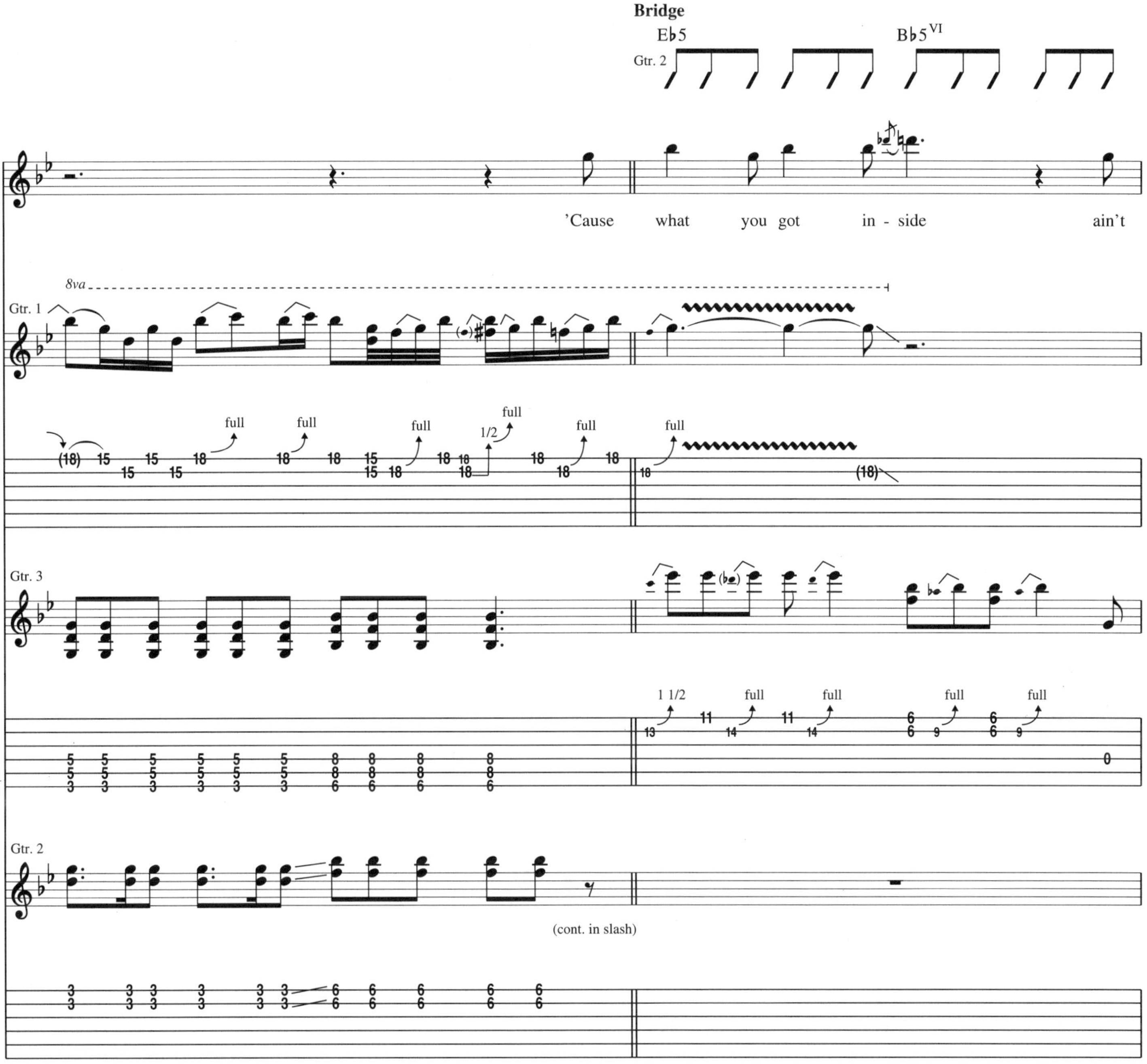

Bridge
Eb5
Bb5VI
Gtr. 2
'Cause what you got in - side ain't
8va
Gtr. 1
full
1/2
Gtr. 3
1 1/2
Gtr. 2
(cont. in slash)

Gtr. 1 tacet
Eb5
Bb5VI
Ab5
Eb5
Gtr. 2
where your love should stay. Yeah, our love, sweet love, ain't love till you
Gtr. 3
full

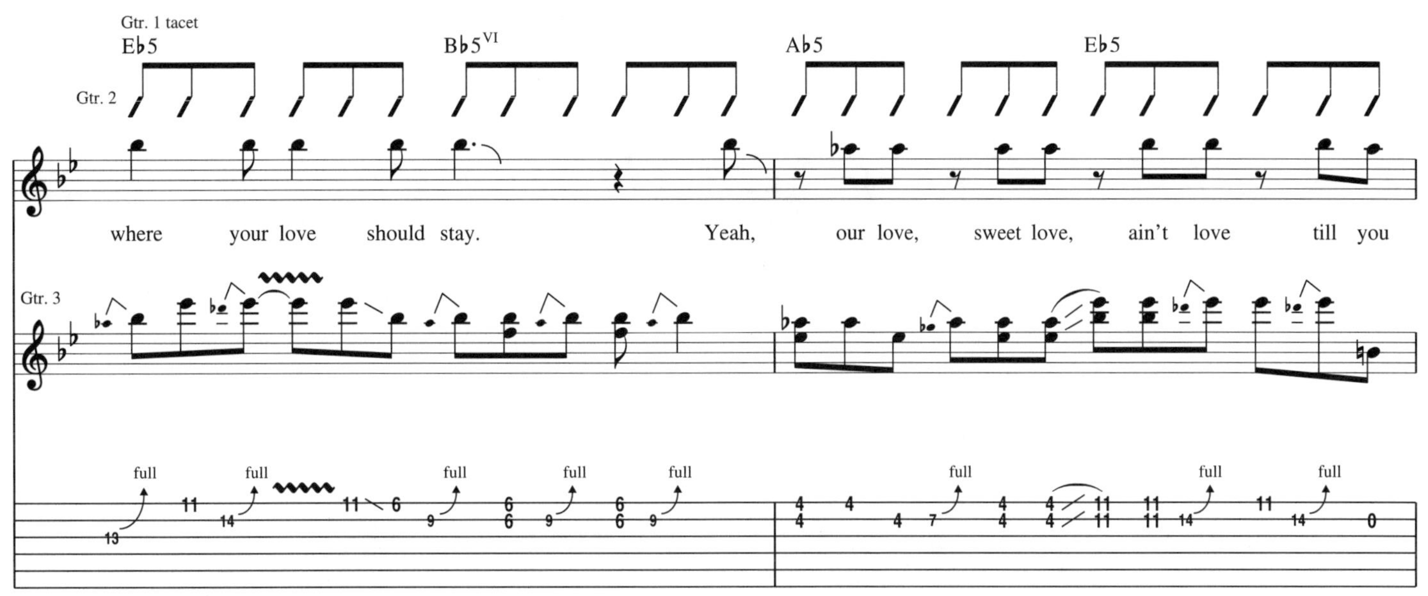

E5
(cont. in notation)
give your heart a - way. Yeah I was
Chorus
A E C#m D A E
cry - in' when I met you. Now I'm try - in' to for-get you. Your love is sweet mis-er -
Gtr. 2
Rhy. Fig. 4
Gtr. 3
D A E F#m D
y. I was cry - in' just to get you. Now I'm dy - in' to let you
End Rhy. Fig. 4

A
E
D
do what you, do what you do down to me, ba-by, ba-by, ba-by, ba-by, ba-by, ba-by.
Rhy. Fig. 5
End Rhy. Fig. 5

Interlude
(w/ harmonica)
Gtr. 2: w/ Rhy. Fig. 4, simile
Gtr. 3
A
E
C♯m
D
A
E

Gtr. 2: w/ Rhy. Fill 1
D
A
E
F♯m
D

Rhy. Fill 1
Gtr. 2

Gtr. 2: w/ Rhy. Fig. 5, simile
A
E
D
8va
loco
Gtr. 1
full
full
Gtr. 3
Outro Chorus
Gtr. 2: w/ Rhy. Fig. 4, simile
A
E
I was cry - in' when I met you. Now I'm
8va
full
C♯m
D
A
E
D
try - in' to for-get you.
Your love is sweet mis - er - y.
Yeah! I was
1/2

Gr. 2: w/ Rhy. Fill 2
A
E
F♯m
D
cry - in' when I met you. Now I'm dy - in' 'cause I let you
8va
loco
full

Gr. 2: w/ Rhy. Fig. 5, simile
A
E
D
do what you do down to, down to, down to, down to, down to.
8va
full
1/2

Rhy. Fill 2
Gtr. 2

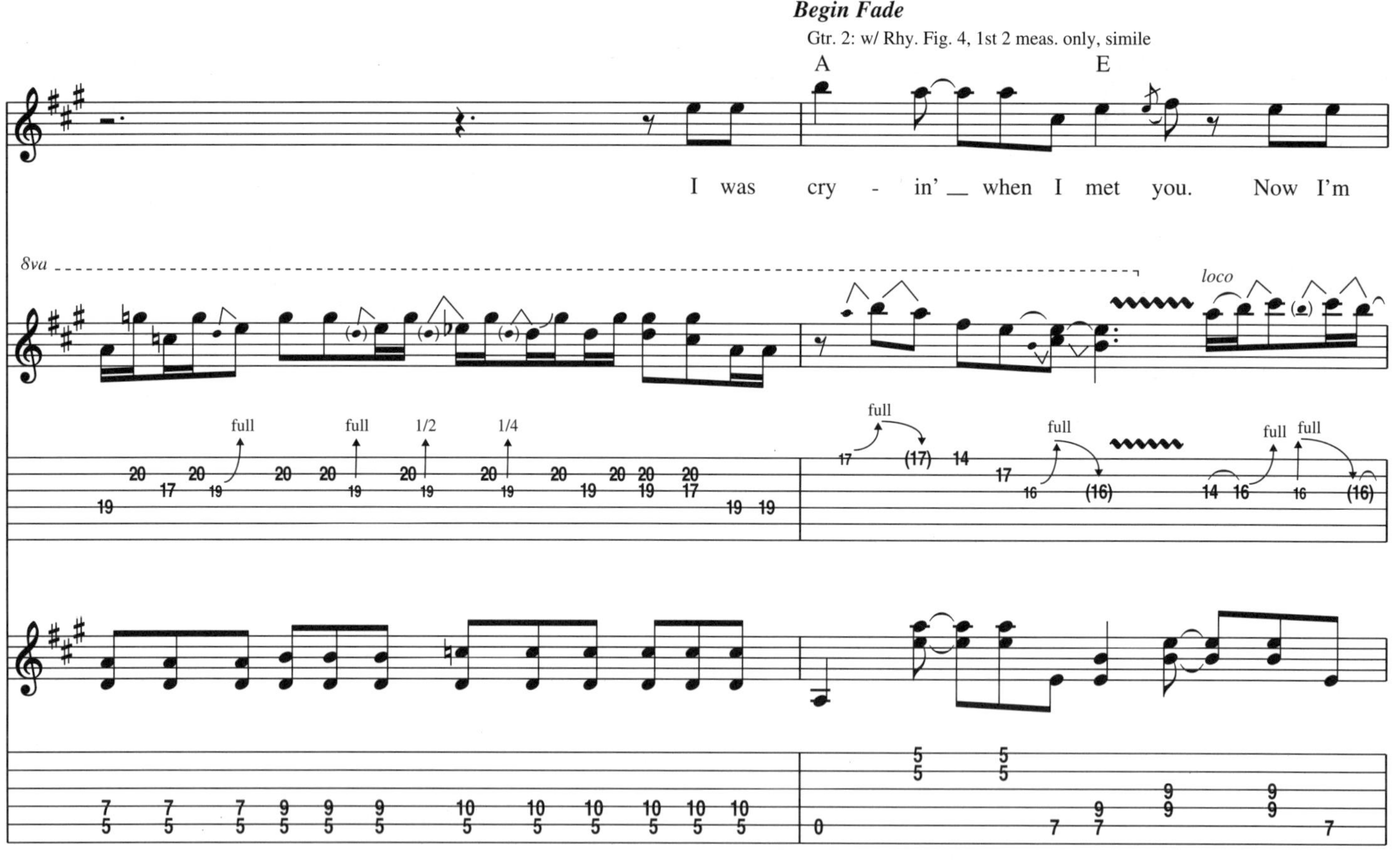

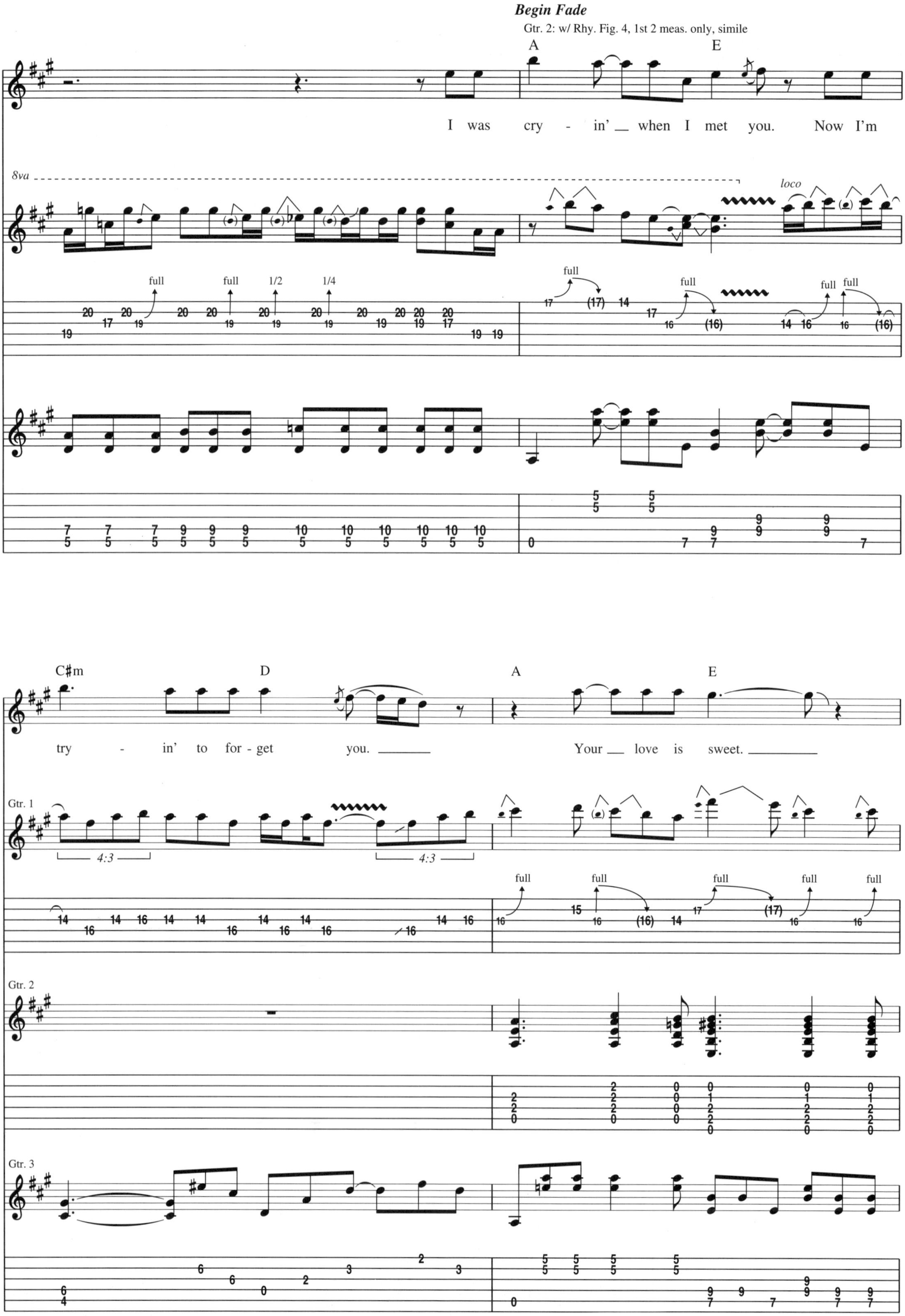

C♯m D A E

try - in' to for - get you. Your love is sweet.

Gtr. 1

4:3

full

Gtr. 2

Gtr. 3

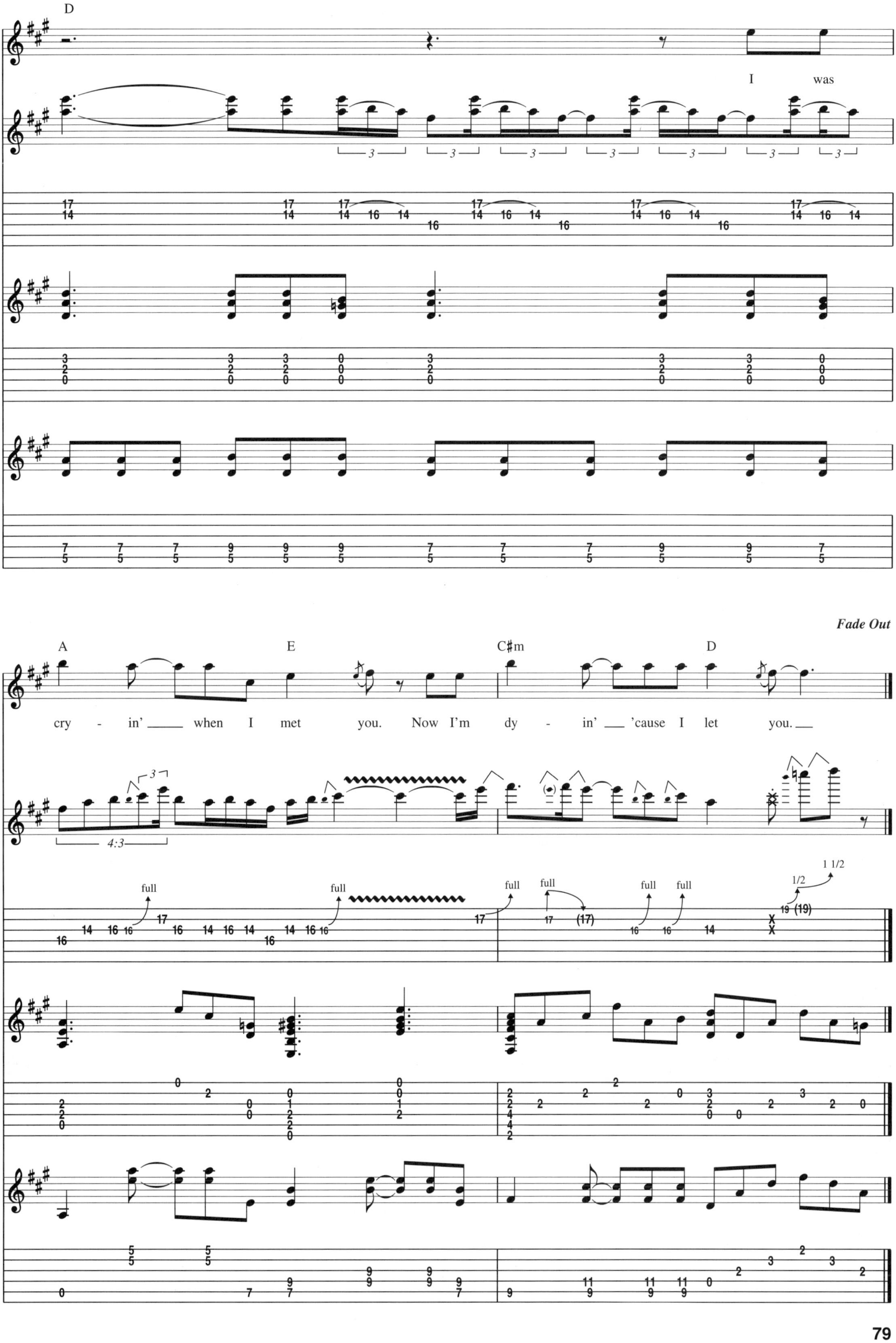

D

I was

Fade Out

A E C♯m D

cry - in' ___ when I met you. Now I'm dy - in' ___ 'cause I let you. ___

Enter Sandman

Words and Music by James Hetfield, Lars Ulrich and Kirk Hammett

Intro

Moderate Rock ♩ = 124

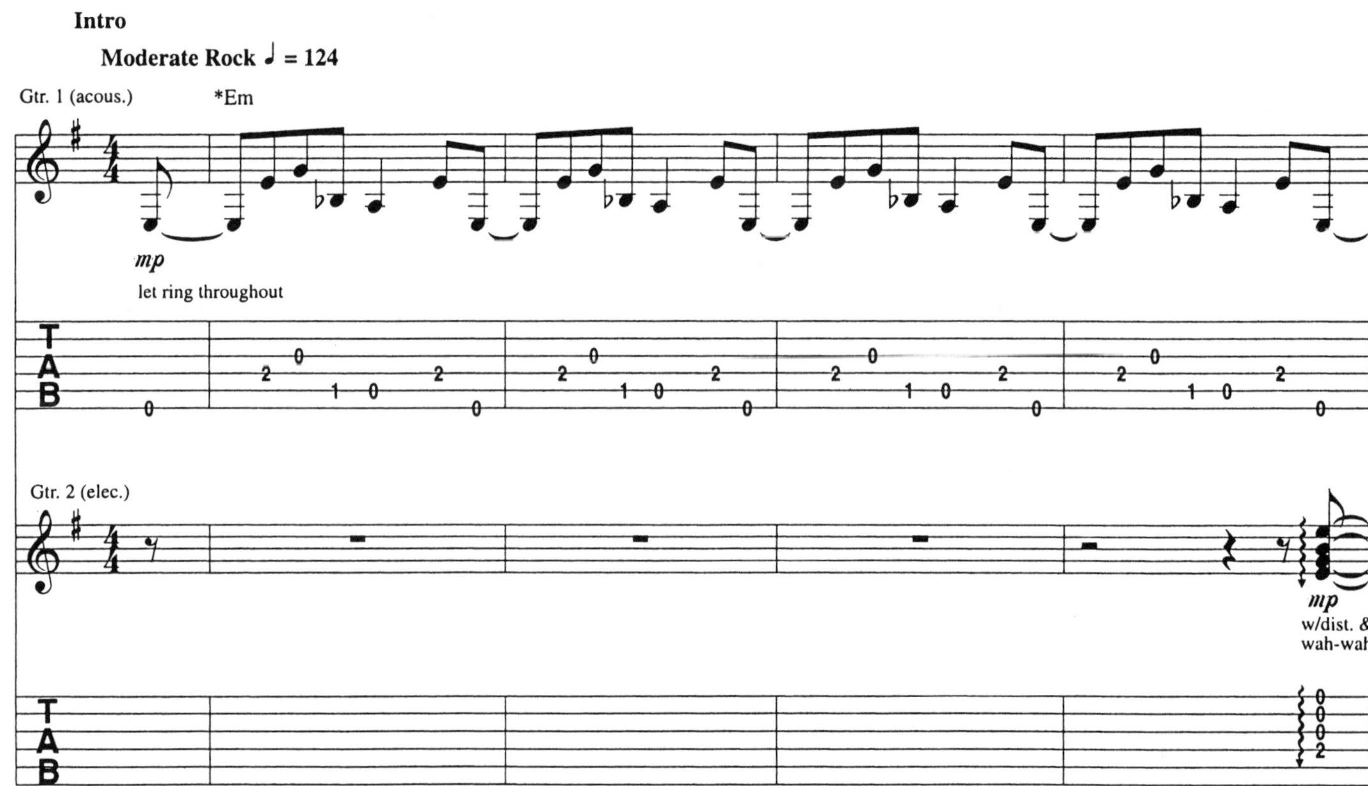

*Chord symbols reflect implied tonality.

Copyright © 1991 Creeping Death Music (ASCAP)
International Copyright Secured All Rights Reserved

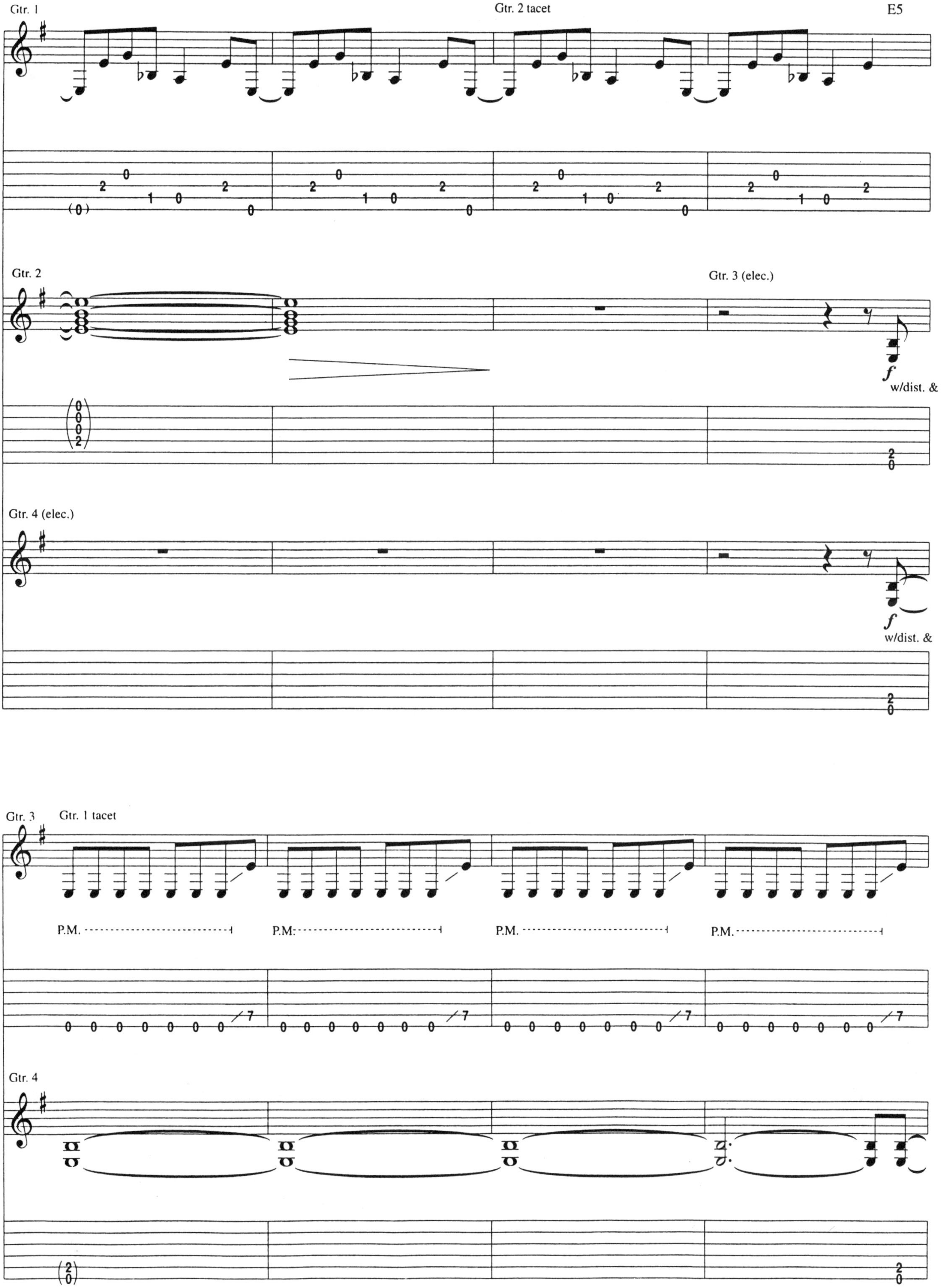

Gtr. 1
Gtr. 2 tacet
E5
Gtr. 2
Gtr. 3 (elec.)
f
w/dist. &
Gtr. 4 (elec.)
f
w/dist. &
Gtr. 3
Gtr. 1 tacet
P.M.
P.M.
P.M.
P.M.
Gtr. 4

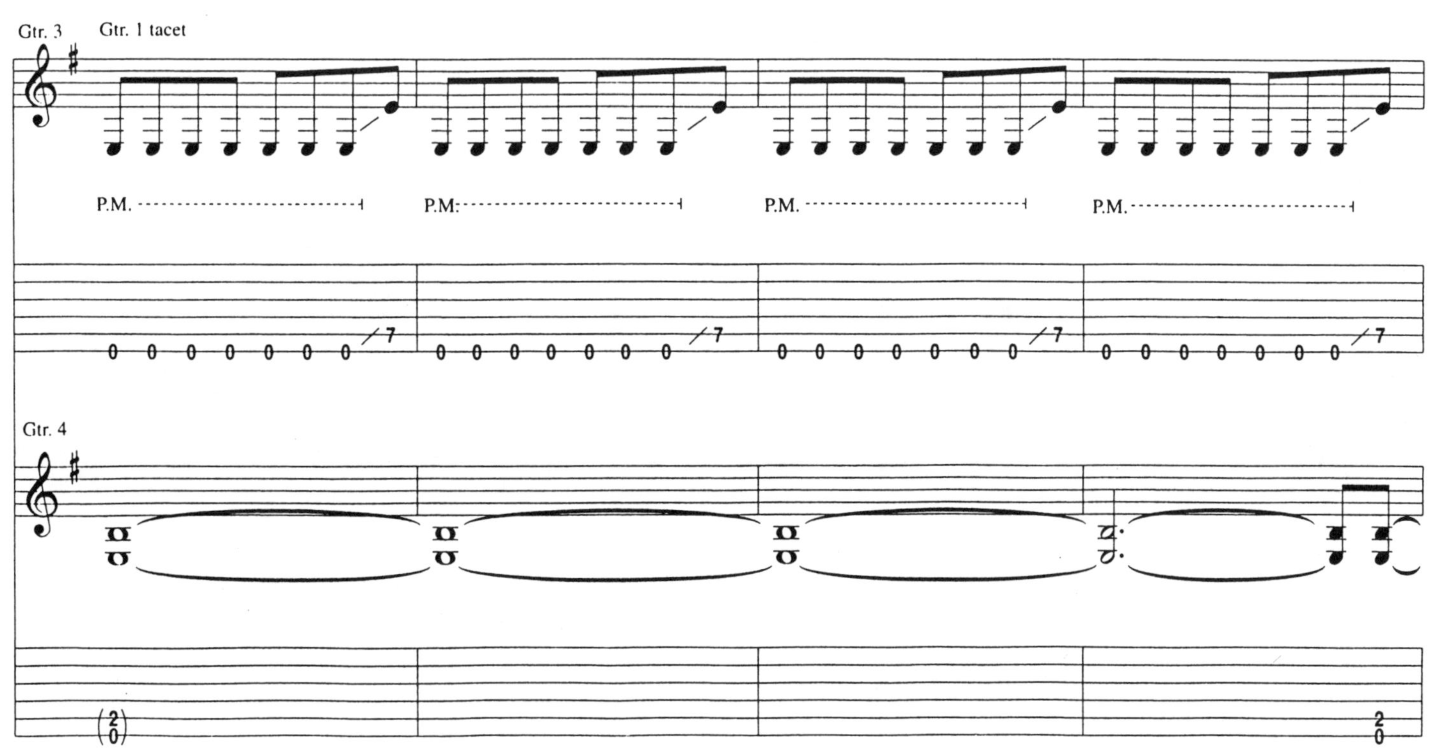

P.M.
A5
E5

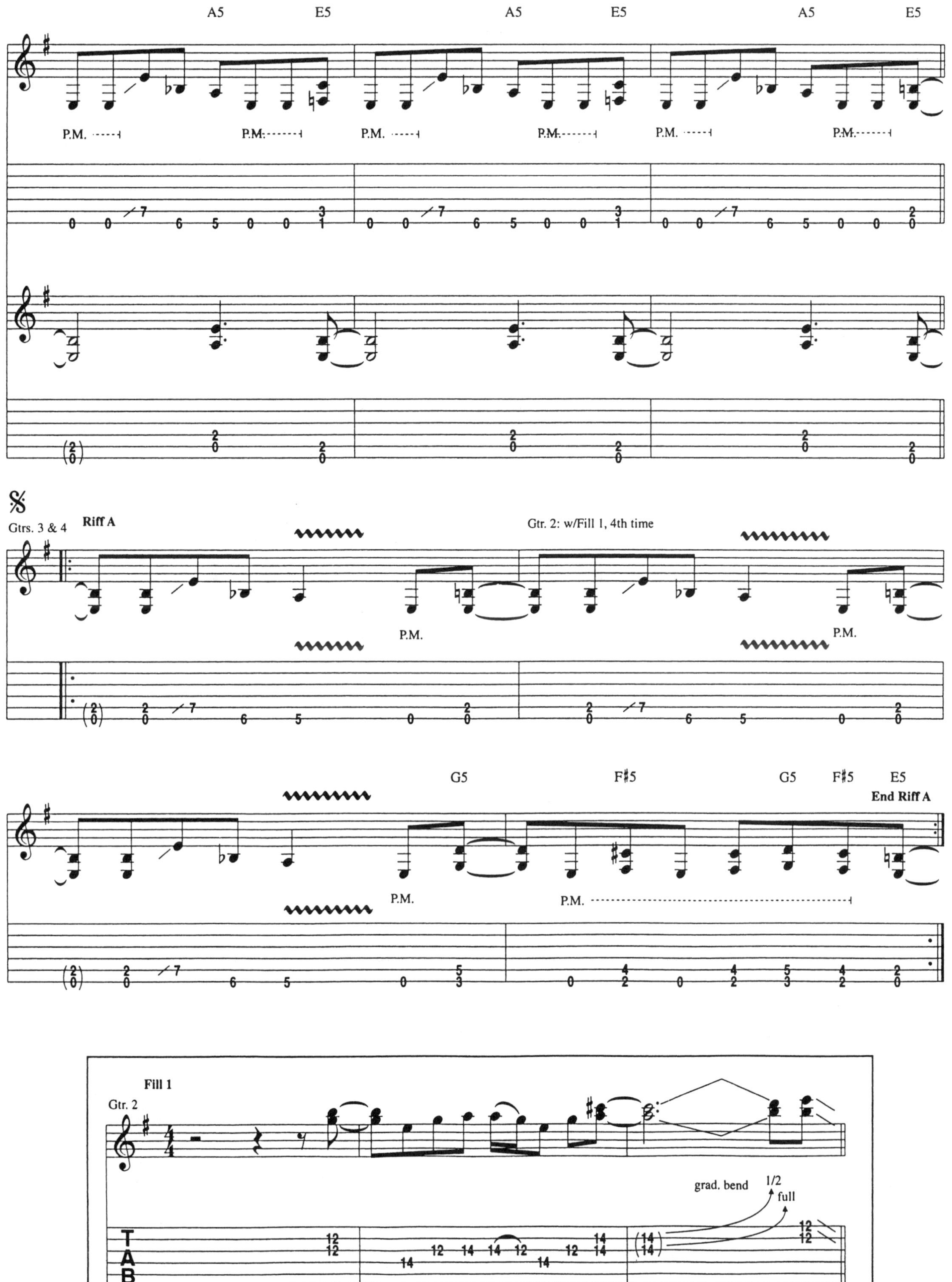
A5
E5
A5
E5
A5
E5
P.M.
Gtrs. 3 & 4
Riff A
Gtr. 2: w/Fill 1, 4th time
P.M.
G5
F♯5
G5
F♯5
E5
End Riff A
Fill 1
Gtr. 2
grad. bend
1/2
full

Verse
E5
F5
E5
F5
1. Say your prayers, lit - tle one. Don't for - get, my son,
2. Some - thing's wrong, shut the light. Heav - y thoughts to - night,
P.M.
P.M.
Gtr. 2: w/Fill 2, 2nd time
E5
G5
F♯5
G5
F♯5
E5
to in - clude ev - 'ry - one.
and they aren't of Snow White.
P.M.
P.M.
F5
E5
F5
I tuck you in, warm with - in, keep you free from sin
Dreams of war, dreams of liars, dreams of drag - on's fire,
P.M.
P.M.
Fill 2
Gtr. 2
T
A
B

Pre-Chorus
Half-Time Feel
E5
G5
F#5
G5 F#5
F#5
till the sand - man, he comes, ah.
and of things that will bite, yeah.
Sleep with one
Riff B
P.M.
End Half-Time Feel
eye o - pen, grip - ping your pil - low tight.
End Riff B
Chorus
F#5 B5 F#5 B5 F#5 B5 E5
Ex - it: light.
En - ter: night.
Gtr. 3
Riff C
Gtr. 4
P.M.

To Coda
D.S. al Coda
F♯5
B5
E5
G5
F♯5
G5
F♯5
E5
Take my hand.
We're off to nev - er nev - er land.
End Riff C
P.M.
P.M.
Coda
G5
F♯5
G5
E5
off to nev - er nev - er land.
Heh, heh.
Gtr. 2
full
Gtr. 3
P.M.
Gtr. 4

Guitar Solo
Gtrs. 3 & 4: w/Riff A, 1¾ times
E5
Gtr. 2
hold bend
w/bar
-1/2
full
G5
F♯5
E5
8va
5:4
Gtrs. 3 & 4: w/Fill 3
loco
Fill 3
Gtrs. 3 & 4
P.M.

Half-Time Feel
Gtrs. 3 & 4: w/Riff B
1/2
full
End Half-Time Feel
Gtrs. 3 & 4: w/Riff C
B5
F♯5
full
E5
let ring
*grad release
w/bar
*Gradually release bend while articulating trem. bar in rhythm indicated.
8va
5:4

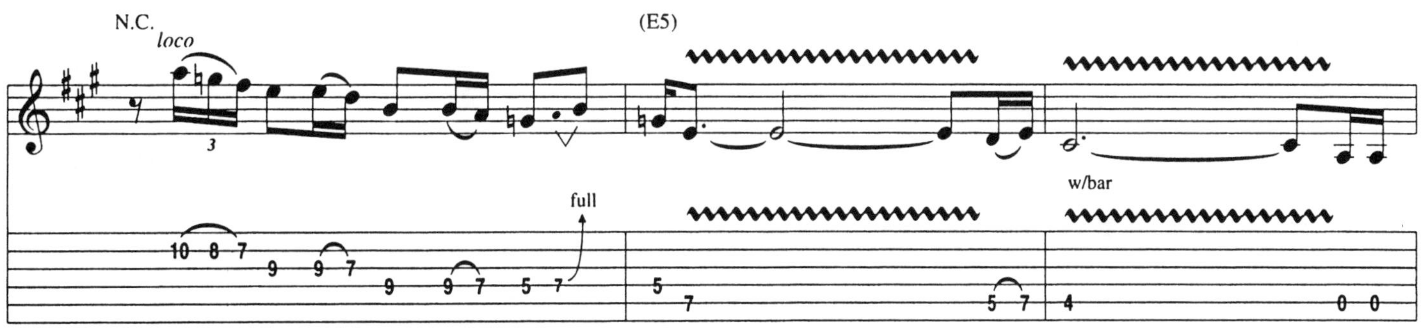
N.C.
loco
(E5)
full
w/bar

Gtr. 2
w/bar
Gtr. 1

Bridge

Em
Spoken: Now I lay me down to sleep. Pray
Child: Now I lay me down to sleep.
8va
w/bar
let ring

Gtr. 2 tacet
the Lord my soul to keep.
Pray the Lord my soul to keep.
If
Gtr. 1
(0)
2 0 1 0 2 0
2 0 1 0 2 0
I die before I wake,
If I die before I wake,
pray
(0)
2 0 1 0 2 0
2 0 1 0 2 0
F♯5
the Lord my soul to take.
pray the Lord my soul to take.
Gtr. 1
(0)
2 0 1 0 2 0
2 0 1 0 2
Gtr. 3
2

Hush, lit - tle ba - by, don't say a word.
Gtr. 3
P.M.
P.M.
And nev - er mind that noise you heard.
It's just the beasts un - der
P.M.
P.M.
P.M.
B5
your bed,
in your clos - et, in your head.
Gtr. 3
P.M.
P.M.
P.M.
Gtr. 4
P.M.

Chorus
F♯5 B5 F♯5 B5 F♯5 B5 E5
Ex - it: light.
En - ter: night.
P.M.
F♯5 B5 E5 F♯5 B5 F♯5 B5 F♯5
Grain of sand.
Ex - it: light.
P.M.
P.M.

B5 E5
F♯5 B5 E5
En - ter: night.
Take my hand.
We're
P.M.
Outro
G5 F♯5 G5 F♯5 E5
E5
off to nev-er nev-er land.
Yeah.
Heh, heh, heh, ha, ha, ha.
Oo!

Yeah,
yeah!
Gtrs. 3 & 4
P.M.
P.M.
P.M.
P.M.
G5
F♯5
G5
F♯5
Em
F5
Yo,
whoa!
Gtrs. 3 & 4
P.M.
P.M.
P.M.
Gtr. 1

w/ad lib voc., till fade
Em
F5
Em
F5
Em
F5
P.M.
P.M.
P.M.
P.M.
P.M.
P.M.

Gtr. 2: w/Fill 4, 5th & 9th time
Em
F5
Em
play 4 times
Play 12 Times and Fade
P.M.
P.M.
P.M.
P.M.

Fill 4
Gtr. 2
wah-wah off

(Everything I Do) I Do It for You

Words and Music by Bryan Adams, Robert John Lange and Michael Kamen

Copyright © 1991 ALMO MUSIC CORP., 2855 MUSIC, MIRACLE CREEK MUSIC, INC., ZOMBA ENTERPRISES, INC. and ZACHARY CREEK MUSIC, INC.
All Rights for 2855 MUSIC Controlled and Administered by ALMO MUSIC CORP.
All Rights Reserved Used by Permission

Pre-Chorus

Chorus

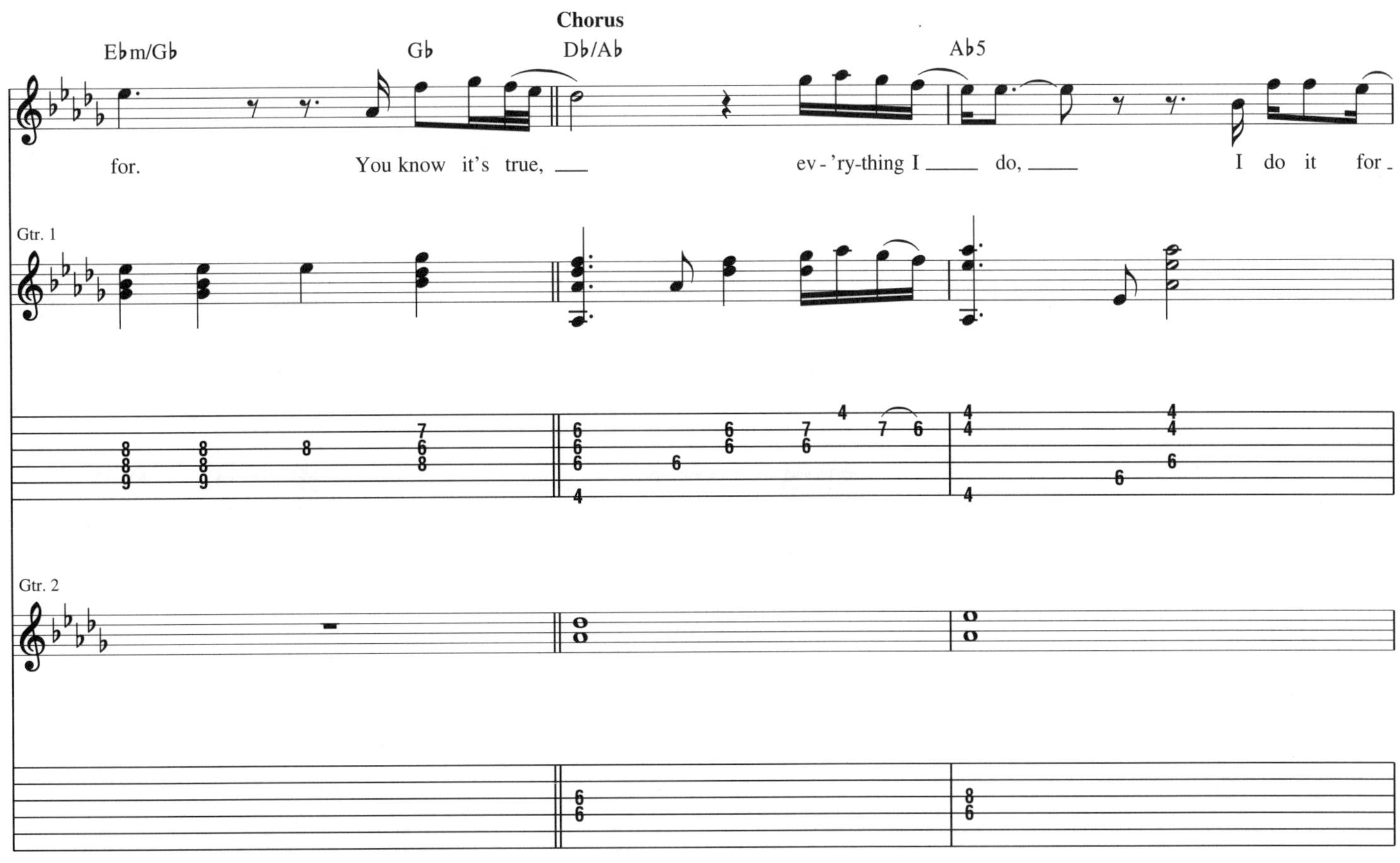

Verse
Gtr. 1 tacet
Gtr. 4: w/ Rhy. Fill 1
Dbsus2
Db
you.
2. Look in - to your heart,
Gtr. 1
Gtr. 3 (elec.)
mp w/ dist.
** w/ bar
** Bar used for vibrato throughout.
Gtr. 2
Rhy. Fig. 1
mp
* Vol. swell
Ab/Db
Gb
Ab5
you will find there's noth - in' there to hide.
Take me as I
End Rhy. Fig. 1
Gtr. 2: w/ Rhy. Fig. 1
Db
Ab/Db
Gb
Db
Ab5
am, take my life.
I will give it all, I would sac - ri - fice. Don't
Gtr. 3
* Vol. swell
Rhy. Fill 1
Gtr. 4 (elec.)
1.
2.
w/ dist.
mp

Pre-Chorus
Gtr. 4 tacet
(Dm)
(C/E)
(Dm)
Gtr. 6: w/ Riff A
(C/E)
Gtr. 5 (acous.)
mf
let ring throughout
tell me it's not worth fight - in' for. I can't help it, there's noth - in' I want
p
Gtr. 3
Gtr. 2
divisi
Gtr. 6 (elec.)
Riff A
End Riff A
mf
w/ clean tone
let ring throughout
Chorus
Gtr. 3 tacet
Gtr. 4: w/ Rhy. Fill 1 (1st 2 meas.)
(Dm)
(C)
(G)
more. You know it's true, ev-'ry-thing I do, I do it for
p
Gtr. 3
Gtr. 2
Gtr. 2
Bridge
Gtr. 4 tacet
Gtr. 2 tacet
(C)
(Cadd4)
(C)
(B♭)
you, oh yeah. There's no love like
Gtr. 4
Gtr. 4
Gtr. 7
Gtr. 2
divisi
** Gtr. 7 (elec.)
f
w/ dist.
* Gtr. 4 to left of slash in tab
** Doubled throughout

(E♭)
(B♭)
(F)
your love, and no oth - er could give more love. There's
Gtr. 7
(C)
(G)
(D)
no - where un - less you're there all the time, all the
(G)
(Gsus4)
Guitar Solo
Gtr. 7 tacet
(F)
way, yeah.
pp
Gtr. 8 (elec.)
mf
w/ slight dist.

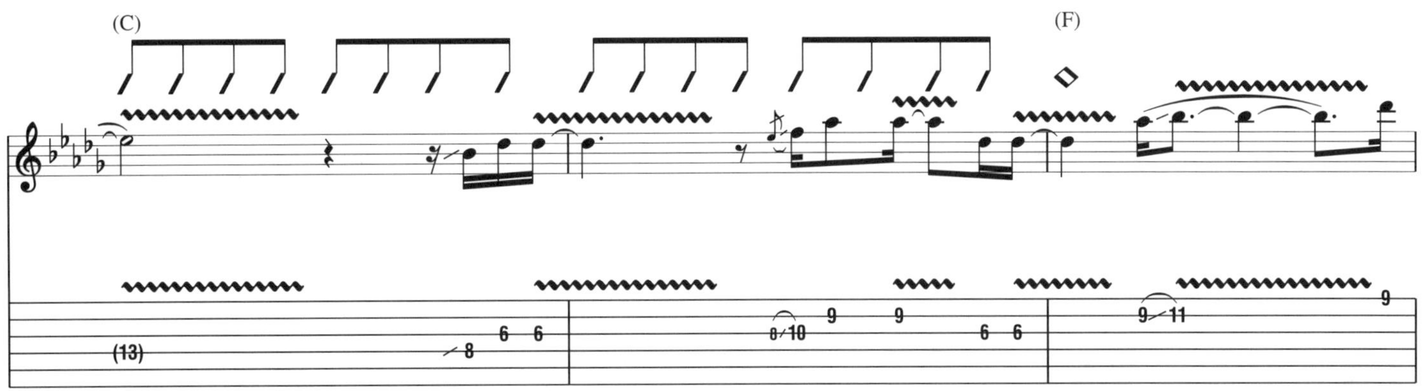
(C)
(F)

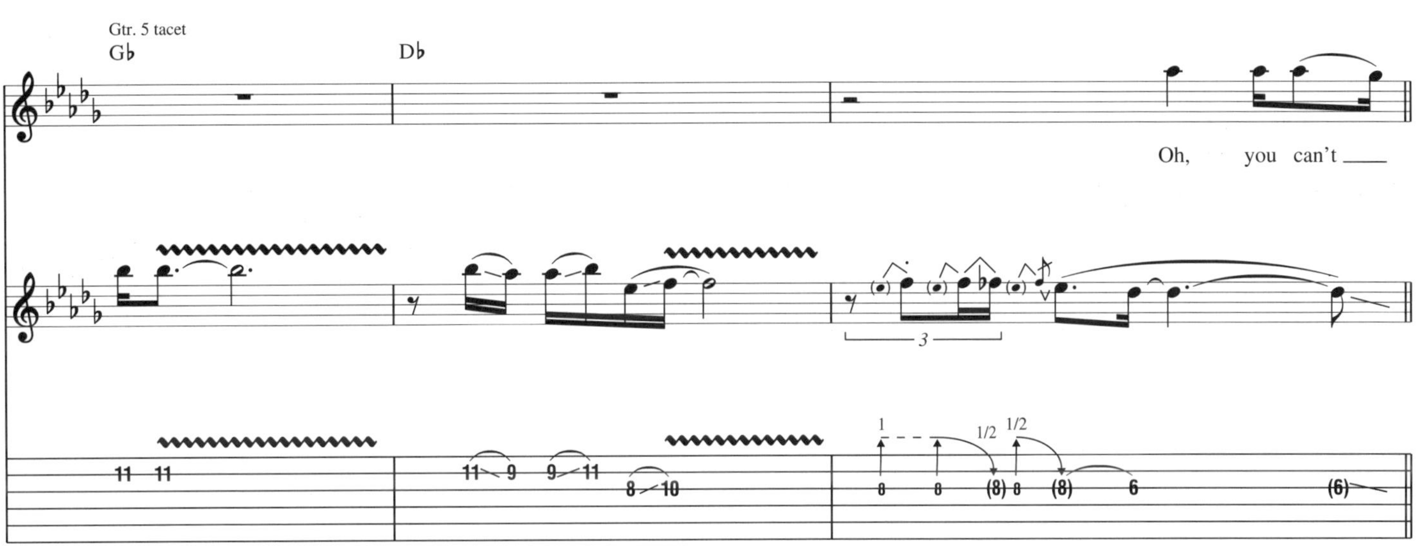
Gtr. 5 tacet
G♭
D♭
Oh, you can't

Pre-Chorus

E♭m
A♭
E♭m
tell me it's not worth try - in' for. I can't help it, there's noth - in' I want
Gtr. 8
mp
w/ bar
Gtr. 4
mp

Ab
Gtr. 4 tacet
(C)
Gtr. 5
Gtr. 8 tacet
(G)
more. Yeah, I would fight for you, I'd lie for you, walk the
Gtr. 8
Gtr. 4
Gtr. 3
Gtr. 7
Gtr. 3 tacet
(F)
(Fm)
Gtrs. 5 & 7 tacet
wire for you. Yeah, I'd die for you. You know it's
Gtr. 7
pp

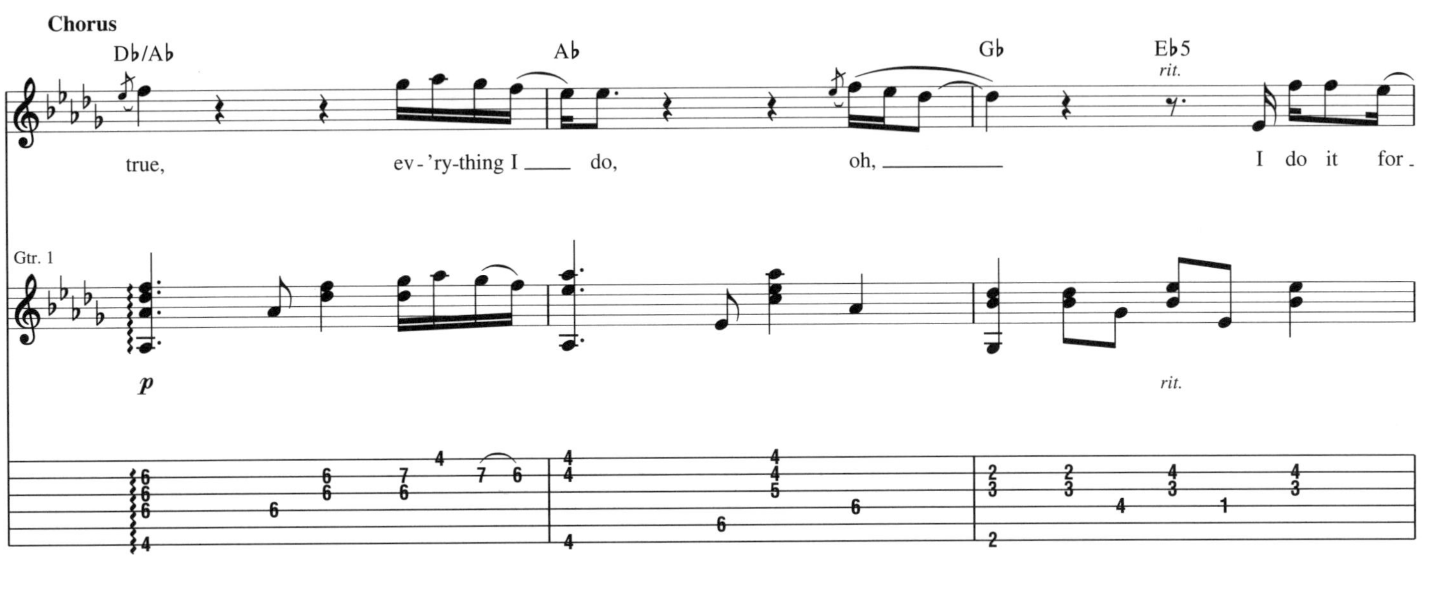

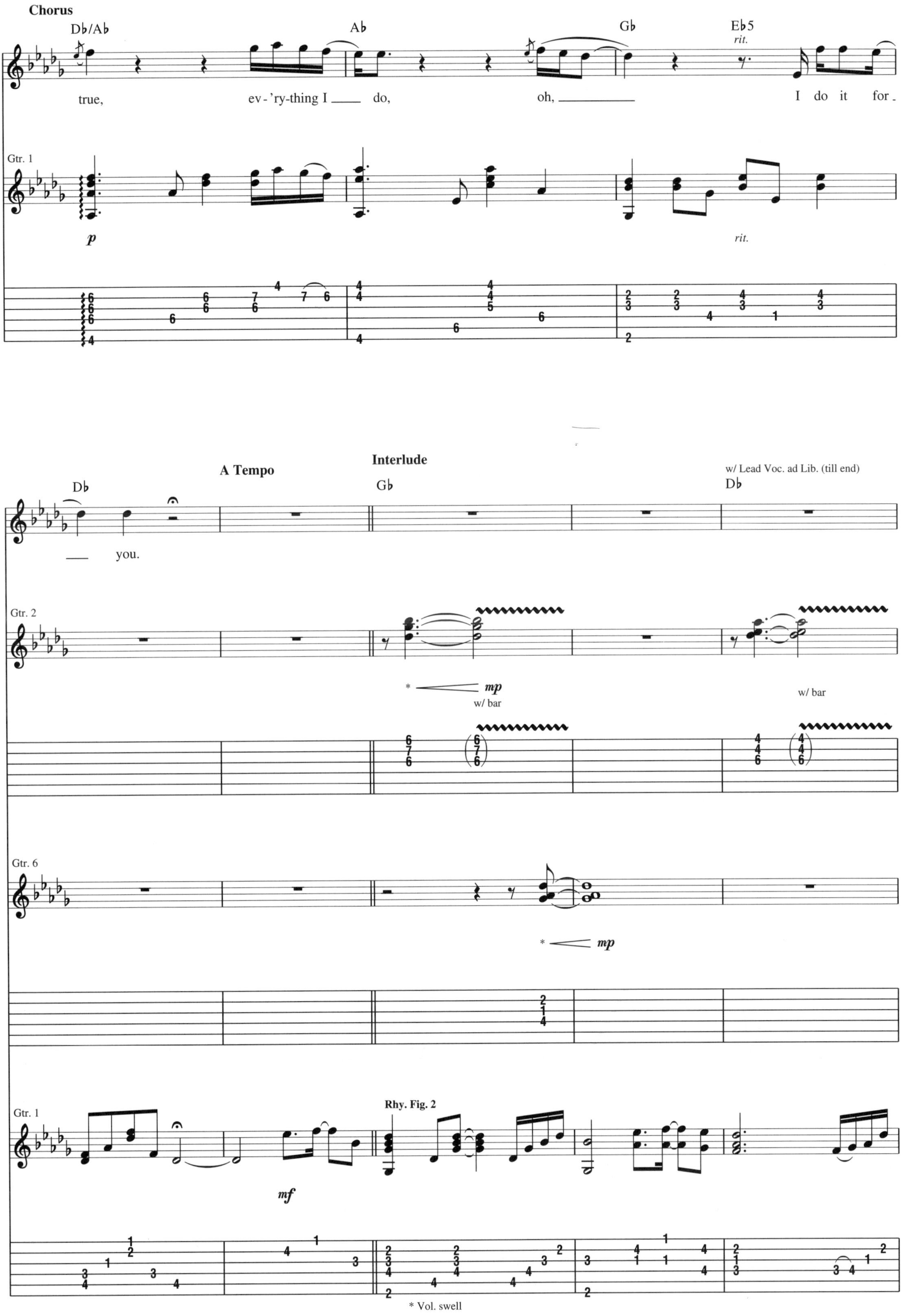

Chorus
Db/Ab
Ab
Gb
Eb5
rit.
true, ev-'ry-thing I ___ do, oh, ___ I do it for
Gtr. 1
p
rit.
Db
A Tempo
Interlude
Gb
w/ Lead Voc. ad Lib. (till end)
Db
___ you.
Gtr. 2
mp
w/ bar
w/ bar
Gtr. 6
mp
Gtr. 1
Rhy. Fig. 2
mf
* Vol. swell

Gtr. 2 tacet
Gb
Db
Gtr. 7
f
w/ bar
End Rhy. Fig. 2
* Vol. swell
Gtr. 1: w/ Rhy. Fig. 2
Gtr. 6 tacet
(F)
(C)
Rhy. Fig. 3
Gtr. 5
End Rhy. Fig. 3
Gtr. 7
Rhy. Fig. 3A
End Rhy. Fig. 3A
Outro-Guitar Solo
Gtr. 1: w/ Rhy. Fig. 2 (till fade)
Gtrs. 5 & 7: w/ Rhy. Figs. 3 & 3A (till fade)
Gb
* (F)
Db
(C)
Gtr. 8
f
1/2
fdbk.
P.H.
w/ bar
-1
* Symbols in parentheses represent chord names respective to capoed guitar.
Symbols above reflect actual sounding chord. Capoed fret is "0" in tab.
Gb
(F)
Db
(C)
1/2

Gb
(F)
Db
(C)
let ring
Gb
(F)
Db
(C)
8va
rake
rake
w/ bar
1
1
1/2
8va
Gb
(F)
Db
(C)
1 1/2
w/ bar
let ring
Begin fade
8va
Gb
(F)
Db
(C)
8va
loco
w/ bar
let ring
Gb
(F)
Db
(C)
Fade out
1/2

Fields of Gold

Written and Composed by Sting

© 1993 G.M. SUMNER
Published by MAGNETIC PUBLISHING LTD. and Administered by EMI BLACKWOOD MUSIC INC. in the USA and Canada
All Rights Reserved International Copyright Secured Used by Permission

(Gadd9)
(D)
Bm7
So she took her love for to
See the west wind move like a
let ring throughout
Gadd9
D
gaze a while upon the fields of barley. In his
lover so upon the fields of barley. Feel her
Bm7
Gadd9
D
G/*B
Asus4
arms she fell as her hair came down among the fields of gold.
body rise when you kiss her mouth among the fields of gold.
*bass plays B
1.
N.C.(D)
2. Will you
2.
Dsus2
Bridge
Asus4
D
I never made promises lightly

Asus4
D
Asus4
D
and there have been some that I've bro - ken, but I swear in the days still left we'll walk
G/B
Asus4
N.C.(D)
G/B
Asus4
N.C.(D)
in fields of gold. We'll walk in fields of gold.
w/ octave divider
Guitar Solo
N.C. *(Bsus2)
(G)
(D)
*Chord symbols in parentheses reflect overall tonality.
(Bsus2)
(G)
(D)
(G/B)
(A)
(D)
3. Man - y
(octave divider off)
Verse
Bm7
Gadd9
years have passed since those sum-mer days a - mong the fields of bar -
mem - ber me when the west wind moves up - on the fields of bar -
simile on repeat

Dadd9
Bm7
Gadd9
Dsus4
D
- ley. See the chil - dren run as the sun goes down a - mong -
- ley. You can tell the sun in his jeal - ous sky when we
G/B
A
1.
Dadd9
2.
Dadd9
the fields of gold. 4. You'll re -
walked in fields of gold.
when we
G/B
A
Dadd9
G/B
A
walked in fields of gold,
when we walked in fields of gold.
Outro
D
Gsus2
D/F♯
D5
D/F♯
Gsus2
D
D5
D/F♯
Gsus2
D/F♯
1.
D5
D/F♯
Gsus2
D/F♯
2.
D5

Free As a Bird

Words and Music by John Lennon, Paul McCartney, George Harrison and Ringo Starr

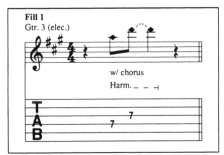

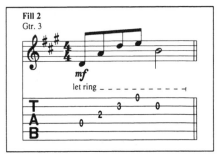

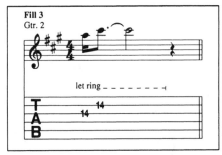

© 1977, 1985, 1995 LENONO.MUSIC
All Rights Controlled and Administered by EMI BLACKWOOD MUSIC INC.
All Rights Reserved International Copyright Secured Used by Permission

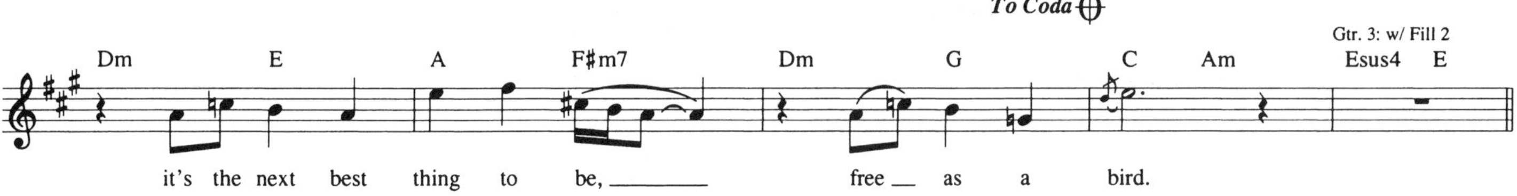
To Coda
Gtr. 3: w/ Fill 2
Dm E A F♯m7 Dm G C Am Esus4 E
it's the next best thing to be, free as a bird.

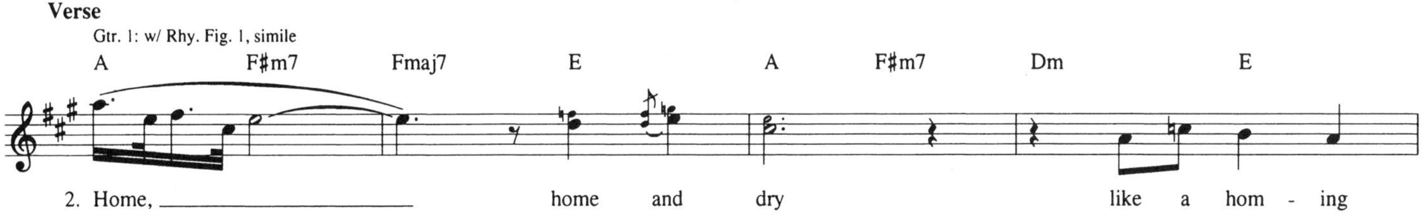
Verse
Gtr. 1: w/ Rhy. Fig. 1, simile
A F♯m7 Fmaj7 E A F♯m7 Dm E
2. Home, home and dry like a hom - ing

Gtr. 3: w/ Fill 2
A F♯m7 Dm G C Am Esus4 E
bird I fly, as a bird on wings.

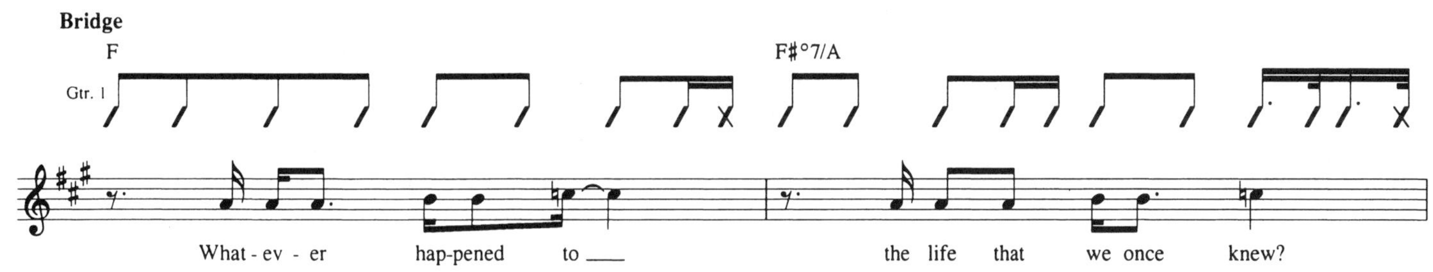
Bridge
F F♯°7/A
Gtr. 1
What - ev - er hap-pened to the life that we once knew?

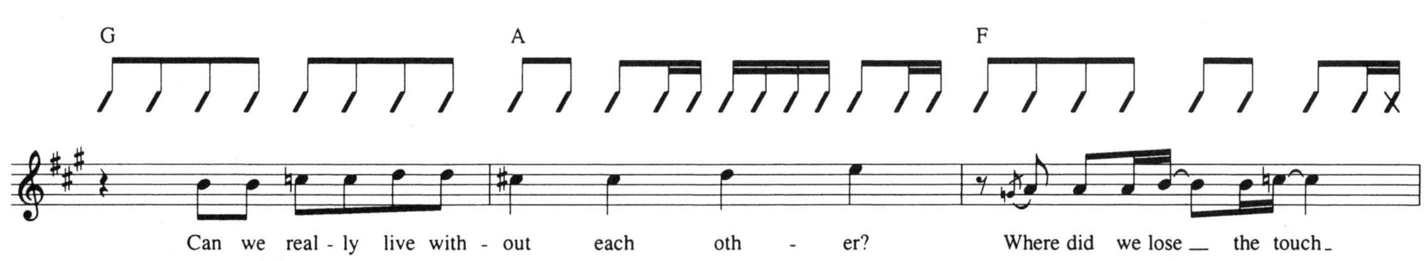
G A F
Can we real - ly live with - out each oth - er? Where did we lose the touch

F♯°7/A G Esus4 E
that seemed to mean so much? It al - ways made me feel so...

Verse
Gtr. 1: w/ Rhy. Fig. 1, simile
A F♯m7 Fmaj7 E A F♯m7 Dm E
3. Free as a bird, it's the next best
Gtr. 3
mf
let ring let ring let ring simile
A F♯m7 Dm G C Am Esus4 E
thing to be, free as a bird.
Riff A
End Riff A
Verse
Gtr. 1: w/ Rhy. Fig. 1, 1st 7 meas. only
A F♯m7 Fmaj7 E A F♯m7
4. Home, home and dry
(Home,)
let ring let ring
Dm E A F♯m7 Dm G
like a hom - ing bird I fly, a bird on
let ring let ring let ring simile

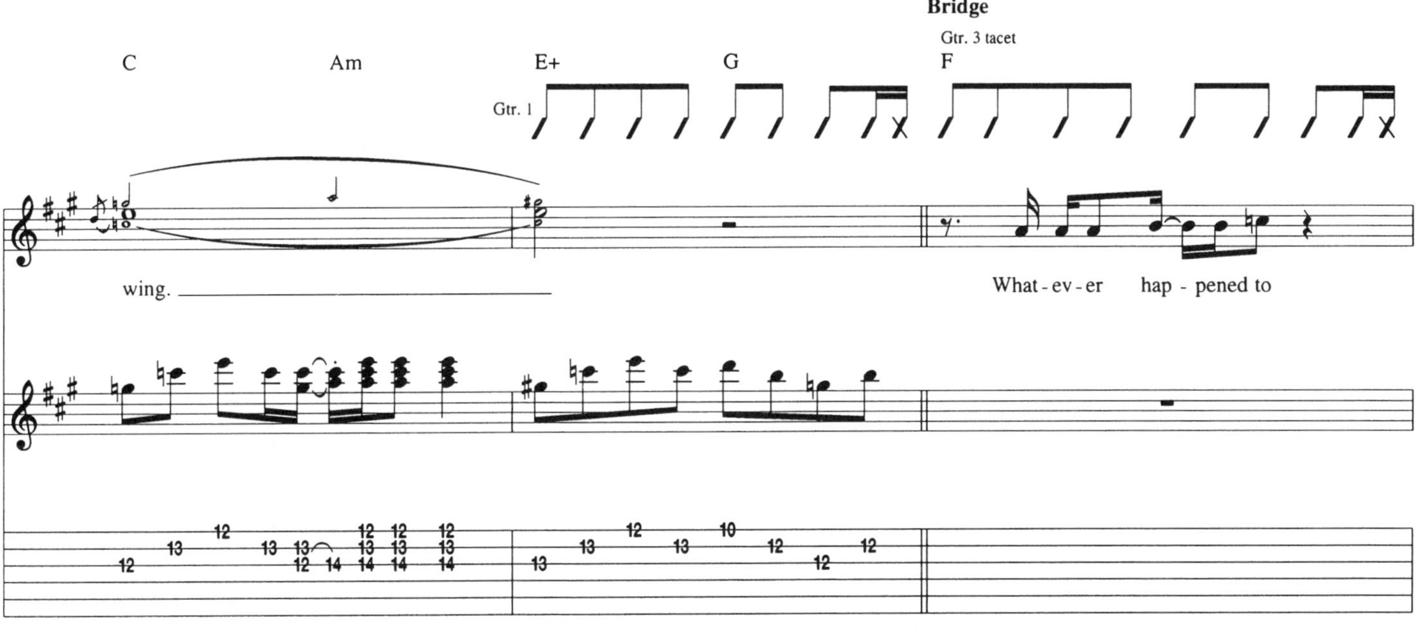

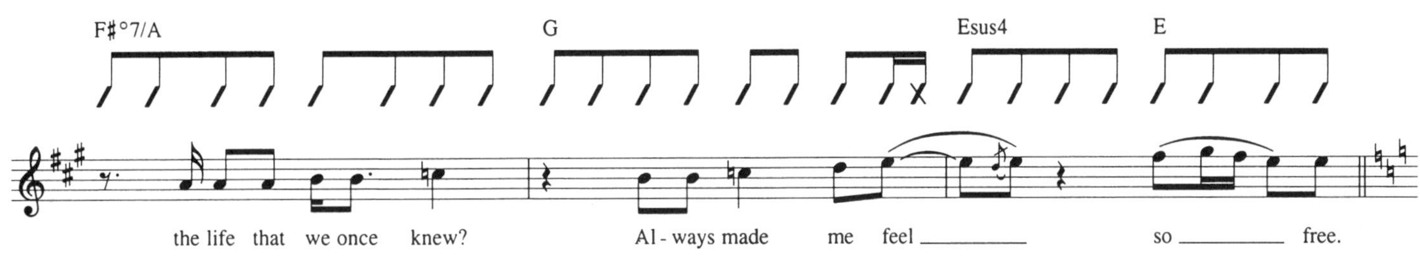

Guitar Solo

C Am7 A♭maj7 G C Am7

Gtr. 1

Ah. Ah.

Gtr. 2

w/ slide

17 17 15 17 15 17

Gtr. 3

Rhy. Fig. 2

0 1 0 2 3 | 0 1 0 2 0 | 3 4 5 6 | X X X X | X X X X | 3 3 4 5 5 3 | 0 1 0 2 3 | 0 1 0 2 0

D.S. al Coda
Gtr. 3: w/ Rhy. Fig. 2
Fm7
G
C
Am7
Ah.
(Ah. Wee. Ah.)
End Rhy. Fig. 2
Coda
Gtr. 3: w/ Riff A, 3 times
A
F♯m7
Dm
Gtr. 1
bird.
Free as a bird.
Gtr. 2
w/ slide
* Play between 5th & 6th frets.
Gtrs. 1 & 3
Free as a bird.
Woo.

I Can't Dance

Words and Music by Mike Rutherford, Phil Collins and Tony Banks

© 1991 HIT & RUN MUSIC (PUBLISHING) LTD., MICHAEL RUTHERFORD LTD., PHIL COLLINS LTD. and ANTHONY BANKS LTD.
All Rights in the United States and Canada Controlled and Administered by EMI BLACKWOOD MUSIC INC.
All Rights Reserved International Copyright Secured Used by Permission

3rd time, Gtr. 2: w/ Fill 1
B♭5
B♭sus4 B♭5
B♭7sus4
B♭5
E♭/E♭
A♭
can't dance, I can't sing. I'm just stand - ing here
Gtr. 1
Rhy. Fig. 2
1.
E♭/B♭
A♭5
E♭sus4/B♭
B♭5
E♭5/B♭
2.
E♭/B♭
A♭
E♭/B♭
sell - ing ev - 'ry - thing.
sell - ing. Oh and check -
End Rhy. Fig. 2
Bridge
To Coda
G♭
Fm
E♭
- ing ev - 'ry - thing is in place. You nev - er know who's a look - ing on.
* Gtr. 2
(clean)
mf w/ fingers
let ring
* Elec. piano arr. for gtr.
Gtr. 1
D.S. al Coda
(take 2nd ending)
Gtr. 1: w/ Rhy. Fig. 1
B♭5
B♭sus4B♭5
B♭7sus4
B♭5
A♭5
A♭sus4
E♭/B♭
E♭5/B♭
Gtr. 2
Rhy. Fig. 3
End Rhy. Fig. 3
let ring

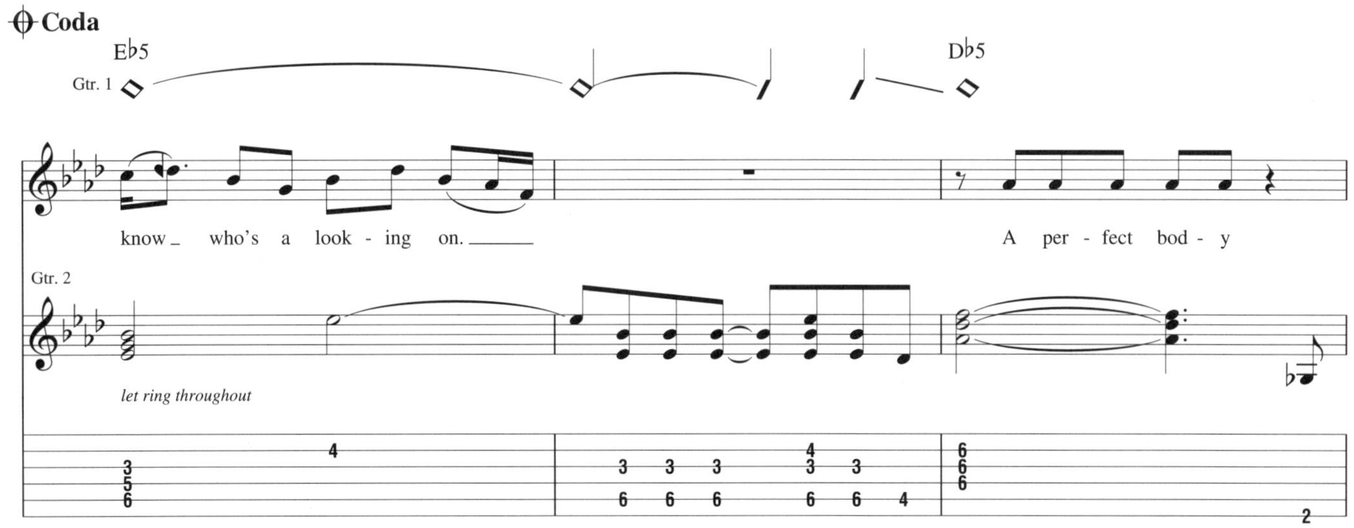
Coda
E♭5
D♭5
Gtr. 1
know_ who's a look - ing on.
A per - fect bod - y
Gtr. 2
let ring throughout

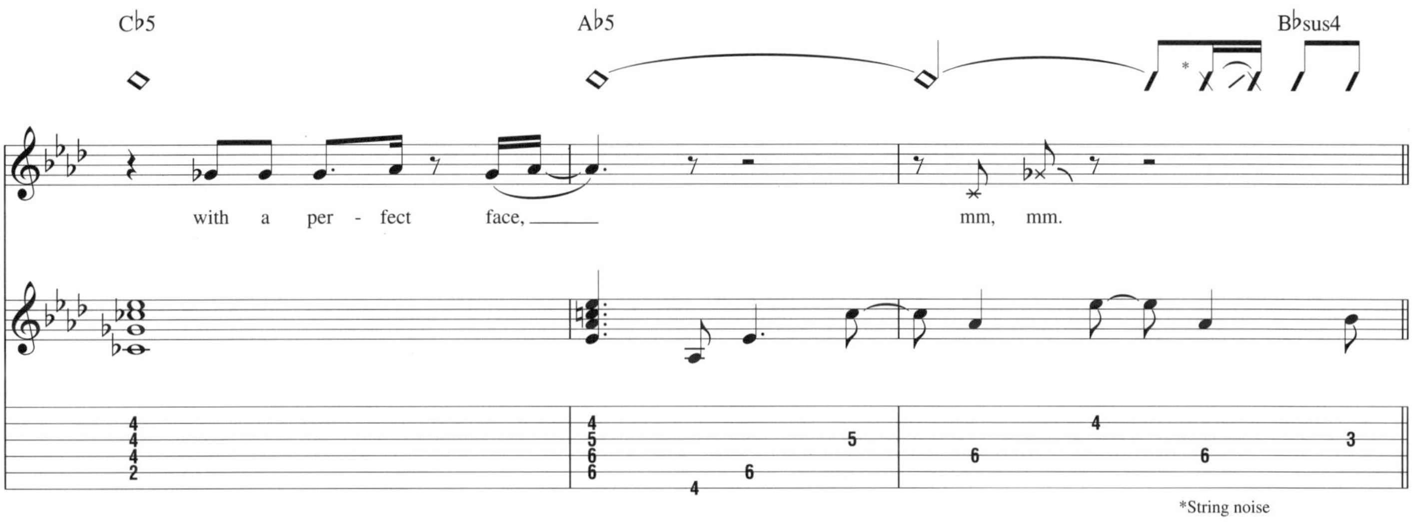
C♭5
A♭5
B♭sus4
with a per - fect face,
mm, mm.
*String noise

Interlude
Gtr. 1: w/ Rhy. Fig. 1 (4 1/2 times)
Gtr. 2: w/ Rhy. Fig. 3 (5 times)
Outro-Chorus
B♭5
B♭sus4 B♭5 B♭7sus4 B♭5
A♭5 A♭sus4 E♭/B♭ E♭5/B♭
B♭5
No I can't dance. I

B♭sus4 B♭5 B♭7sus4 B♭5 A♭5 A♭sus4 E♭/B♭ E♭5/B♭
can't talk. On - ly thing a - bout me is the way I walk. No I

B♭5 B♭sus4 B♭5 B♭7sus4 B♭5 A♭5
can't dance. I can't sing. I'm just stand - ing here

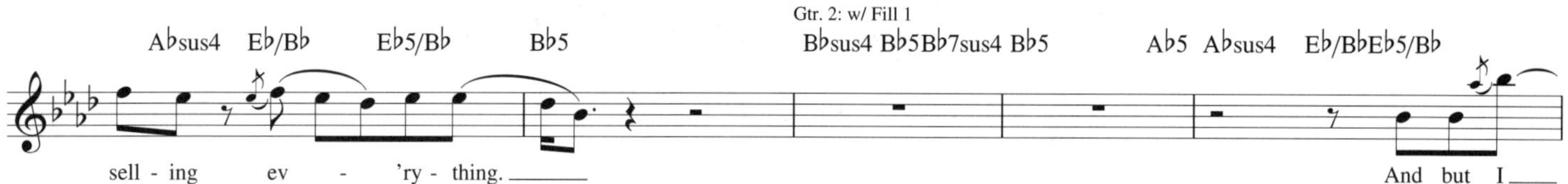
Gtr. 2: w/ Fill 1
A♭sus4 E♭/B♭ E♭5/B♭ B♭5
B♭sus4 B♭5 B♭7sus4 B♭5
A♭5 A♭sus4 E♭/B♭ E♭5/B♭
sell - ing ev - 'ry - thing.
And but I

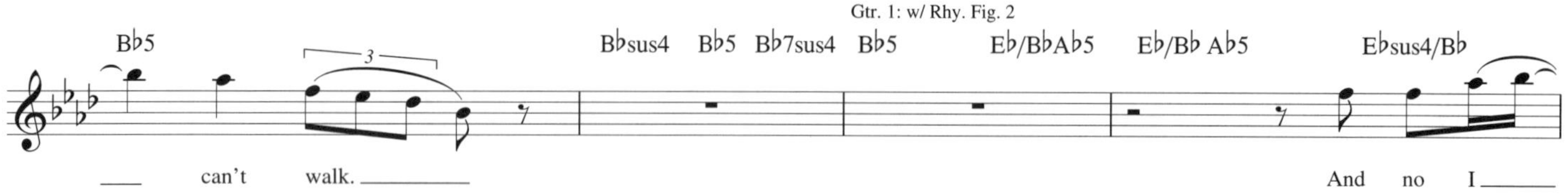
Gtr. 1: w/ Rhy. Fig. 2
B♭5
B♭sus4 B♭5 B♭7sus4 B♭5
E♭/B♭ A♭5 E♭/B♭ A♭5
E♭sus4/B♭
can't walk.
And no I

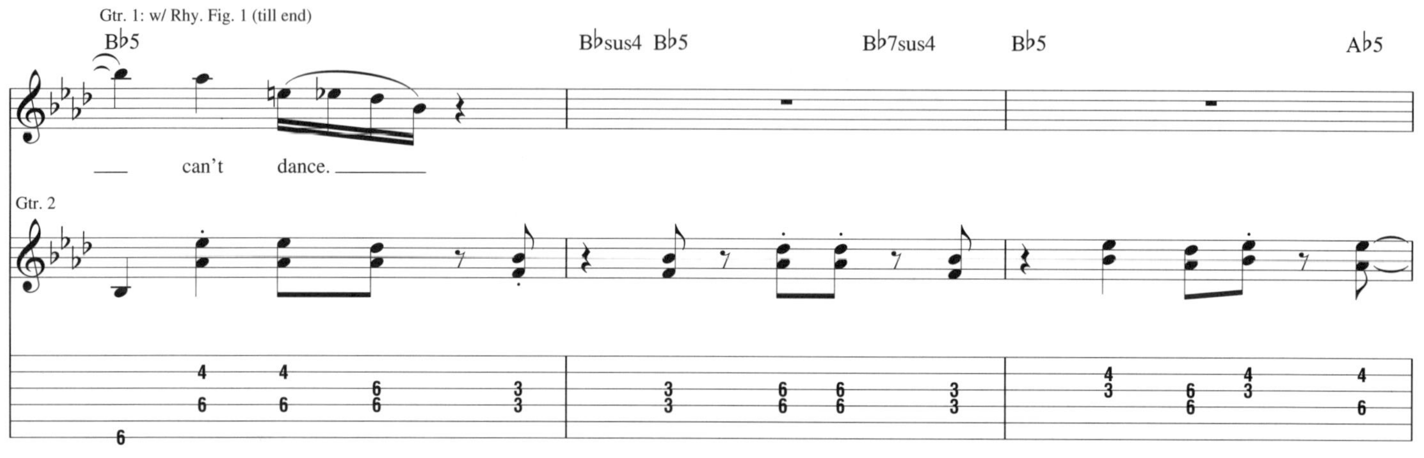
Gtr. 1: w/ Rhy. Fig. 1 (till end)
B♭5
B♭sus4 B♭5
B♭7sus4 B♭5
A♭5
can't dance.
Gtr. 2

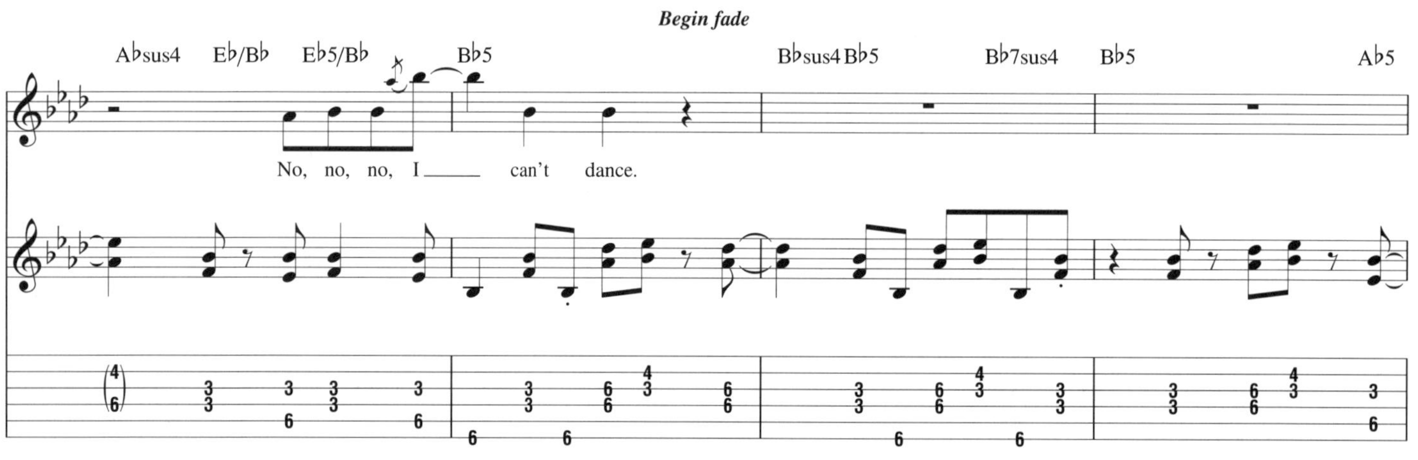
Begin fade
A♭sus4 E♭/B♭ E♭5/B♭ B♭5
B♭sus4 B♭5 B♭7sus4 B♭5
A♭5
No, no, no, I can't dance.

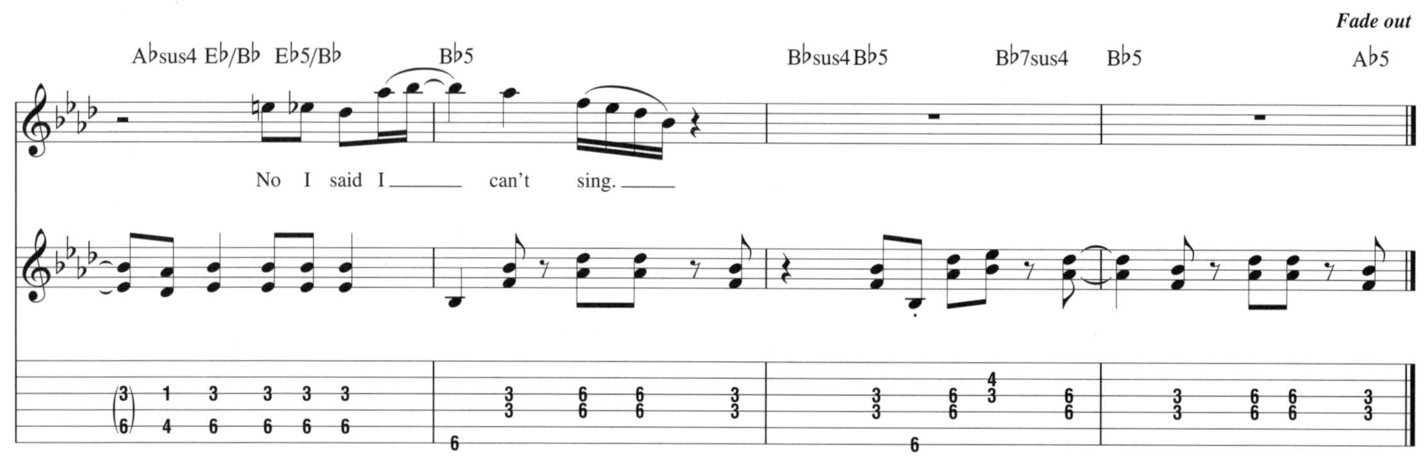
Fade out
A♭sus4 E♭/B♭ E♭5/B♭ B♭5
B♭sus4 B♭5 B♭7sus4 B♭5
A♭5
No I said I can't sing.

I'm the Only One

Words and Music by Melissa Etheridge

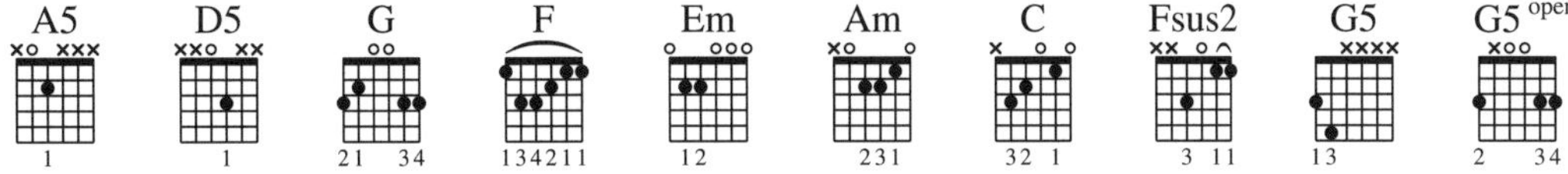

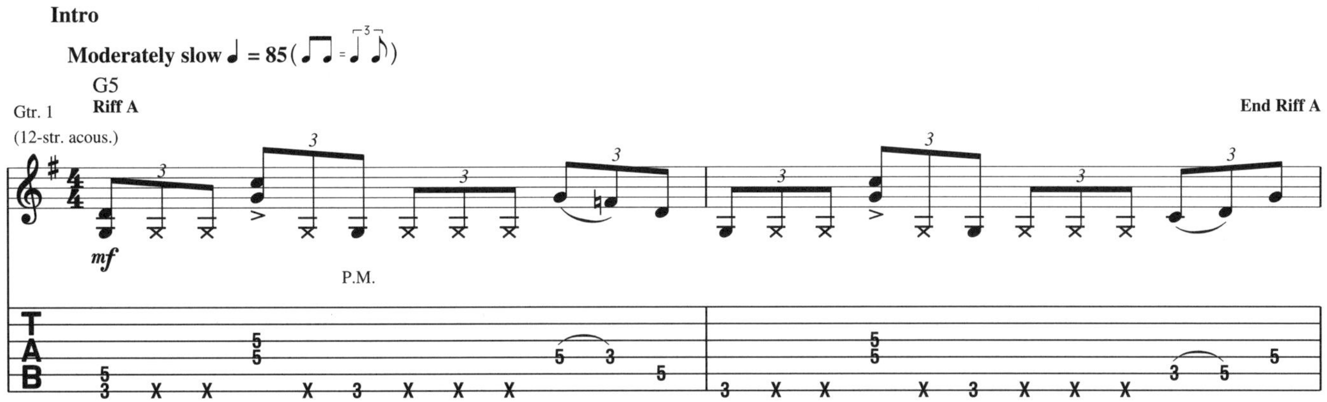

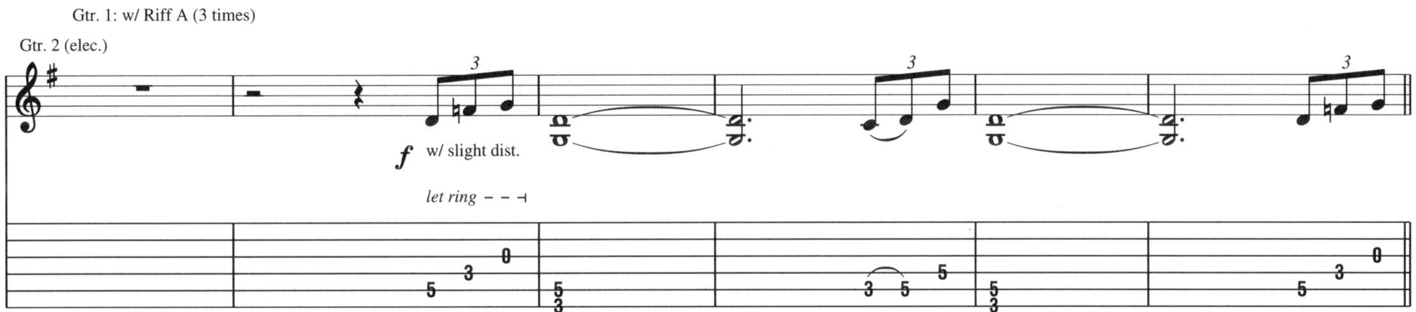

Copyright © 1993 MLE Music (ASCAP)
All Rights Reserved Used by Permission

heart a - part as well.
To - night you told _ me that you ache for some-thin' new, _ and
Rhy. Fig. 1
P.M.
let ring
some oth - er wom - an is look-in' like some-thin' that might be good _ for you.
End Rhy. Fig. 1
Pre-Chorus
A5
Rhy. Fig. 2B
Gtr. 3 (elec.)
mf w/ slight dist.
Go on and hold her 'til the
Rhy. Fig. 2
Gtr. 1
Rhy. Fig. 2A
Gtr. 2
D5
A5
D5
scream-in' is gone. _
Go on, be - lieve her when she tells you noth-in's wrong. _
End Rhy. Fig. 2B
(cont. in notation)
End Rhy. Fig. 2
(cont. in slashes)
End Rhy. Fig. 2A

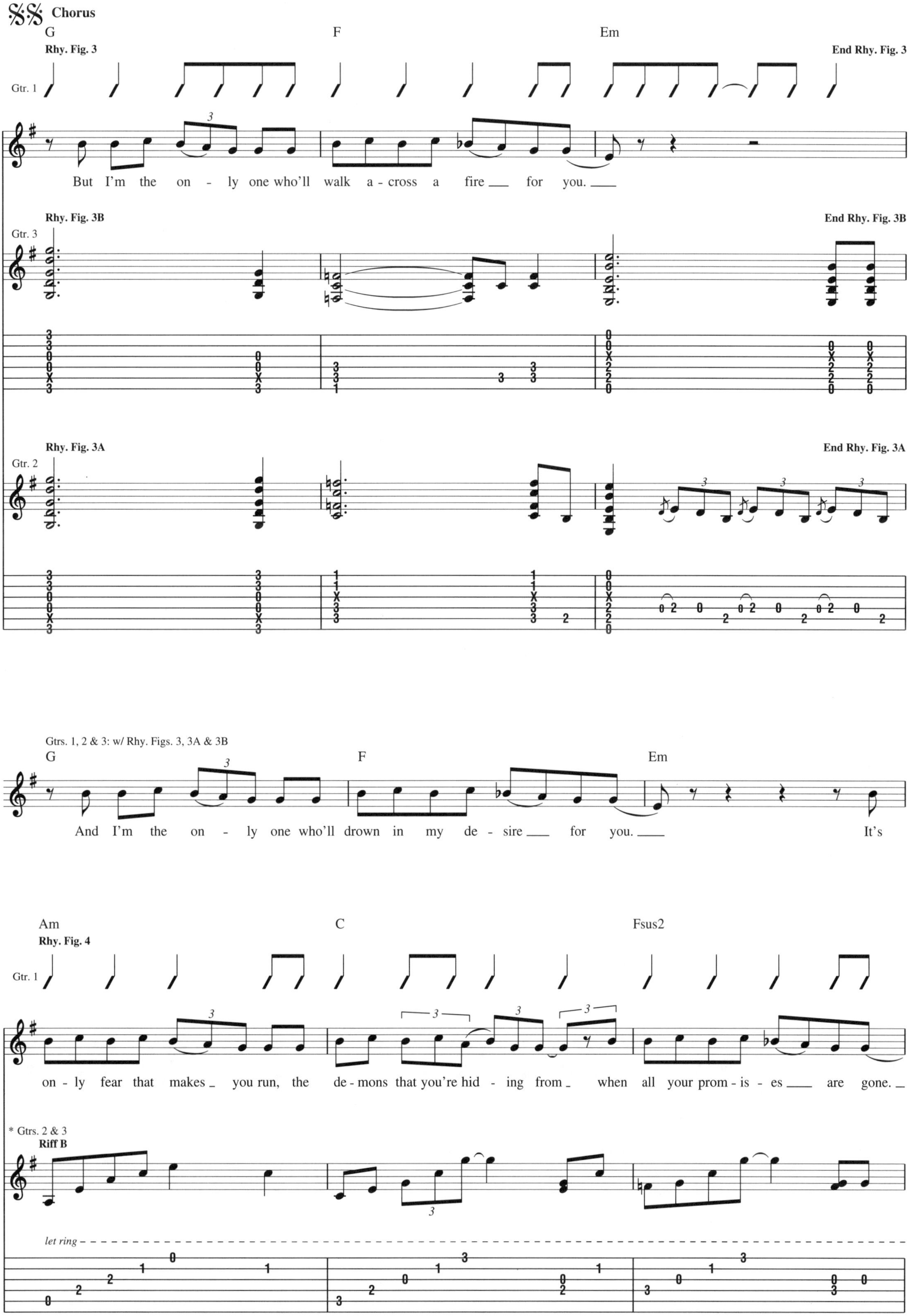

𝄋𝄋 **Chorus**

G F Em

Rhy. Fig. 3 **End Rhy. Fig. 3**

Gtr. 1

But I'm the on - ly one who'll walk a - cross a fire ___ for you. ___

Rhy. Fig. 3B **End Rhy. Fig. 3B**

Gtr. 3

Rhy. Fig. 3A **End Rhy. Fig. 3A**

Gtr. 2

*Composite arrangement.

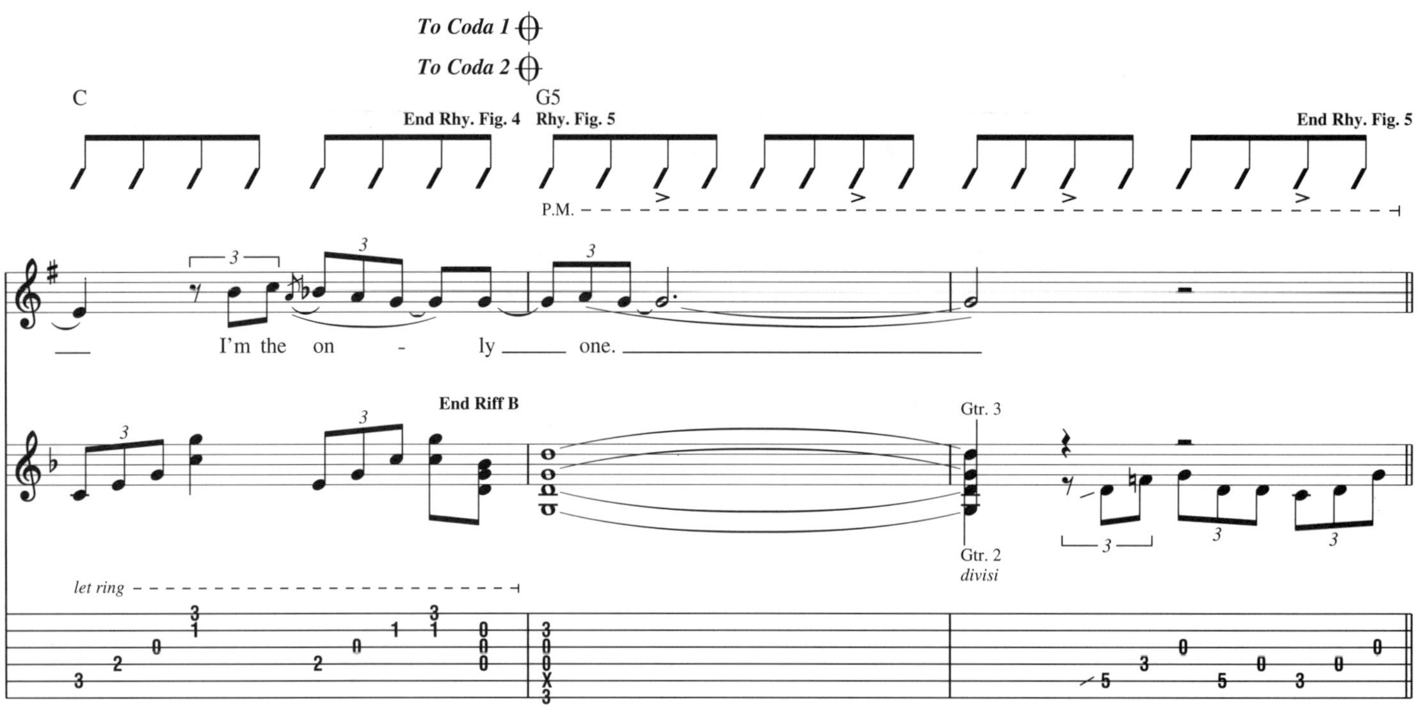
To Coda 1
To Coda 2
C
G5
End Rhy. Fig. 4
Rhy. Fig. 5
End Rhy. Fig. 5
P.M.
I'm the on - ly one.
End Riff B
Gtr. 3
Gtr. 2
divisi
let ring

Verse

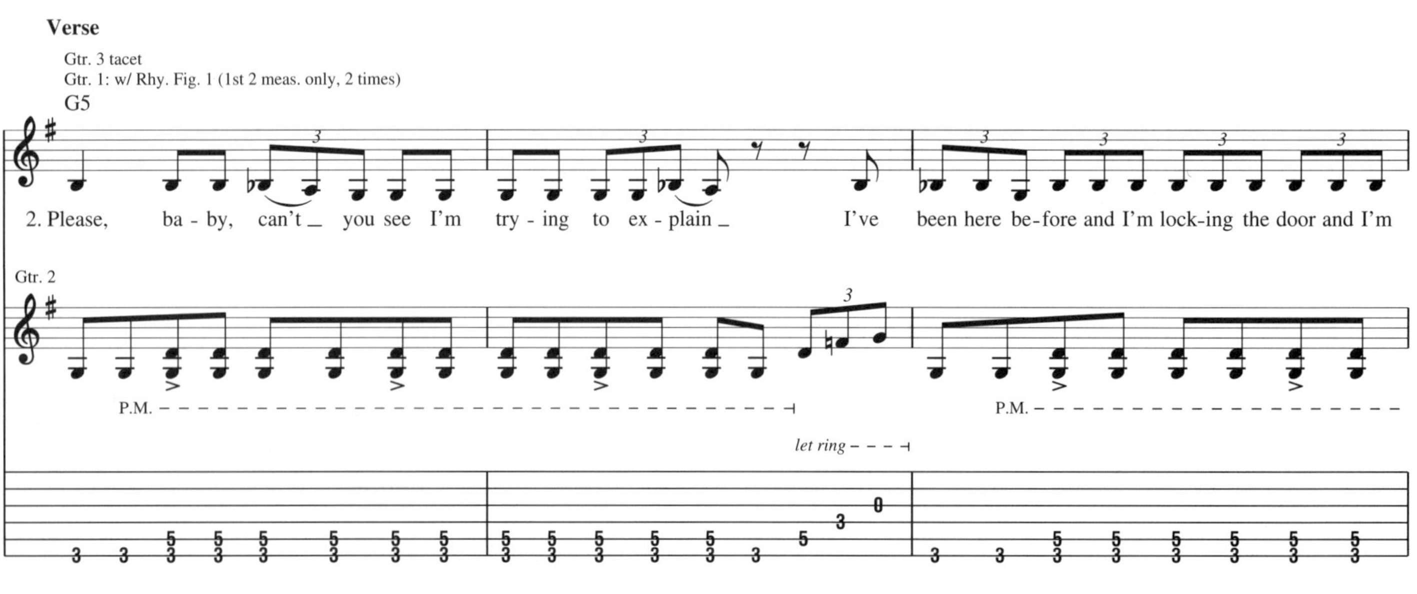
Gtr. 3 tacet
Gtr. 1: w/ Rhy. Fig. 1 (1st 2 meas. only, 2 times)
G5
2. Please, ba - by, can't you see I'm try - ing to ex - plain I've been here be - fore and I'm lock - ing the door and I'm
Gtr. 2
P.M.
let ring

Gtr. 1: w/ Rhy. Fig. 1
not go - ing back a - gain. Her eyes and arms and skin won't make it go a - way. You'll
P.M.
let ring

D.S. al Coda 1
wake up to - mor - row and wres - tle the sor - row that holds you down to - day.
P.M.

Coda 1

Guitar Solo
Gtr. 3 tacet
G5
Fsus2
one.
Gtr. 3
Gtr. 4 (elec.)
Gtr. 4
p
f w/ slight dist.
Gtr. 2
Gtr. 1
Rhy. Fig. 6
(cont. in slashes)

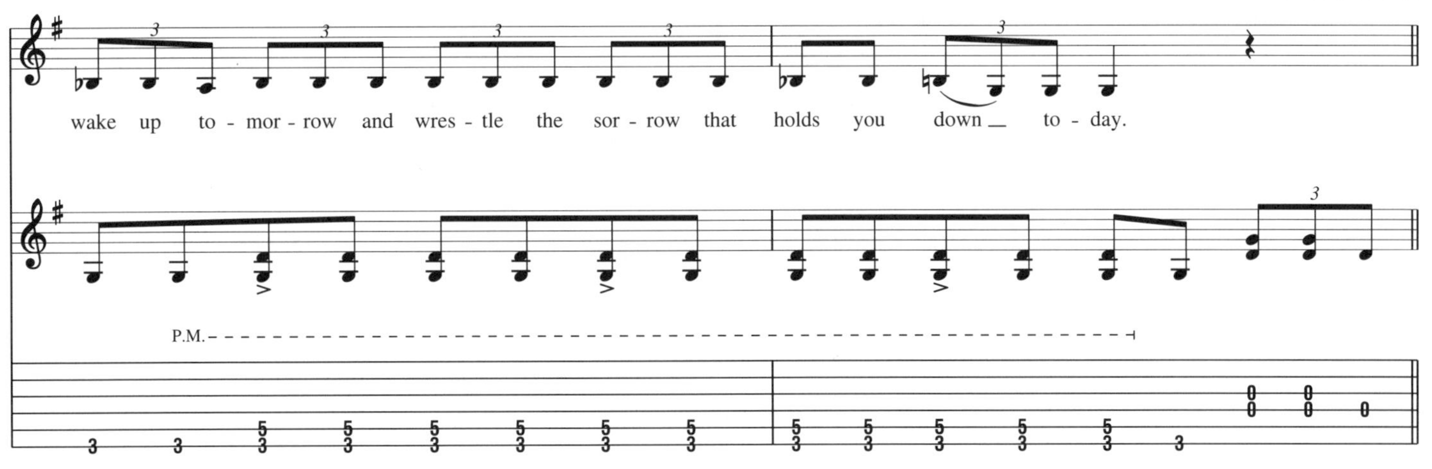

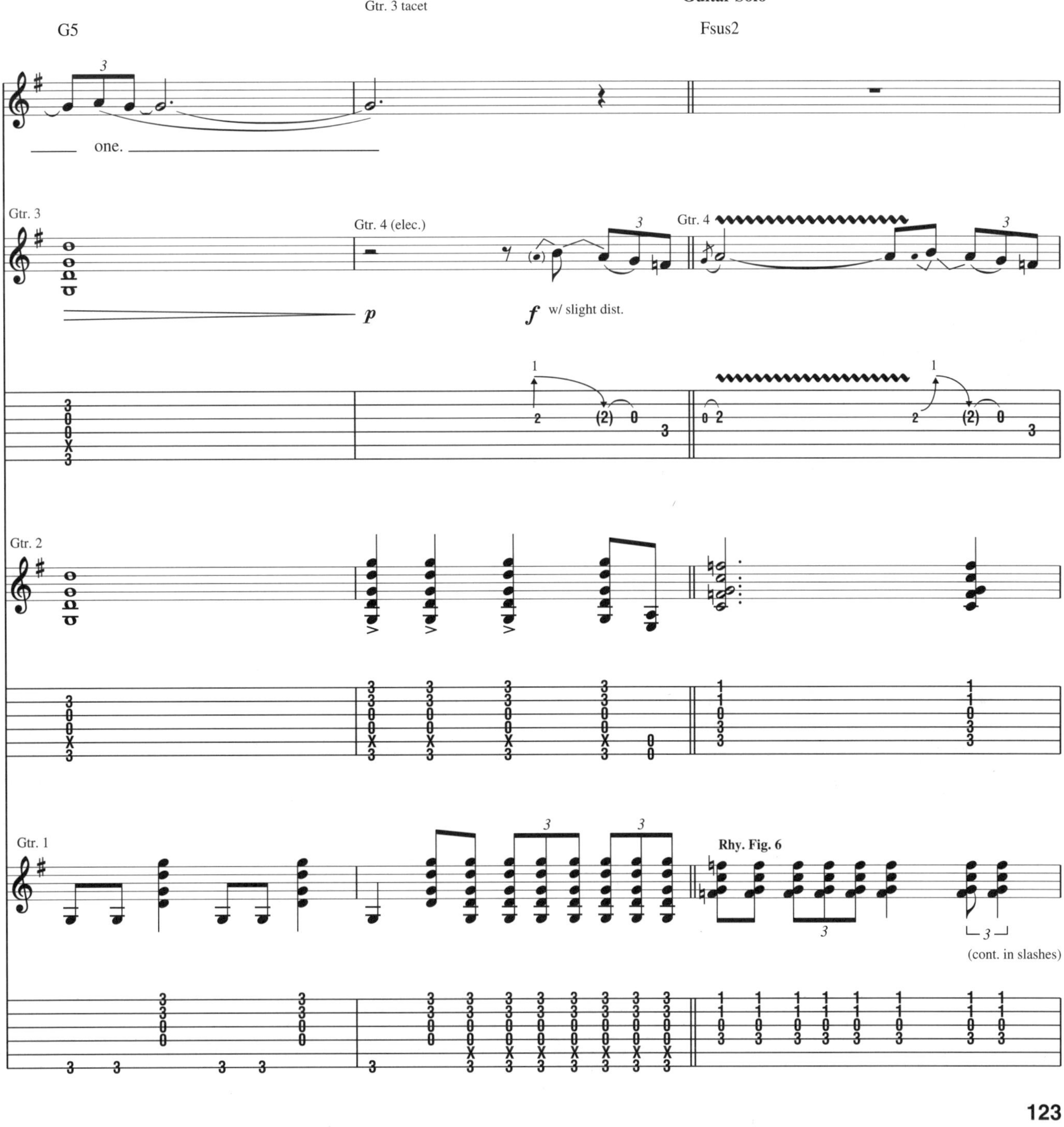

Gtr. 1
G5 open
Gtr. 4
let ring
1/2
Gtr. 2
1/4
Gtr. 1: w/ Rhy. Fig. 6
Fsus2
End Rhy. Fig. 6
let ring
hold bend
G5
Pre-Chorus
Gtrs. 1, 2 & 3: w/ Rhy. Figs. 2, 2A & 2B
A5
Go on and hold her 'til the
Gtr. 4

D5 A5 D5

scream-ing is gone. _ Go on be - lieve _ her when she tells you noth-ing's wrong.

1/2 1 1

(10) 10 (10) 8 10 10 10 13 10 10 13

𝄌 Coda 2

Gtrs. 1, 2 & 3: w/ Rhy. Figs. 3, 3A & 3B (2 times)

G F Em

_____ one, _____ yeah, _____ yeah. _____

G F Em

And I'm the on - ly one who'll drown _ in my de - sire for you. ___ It's

Gtr. 1: w/ Rhy. Fig. 4
Gtrs. 2 & 3: w/ Riff B

Am C

on - ly fear that makes _ you run, the de - mons that you're hid - in' from ___ when

Fsus2 C

all your prom - is - es _____ are gone. _____ I'm the on -

Outro

Gtr. 1: w/ Rhy. Fig. 5 (till fade)

G5

- ly ____ one. _____

Gtr. 2

let ring let ring

5 3 5 3 0 3 0 0 3 5 3 0 3

Gtr. 3

pp

5 3

I'm the on - ly one, babe.
I'm the on-ly one.
let ring
Riff C
End Riff C
mp

Begin fade
Gtr. 1: w/ Riff C (till fade)
Ain't no - bod - y else is gon - na love you,
ain't no-bod-y else is gon-na love
Gtr. 2
let ring

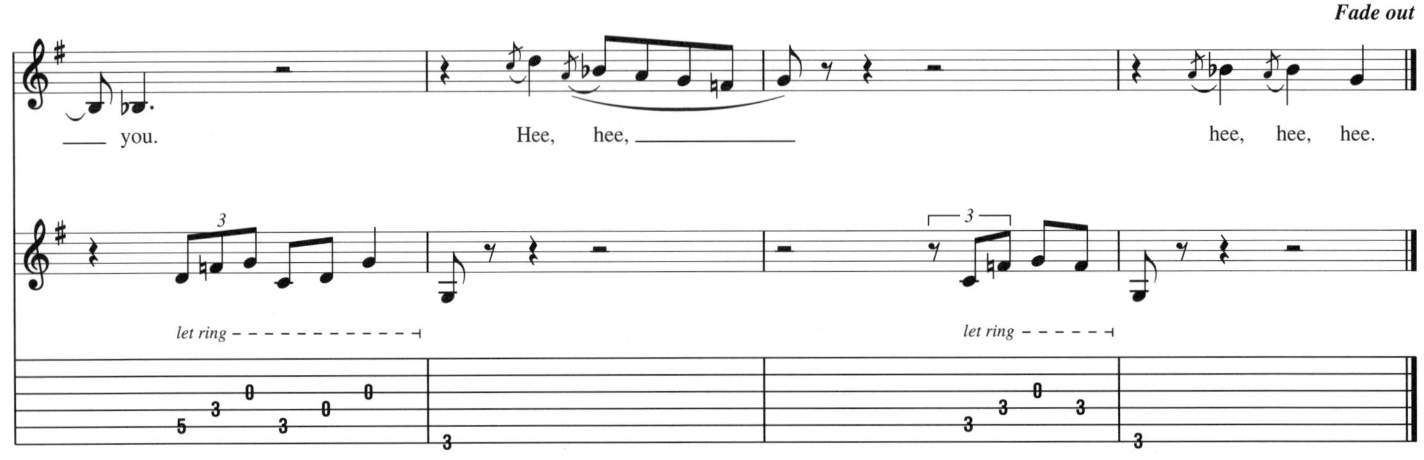
Fade out
you.
Hee, hee,
hee, hee, hee.
let ring

Jeremy

Music by Jeff Ament
Lyric by Eddie Vedder

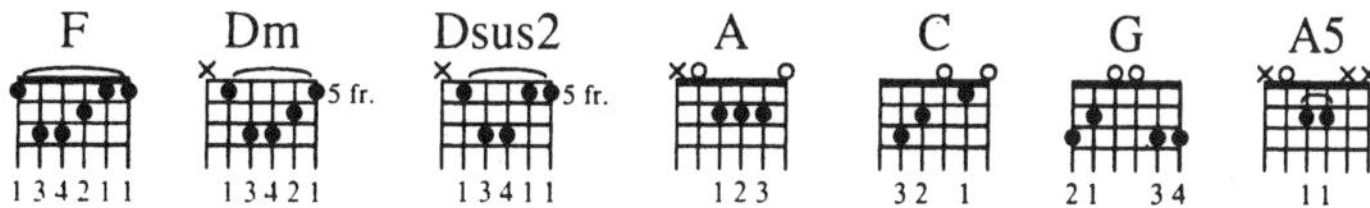

Moderate Rock ♩ = 104
Intro

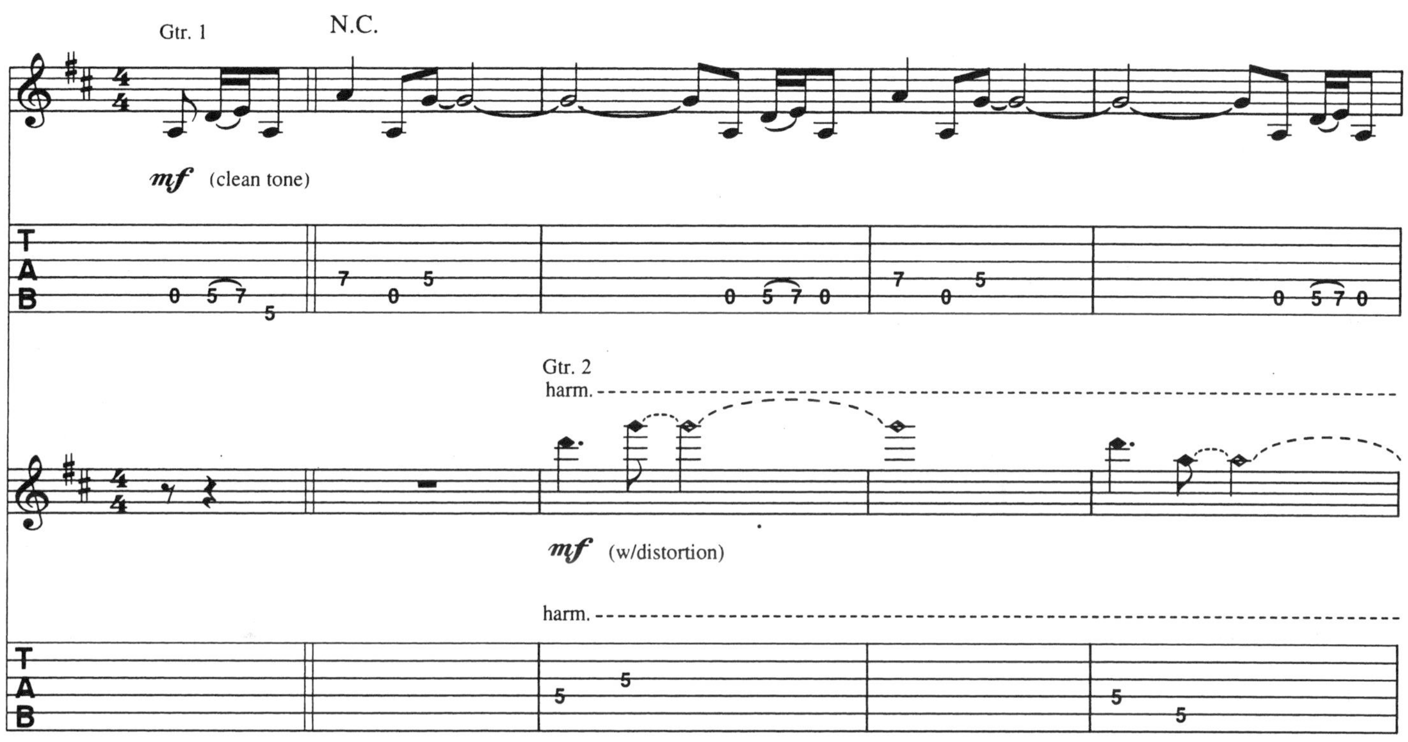

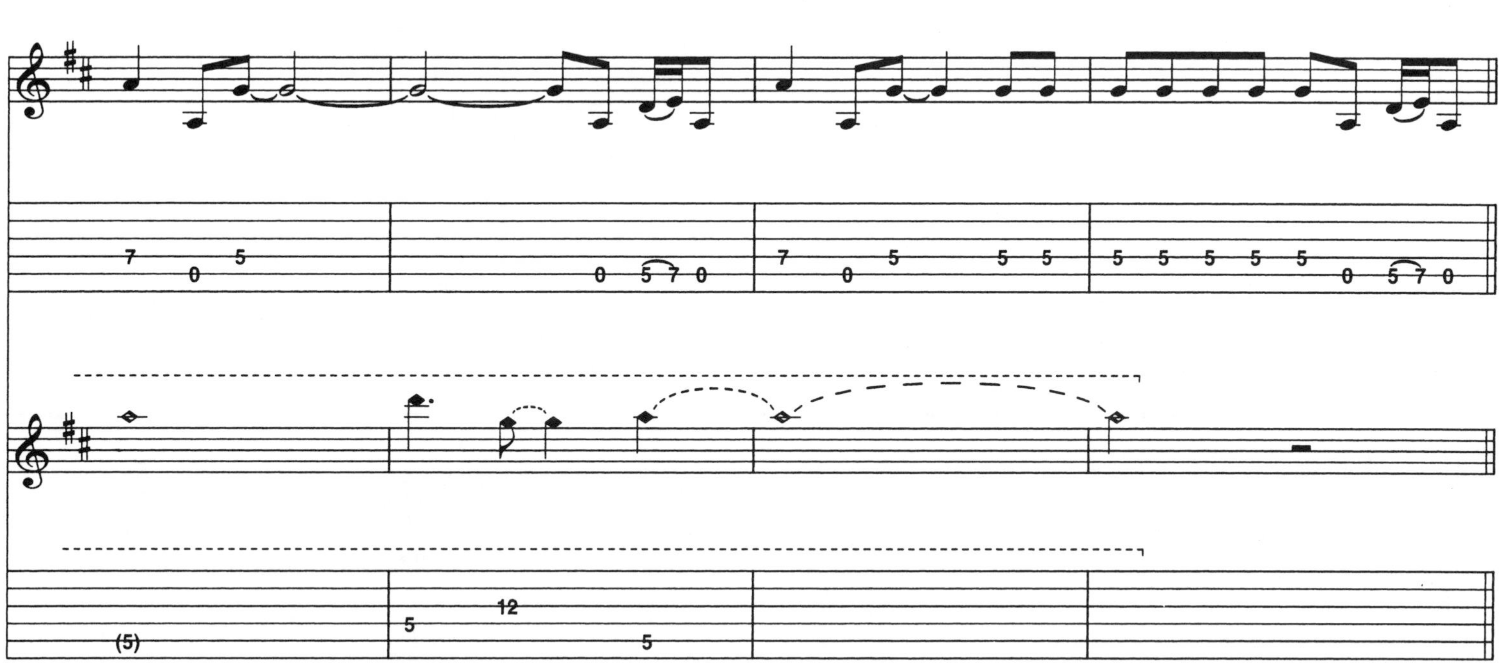

Copyright © 1991 PolyGram International Music, Inc., Scribing C-Ment Songs and Innocent Bystander
International Copyright Secured All Rights Reserved

Verse
w/Rhy. Fill 1 (2nd time only)
1. At home draw - ing pic -tures of ___ moun- tain tops, ___ with ___ him on ___
2. get? And he hit me with a sur - prise, ___ left my jaw left hurt - in,
Rhy. Fig. 1
Gtr. 1
w/Rhy. Fig. 1
w/Rhy. Fill 1 (2nd time only)
top. Lem - on yel - low sun; ___ arms ___ raised ___ in a V.
ooh dropped wide o - pen. ___ Just like the day, ___ oh
(end Rhy. Fig. 1)
A5 D5/A
The dead ___ lay ___ in pools of ma -roon be- low. Dad - dy ___ did - n't
like the ___ day I heard. ___ Dad - dy ___ did - n't
Rhy. Fig. 2
Gtrs. 3 & 4
f (w/distortion)
let ring
let ring
Rhy. Fill 1
Gtr. 1
T
A
B

G5/A
D5/A
A5
w/Rhy. Fill 2
give at - ten - tion, oh, to the fact that mom - my didn't
give af - fec - tion, no, and the boy was some - thing that mom - my would - n't
(end Rhy. Fig. 2)
let ring
w/Rhy. Fig. 2
A5 D5/A G5/A D5/A A5
w/Rhy. Fill 2
care. King Jer - e - my the wick - ed oh ruled his world.
wear. King Jer - e - my the wick - ed oh ruled his world.
w/Rhy. Fill 3 (3rd time only)
F Dm Dsus2 Dm A
Gtr. 5
Rhy. Fig. 3B
mf (acoustic)
(end Rhy. Fig. 3B)
Jer- e- my spoke in class to - day.
Rhy. Fig. 3A
Gtr. 3
(end Rhy. Fig. 3A)
Rhy. Fig. 3
Gtr. 4
(end Rhy. Fig. 3)
let ring
Rhy. Fill 2
Gtr. 4
let ring
Rhy. Fill 3
Gtr. 3
T
A
B

w/Rhy. Fig. 3 (1st 3 bars)
w/Rhy. Fill 4 (2nd & 3rd time)
w/Rhy. Fill 5 (2nd & 3rd time)
To Coda
* F
Dm
Dsus2
C
A
w/Rhy. Fill 6 (1st time only)
Jer - e - my spoke in class to - day.
Gtrs. 3 & 4
* 2nd & 3rd times Rhy. Fill 4 implies F(add9)
1. Verse
w/Rhy. Fig. 1 (twice)
N.C.
2. Clear - ly I re - mem - ber pick - ing on the boy, seemed a harm - less
lit - tle fuck. Ooh but we un - leashed a li - on. Gnashed
2.
w/Rhy. Figs. 3, 3A & 3B
F
his teeth and bit the re - cess la - dies breast. How could I for - Jer - e - my spoke in
Rhy. Fill 4
Gtrs. 3 & 4
Rhy. Fill 6
Gtr. 1
Rhy. Fill 5
Gtrs. 4
let ring
let ring

w/Rhy. Fill 5
Dm
Dsus2
Dm
A
class
day.
N.C.
Ooh, ooh, ooh, ooh, ooh, ooh, ooh, ooh, ooh, ooh, ooh, ooh,
Rhy. Fig. 4
w/Rhy. Fig. 4
ooh, ooh. Try to for-get this. Try to e-rase
(Try to for-get this.
(end Rhy. Fig. 4)
w/Rhy. Fill 7
D.S. al Coda
this from the black
Try to e-rase this,)
CODA
w/Rhy. Fig. 3, 3A & 3B
F
Dm
Dsus2
Dm
w/Rhy. Fill 5
A
Jer-e-my spoke in class to-day.
Rhy. Fill 7
Gtrs. 3 & 4
P.M.
T
A
B

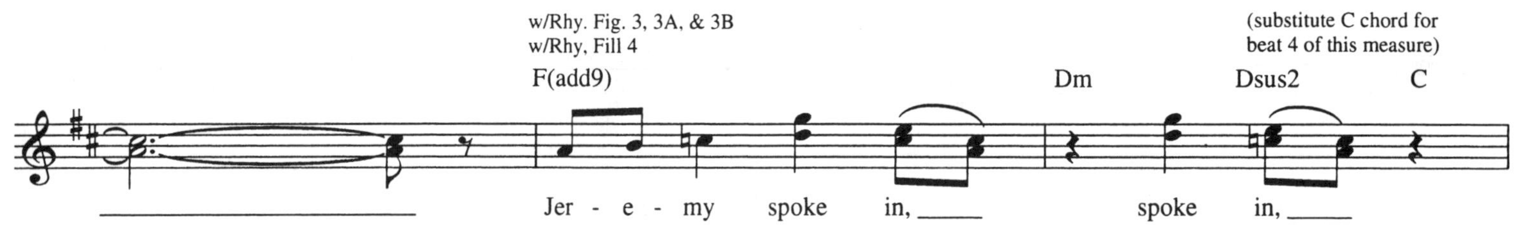

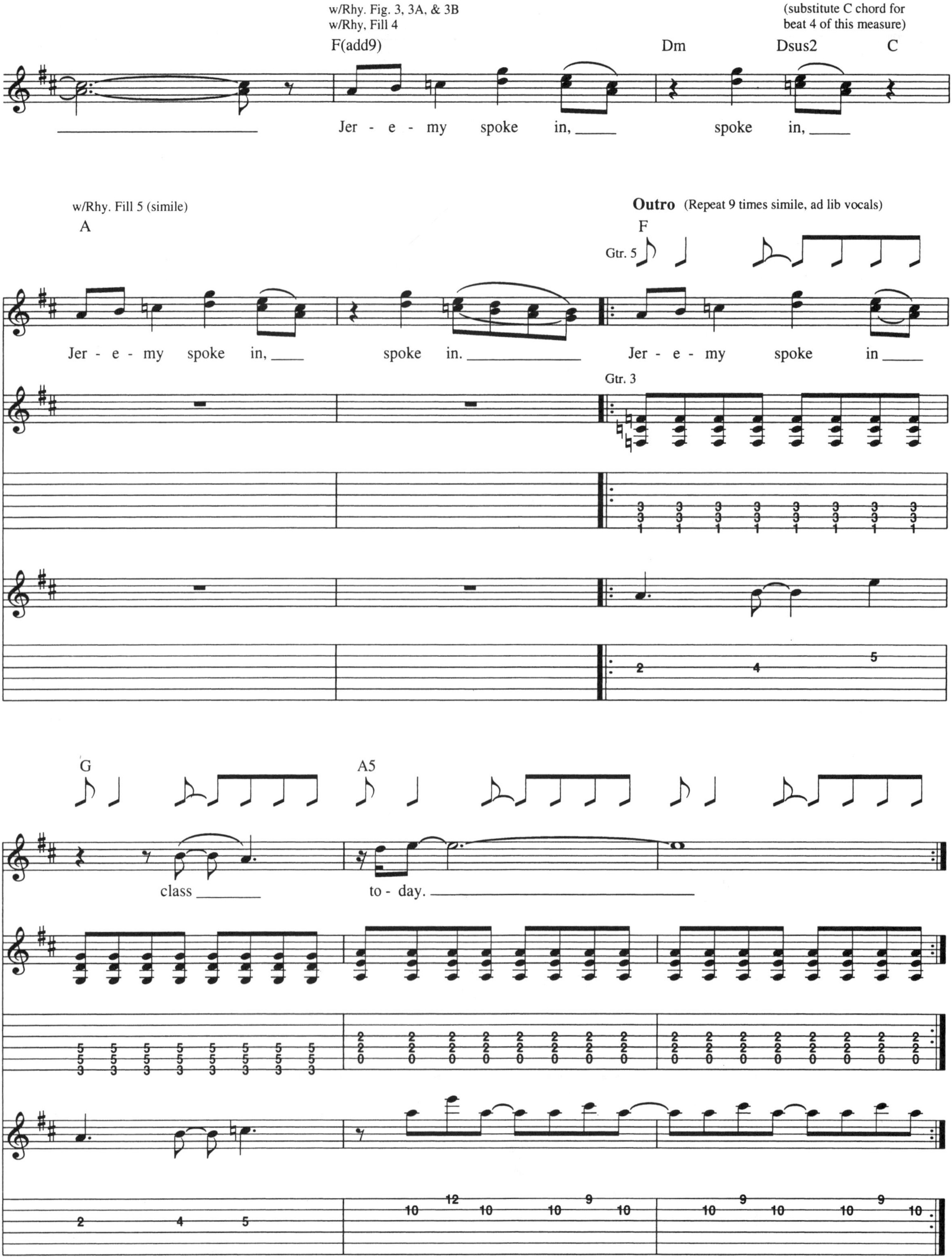

w/Rhy. Fill 5 (simile)

Outro (Repeat 9 times simile, ad lib vocals)

A

F

Gtr. 5

Jer - e - my spoke in,

spoke in.

Jer - e - my spoke in

Gtr. 3

Ah - ha,
ah - ha,
ah - ha
Gtr. 5
Gtr. 3
harm
w/bar
harm
rit.
ah - ha.
Gtr. 5
harm.
harm.

Jump, Jive an' Wail

Words and Music by Louis Prima

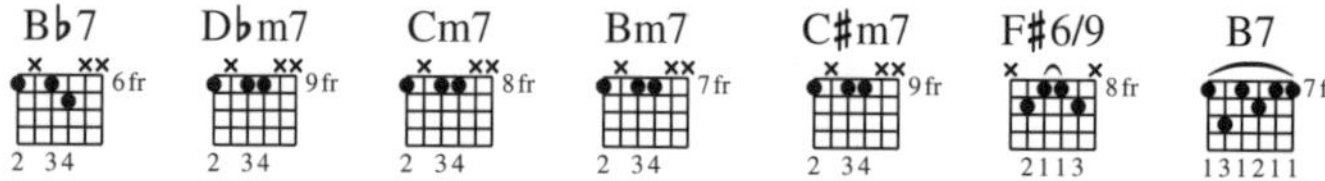

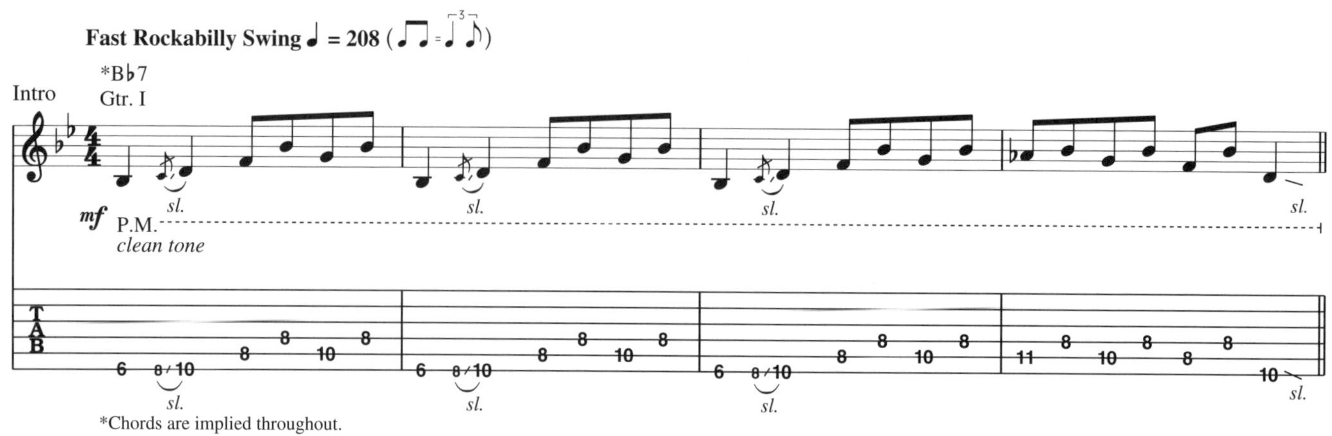

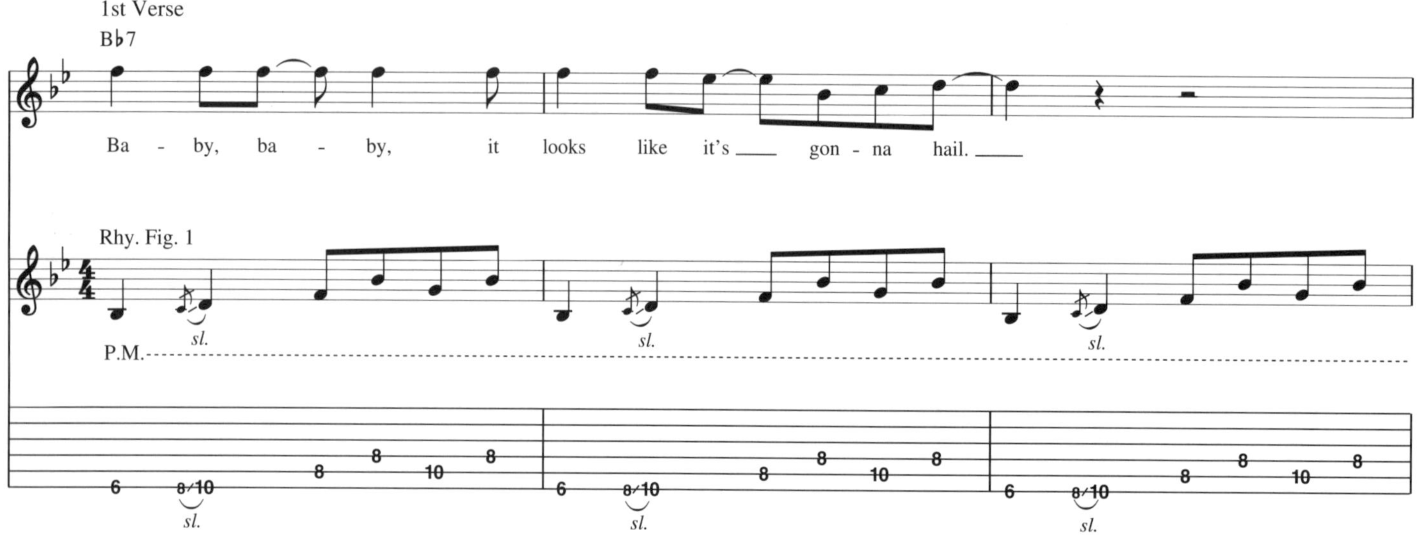

Copyright © 1956; Renewed and Assigned to LGL Music Co.
Administered by Larry Spier, Inc., New York
International Copyright Secured All Rights Reserved

Bb7
Cm7
You bet - ter come in - side; let me
sl.
F7
Bb
teach you how to jive and wail. Oh, you got - ta
(end Rhy. Fig. 1)
Chorus
w/Rhy. Fig. 1 (1st 8 bars only)
Bb9
jump, jive and then you wail. You got - ta jump, jive and then you wail. You got - ta
*Gtr. II
mf
w/light dist.
*Play w/slight variations ad lib on repeat.
Eb13
Bb9
jump, jive and then you wail. You got - ta jump, jive and then you wail. You got - ta
*1/2
trem. bar
(Gtr. II out)
*Depress bar before striking chord.

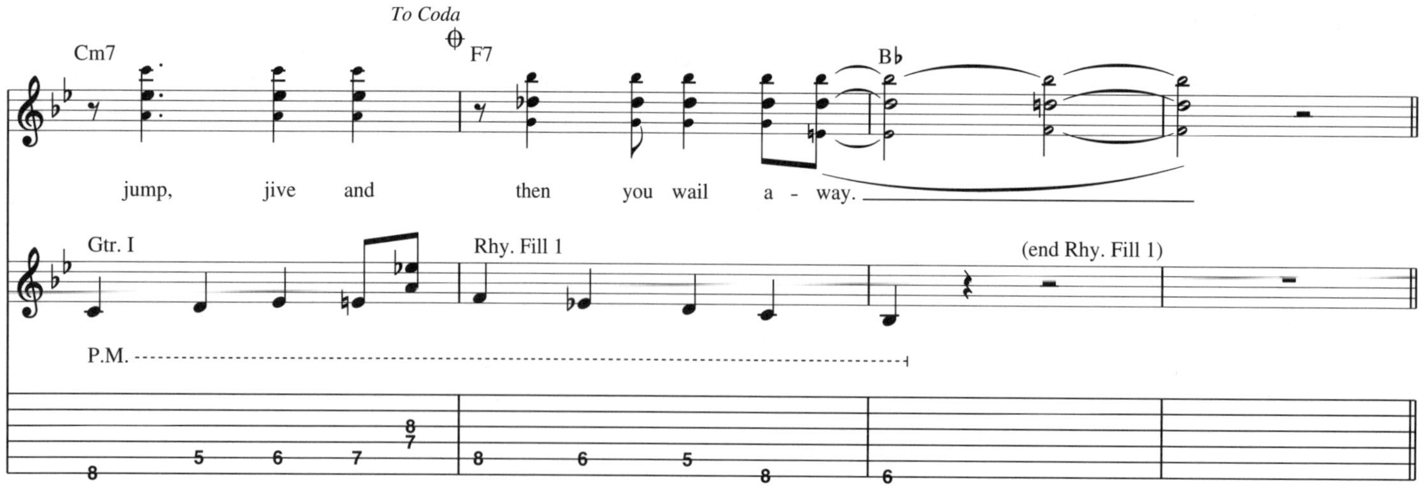
To Coda
Cm7
F7
B♭
jump, jive and then you wail a - way.
Gtr. I
Rhy. Fill 1
(end Rhy. Fill 1)
P.M.
8 5 6 7 8 7 8 6 5 8 6

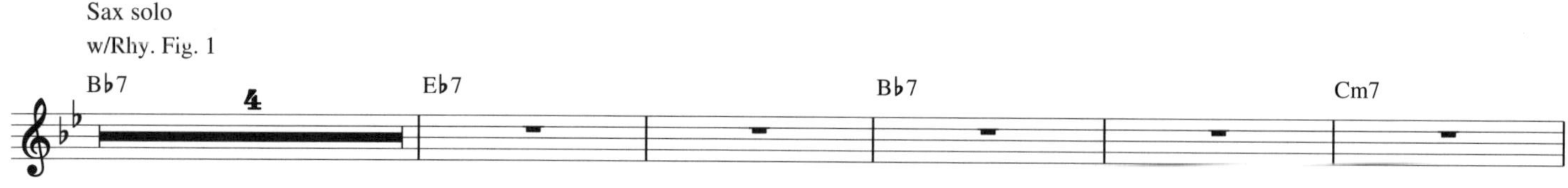
Sax solo
w/Rhy. Fig. 1
B♭7
4
E♭7
B♭7
Cm7

F7
B♭
2nd Verse
w/Rhy. Fig. 1 (1st 10 bars only)
B♭7
Pa - pa's in the ice - box

E♭7
look - in' for a can of ale.
Pa - pa's in the ice - box

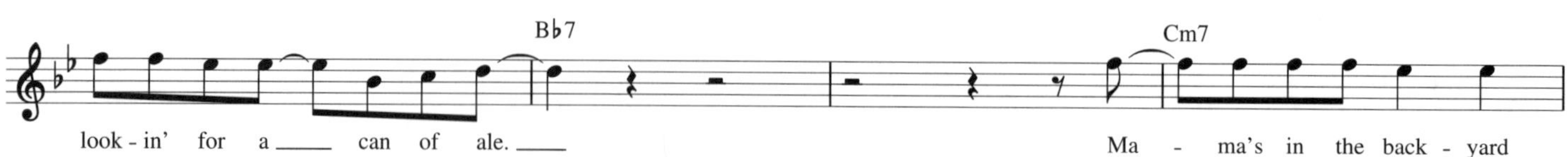
B♭7
Cm7
look - in' for a can of ale.
Ma - ma's in the back - yard

D.S. al Coda
F7
B♭7
D♭m7
Cm7
Bm7
Gtrs. I & II
learn - in' how to jive and wail.
Woh, you got - ta

Coda
w/Rhy. Fill 1
F7
B♭
(Gtr. I out)
then you wail a - way.
Gtr. II
Guitar Solo
B♭7
trem. bar
1/2
E♭7
B♭7
Cm7
F7
B♭
N.C.
Full
1/2
sl.
A

3rd Verse
w/Rhy. Fig. 1 (1st 10 bars only)
B♭7
wom - an is a wom - an and a man ain't noth - in' but a male. _ Wom-

E♭7
B♭7
an is a wom - an and a man ain't noth - in' but a male._ One good_

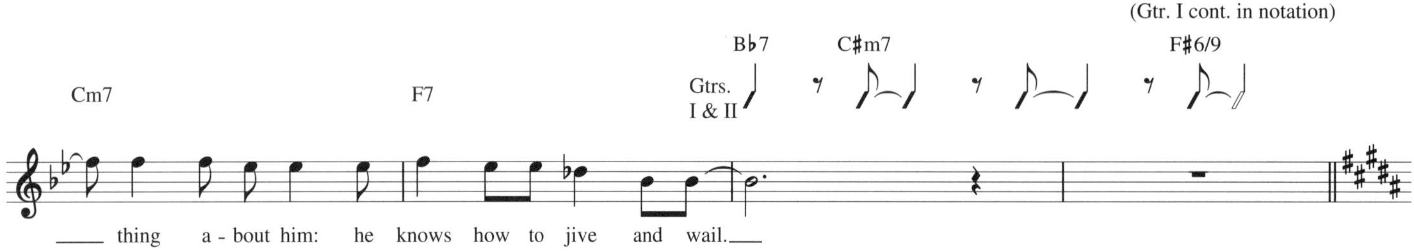
(Gtr. I cont. in notation)
B♭7
C♯m7
F♯6/9
Cm7
F7
Gtrs. I & II
_ thing a - bout him: he knows how to jive and wail._

4th Verse
B7
(Gtr. II out)
Gtr. II
Jack and Jill_ went up_ the hill to_ get a pail._
Rhy. Fig. 2 (Gtr. I)
sl.
P.M.

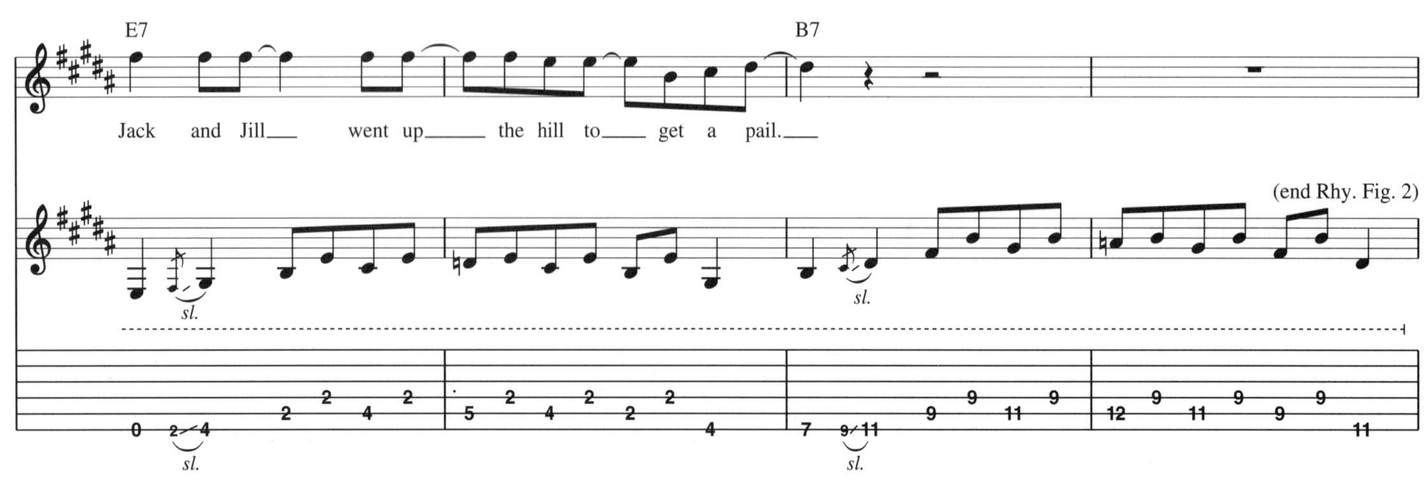
E7
B7
Jack and Jill_ went up_ the hill to_ get a pail._
(end Rhy. Fig. 2)
sl.

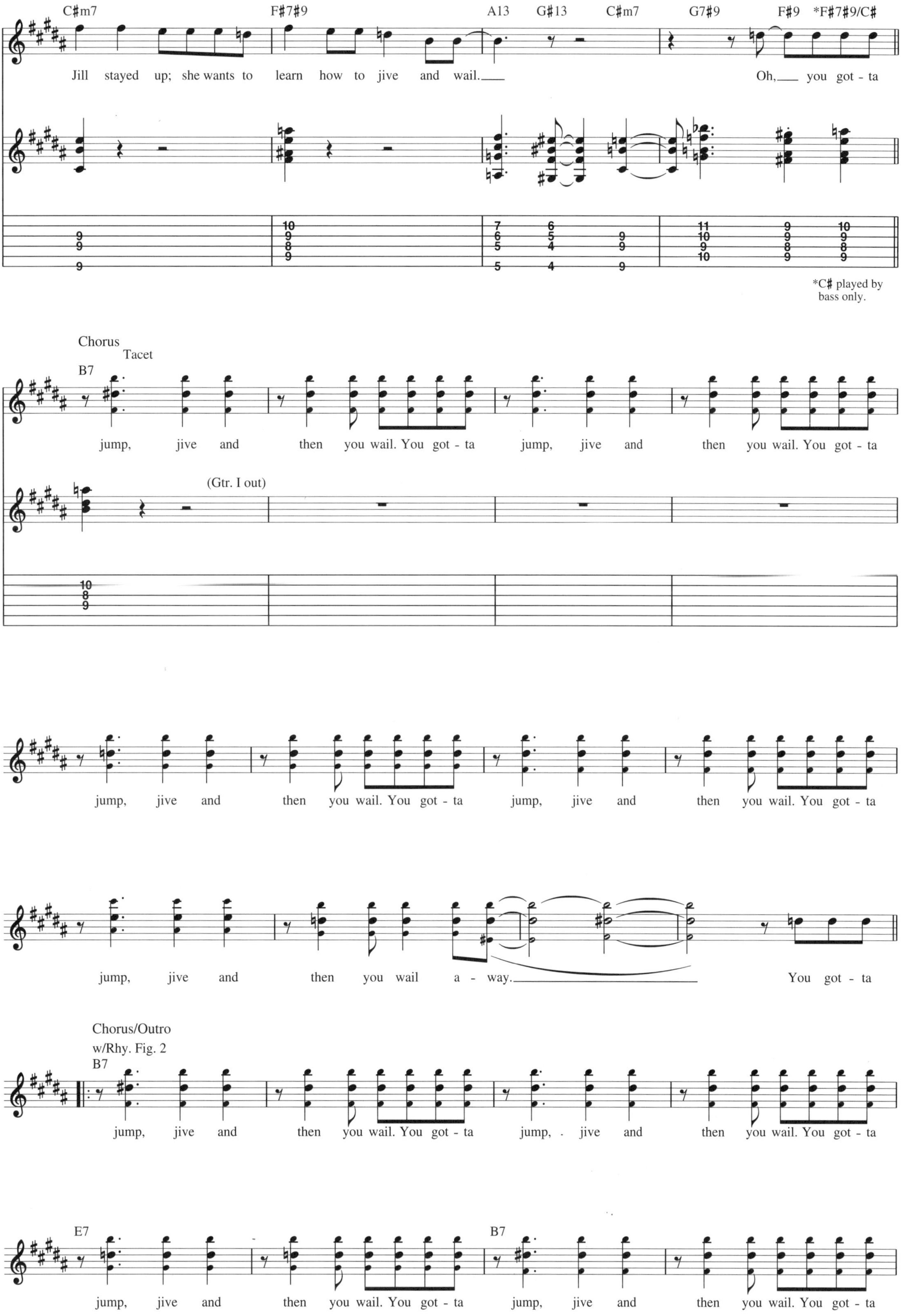

C♯m7 F♯7♯9 A13 G♯13 C♯m7 G7♯9 F♯9 *F♯7♯9/C♯

Jill stayed up; she wants to learn how to jive and wail.___ Oh,___ you got - ta

*C♯ played by bass only.

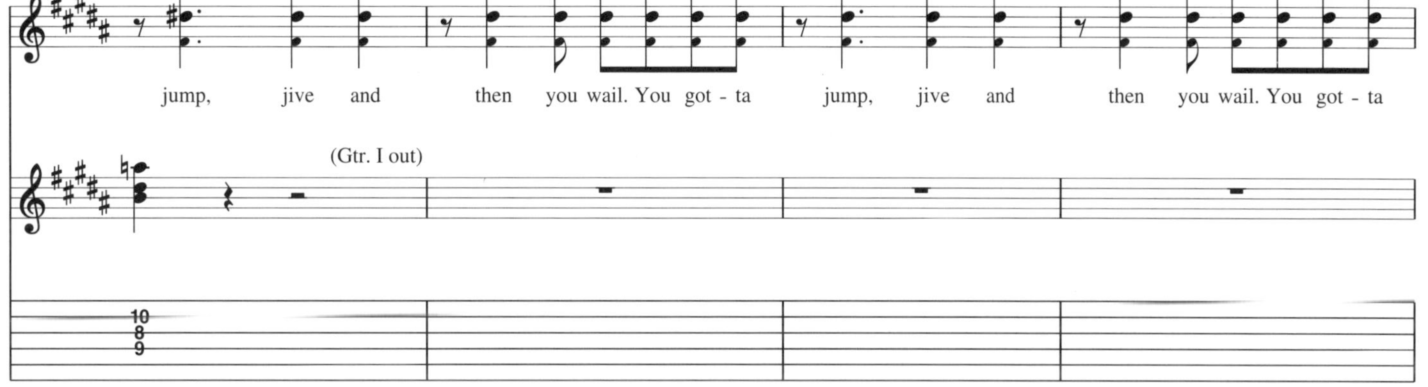

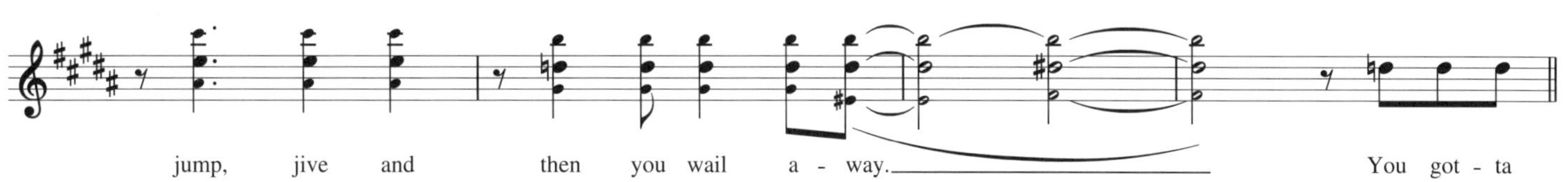

1.
C#m7
F#7
B7
A7
G#7
Dm7
C#m7
G7
F#7
jump, jive and then you wail a - way.
Oh, you got - ta.
Gtr. I
P.M.
2.
Begin fade
N.C.
B
You got - ta jump, jive and...
Jump, jive and...
E
Jump, jive and...
B
Jump, jive and...
Fade out

Lightning Crashes

Lyrics by Edward Kowalczyk
Music by Edward Kowalczyk, Chad Taylor, Patrick Dahlheimer and Chad Gracey

Copyright © 1994 Loco de Amor Music and Audible Sun Music (BMI)
All Rights Reserved Used by Permission

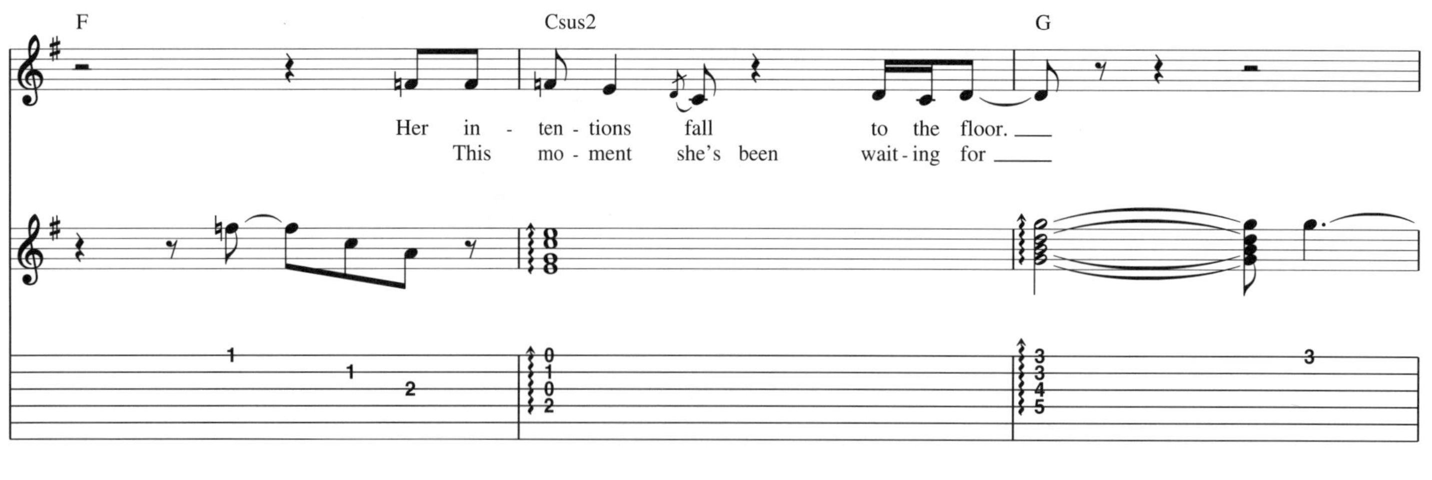
F
Csus2
G
Her in - ten - tions fall to the floor.
This mo - ment she's been wait - ing for

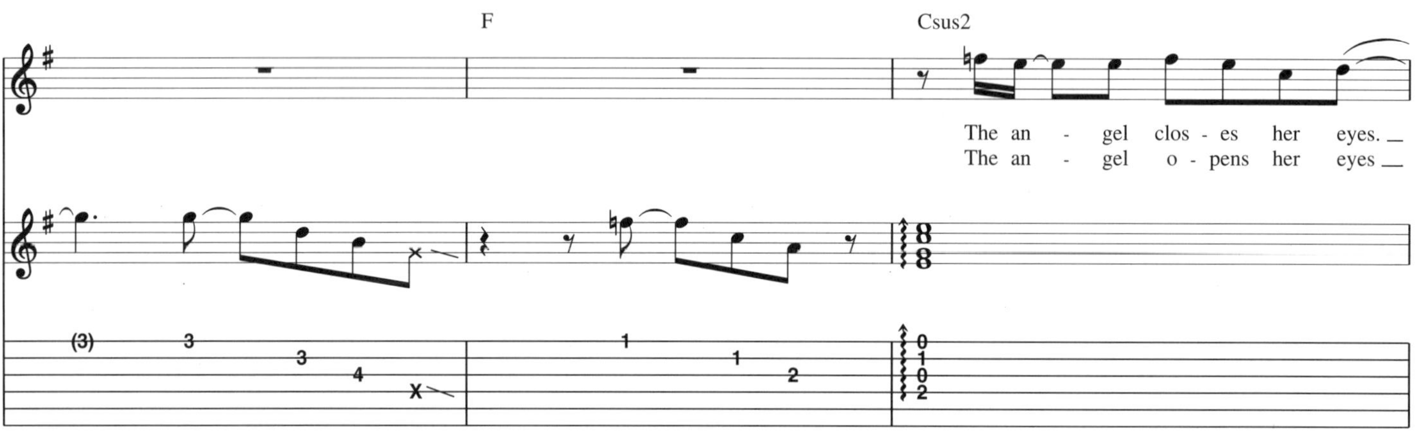
F
Csus2
The an - gel clos - es her eyes.
The an - gel o - pens her eyes

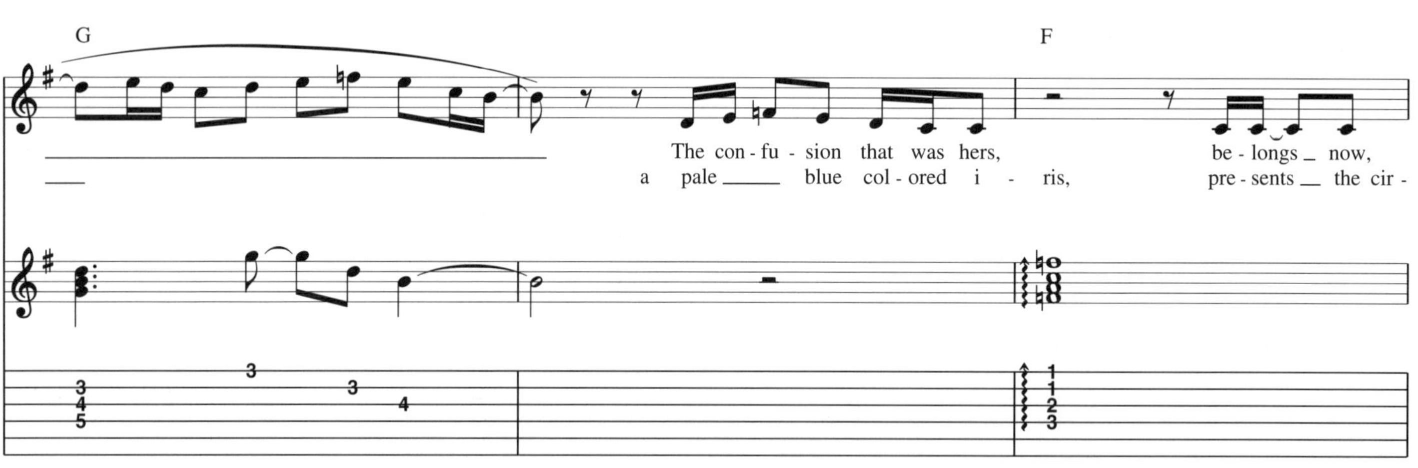
G
F
The con - fu - sion that was hers, be - longs now,
a pale blue col - ored i - ris, pre - sents the cir -

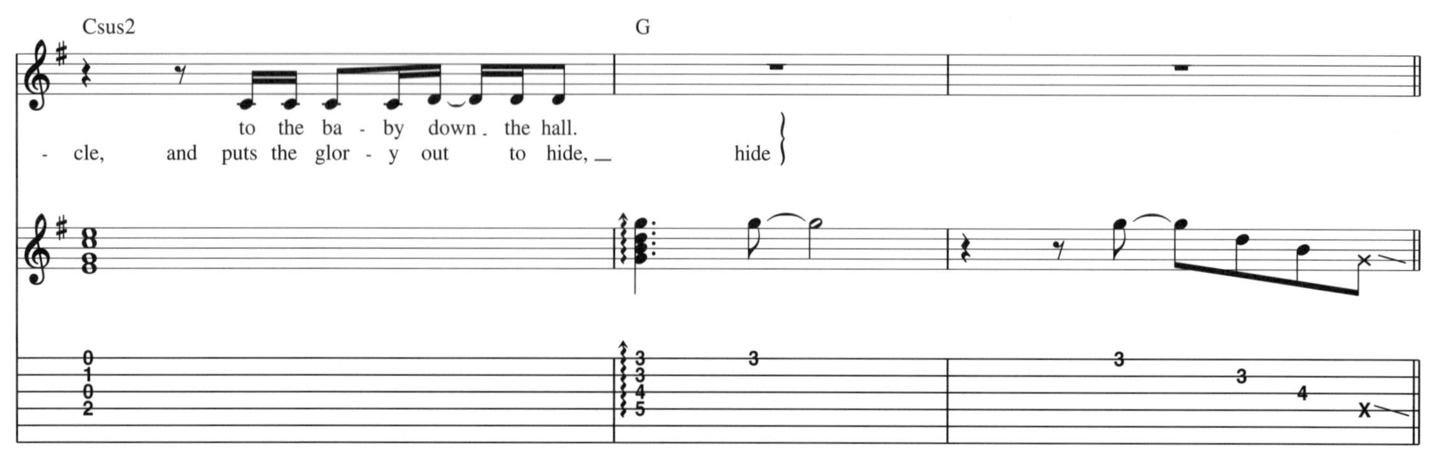
Csus2
G
to the ba - by down the hall.
- cle, and puts the glor - y out to hide, hide

Chorus
* Gtr. 2: w/ Rhy. Fig. 3A, 5 times, 2nd time only
Gtr. 1: w/ Rhy. Fig. 3, 2 times, simile
F
Csus2
G
F
Csus2
Rhy. Fig. 3
End Rhy. Fig. 3
Gtr. 1
mf
Oh, now feel it com - in' back a - gain like a roll - in'
* amp tremolo off
G
F
Csus2
G
thun - der chas - ing the wind Forc - es pull - in' from the cen - ter of the Earth a - gain
1.
F
Csus2
G
E
G
D
G
2.
F
Csus2
6
open
5
5fr
Gtr. 1
Gtr. 1
f
I can feel it
I can feel it
G
F
Csus2
G
I can feel it
* with added gain
Interlude
Am
Em7
F
Gtr. 1
play 3 times
Gtr. 2
Gtr. 3
Rhy. Fig. 3A
Gtr. 2
Fadd9
Csus2
G

G Am Em7

Am Em7 F G

Chorus
Gtr. 3 tacet
Gtrs. 1 & 2: w/ Rhy. Figs. 3 & 3A, 14 times
F Csus2 G F Csus2
Oh, now feel it com - in' back a - gain like a roll - in'
G F Csus2
thun - der chas - ing the wind Forc - es pull - in' from the
G F Csus2 G
cen - ter of the Earth a - gain I can feel it.

Outro-Chorus
F Csus2 G
Oh, now feel it com - in' back a - gain
F Csus2 G F Csus2
like a roll - in' thun - der chas - ing the wind Forc - es pull - ing from the
1.
G F Csus2 G
cen - ter of the Earth a - gain I can feel it

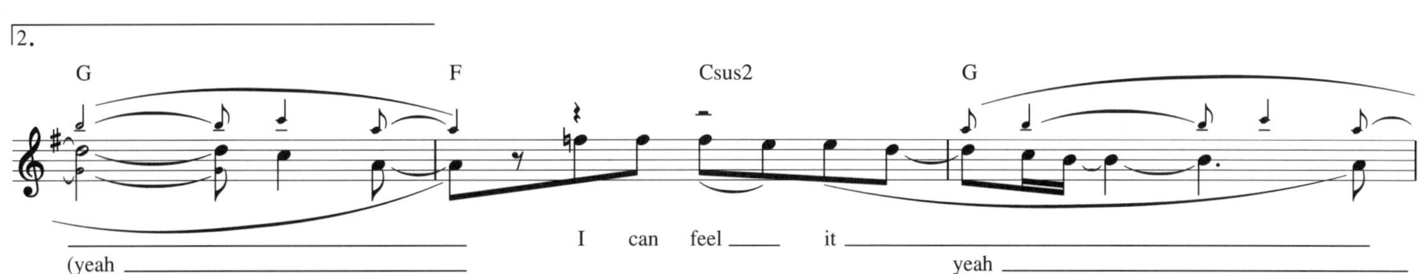
2.
G F Csus2 G
I can feel it
(yeah yeah

F Csus2 G F Csus2 G
Gtrs. 1 & 2
mp rit.
I can feel it
yeah)

Loser

Words by Beck Hansen
Music by Beck Hansen and Karl Stephenson

Copyright © 1993 by BMG Songs, Inc., Cyanide Breathmint Music and Nothin' Fluxin' Music
All Rights Administered by BMG Songs, Inc.
International Copyright Secured All Rights Reserved

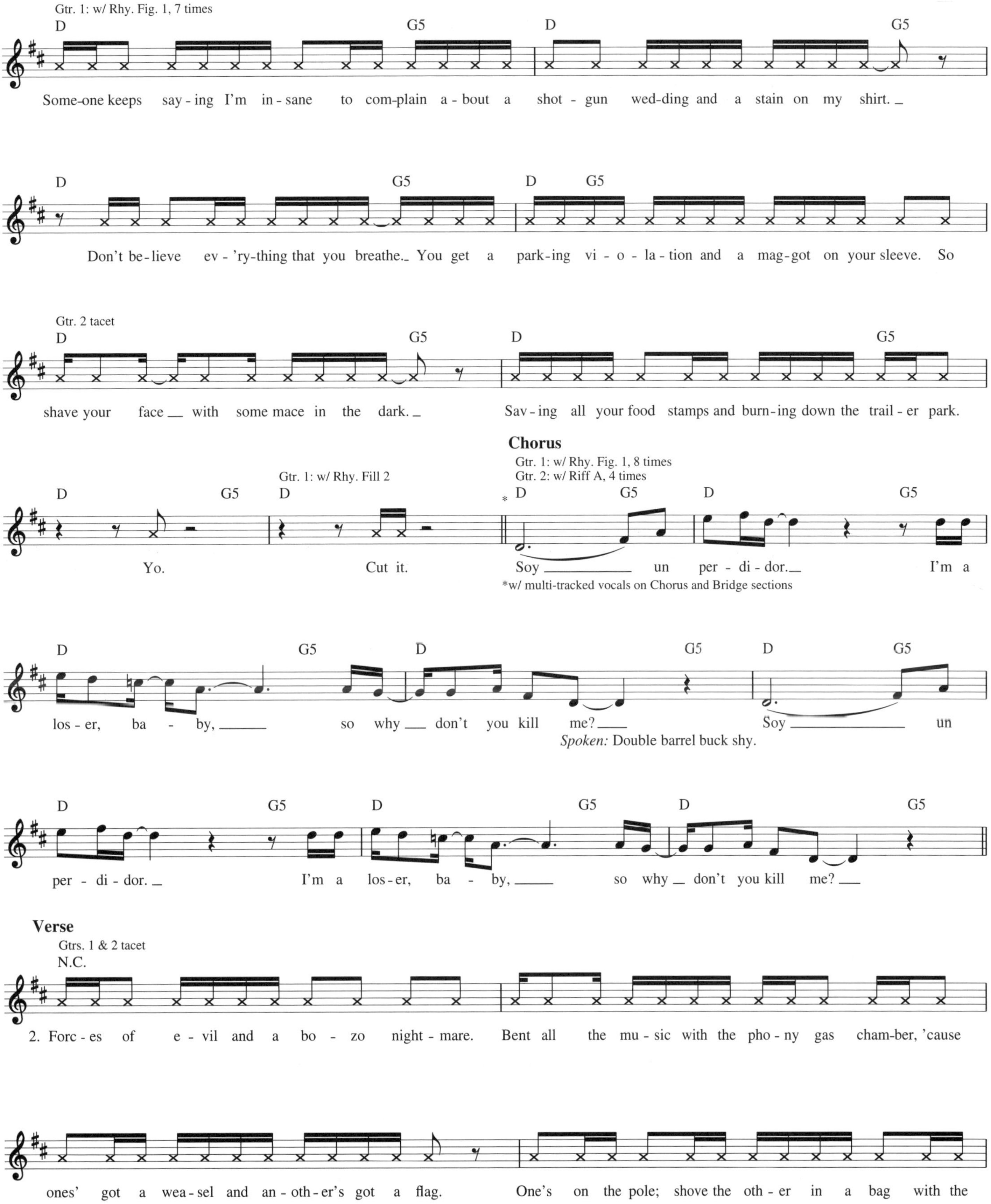

Gtr. 1: w/ Rhy. Fig. 1, 7 times

D G5 D G5

Some-one keeps say-ing I'm in-sane to com-plain a-bout a shot-gun wed-ding and a stain on my shirt._

D G5 D G5

Don't be-lieve ev-'ry-thing that you breathe._ You get a park-ing vi-o-la-tion and a mag-got on your sleeve. So

Gtr. 2 tacet

D G5 D G5

shave your face_ with some mace in the dark._ Sav-ing all your food stamps and burn-ing down the trail-er park.

D G5

Gtr. 1: w/ Rhy. Fill 2

D

Yo. Cut it.

Chorus

Gtr. 1: w/ Rhy. Fig. 1, 8 times
Gtr. 2: w/ Riff A, 4 times

* D G5 D G5

Soy_ un per-di-dor._ I'm a

*w/ multi-tracked vocals on Chorus and Bridge sections

D G5 D G5 D G5

los-er, ba-by,_ so why_ don't you kill me?_ Soy_ un

Spoken: Double barrel buck shy.

D G5 D G5 D G5

per-di-dor._ I'm a los-er, ba-by,_ so why_ don't you kill me?_

Verse

Gtrs. 1 & 2 tacet

N.C.

2. Forc-es of e-vil and a bo-zo night-mare. Bent all the mu-sic with the pho-ny gas cham-ber, 'cause

ones' got a wea-sel and an-oth-er's got a flag. One's on the pole; shove the oth-er in a bag with the

Gtr. 1: w/ Rhy. Fig. 1, 4 times
D G5 D G5
re - run shows and the co - caine nose job, the day - time crap of the folk sing - er slob.
D G5 D G5
He hung him - self with a gui - tar string. A slab of tur - key neck, and its' hang - ing from a pi - geon wing.
Gtr. 1 tacet
N.C. (D7)
A - get right if you can't re - late. Trade the cash for the beef, for the bod - y, for the hate. And my
Gtr. 3
time is a piece of wax fall - in' on a ter - mite who's chok - in' on the splin - ters.
Gtr. 3
Chorus
Gtr. 1: w/ Rhy. Fig. 1, 7 times
Gtr. 2: w/ Riff A, 3 1/2 times
Gtr. 3 tacet
D G5 D G5 D G5 D G5
Soy un per - di - dor. I'm a los - er, ba - by, so why don't you kill me?
Spoken: Get crazy with the Cheez Whiz.
Gtr. 1: w/ Rhy. Fill 1
Gtr. 2: w/ Rhy. Fill 3
D G5 D G5 D G5 D
Soy un per - di - dor. I'm a los - er, ba - by, so why don't you kill me?
Spoken: Drive-by body pierce.
Rhy. Fill 3
Gtr. 2
TAB

Bridge
Gtrs. 1 & 2 tacet
N.C.
Yo, bring it on down. Soy.
Gtr. 1: w/ Rhy. Fig. 1, 7 times
w/ Bkgd. voc. ad Lib, next 4 meas.
D G5 D G5 D G5 D G5
Soy.
Gtr. 3
Gtr. 2: w/ Riff A, 1 1/2 times
Gtr. 1: w/ Rhy. Fill 4
Gtr. 2: w/ Rhy. Fill 5
Spoken: I'm a driver, I'm a winner. Things are gonna change. I can feel it.
Chorus
4th time, Begin Fade
Gtr. 1: w/ Rhy. Fig. 1, 4 times
Gtr. 2: w/ Riff A, 2 times
Gtr. 3 tacet
So, un per-di-dor. I'm a los-er, ba-by, so why don't you kill me?
Spoken: I can't believe it.
don't you kill me? don't you kill me? don't you kill me?
Spoken: Uuuuuuuuuh. Spoken: Sprechen Sie Deutsch, baby? Spoken: You know what I'm sayin'?
Outro
Gtr. 3: w/ Rhy. Fill 1
Gtr. 2: w/ Riff A, till fade
Gtr. 1 tacet
Repeat and Fade
N.C. (D)
Rhy. Fill 4
Gtr. 1
Rhy. Fill 5
Gtr. 2

Mmm Mmm Mmm Mmm

Words and Music by Brad Roberts

Gtr. 1: Capo III

Intro

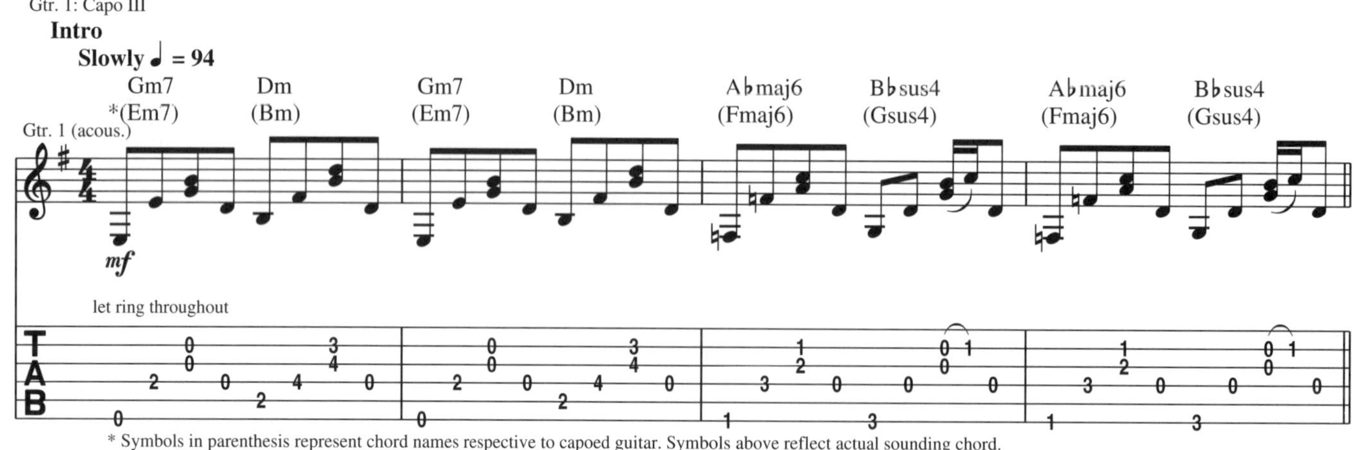

* Symbols in parenthesis represent chord names respective to capoed guitar. Symbols above reflect actual sounding chord.

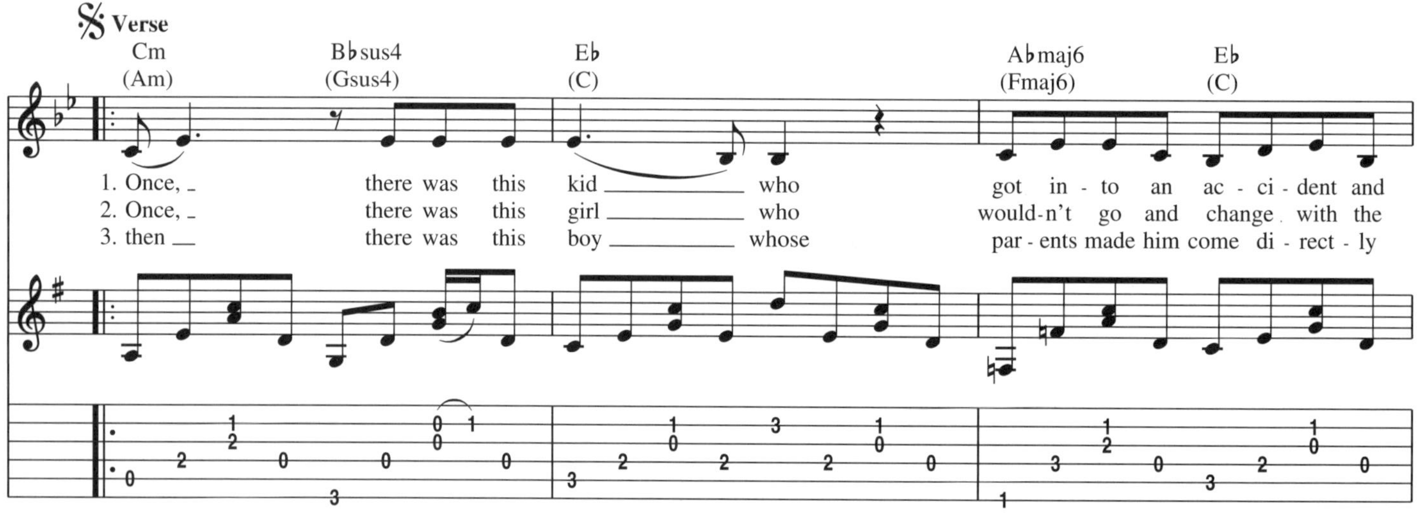

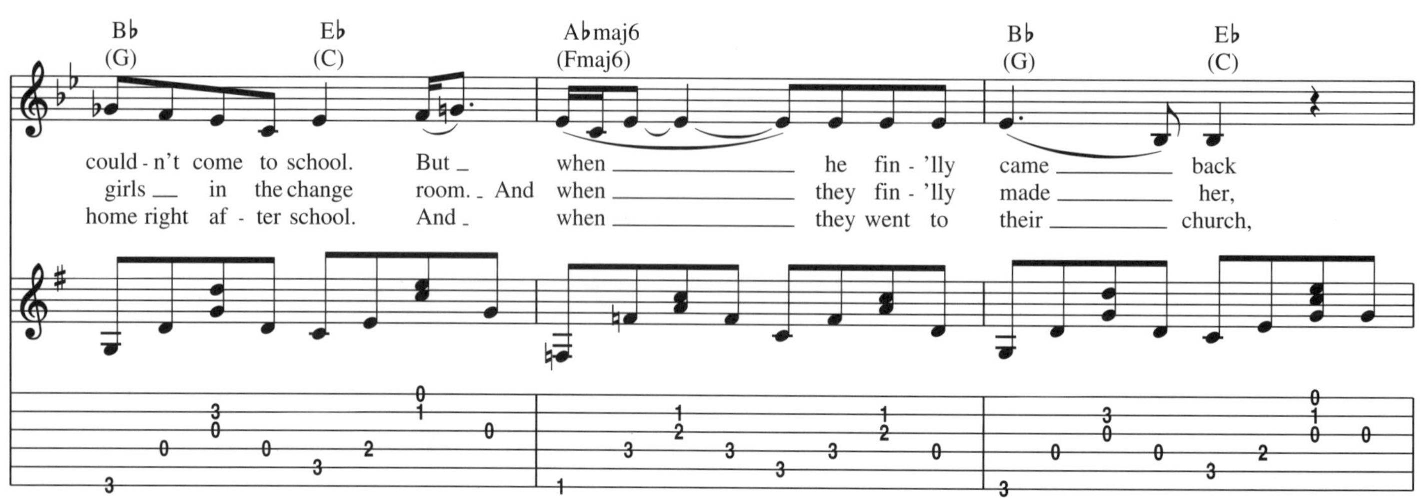

Copyright © 1993 PolyGram International Publishing, Inc., Door Number Two Music and Dummies Productions, Inc.
International Copyright Secured All Rights Reserved

Bb (G) Eb (C) Abadd2 (Fadd2) Eb (C) Ebadd2 (Cadd2) Bb (G)
his hair had turned from black in - to bright white.
they saw birth-marks all o - ver her bod - y.
they shook and lurched all o - ver the church floor.
B (G#) Eb (C) B (G#) Asus2/6 (Fsus2/6)
He said that it was from when the cars had smashed him so hard.
She could-n't quite ex - plain that they'd al - ways just been there.
They could-n't quite ex - plain it. They'd al - ways just gone there.
Ab (F)
Chorus
Gm7 (Em7) Dm (Bm) Gm7 (Em7) Dm (Bm) Abmaj6 (Fmaj6) Bbsus4 (Gsus4)
Mmm, mmm, mmm, mmm. Mmm, mmm, mmm, mmm.
1.
Abmaj6 (Fmaj6) Bbsus4 (Gsus4)
2., 3.
Abmaj6 (Fmaj6) Bbsus4 (Gsus4) Gm7 (Em7) Dm (Bm) Dm7 (Em7) Dm (Bm)
Mmm, mmm, mmm, mmm. Mmm, mmm, mmm, mmm.

To Coda
Bridge
A♭maj6 (Fmaj6)
B♭sus4 (Gsus4)
A♭maj6 (Fmaj6)
B♭sus4 (Gsus4)
Fm (Dm)
E♭ (C)
B♭ (G)
But both girl and boy were glad
Rhy. Fig. 1
Fm (Dm)
E♭ (C)
B♭ (G)
A♭add2 (Fadd2)
D.S. al Coda
'cause one kid had it worse than that.
3. 'Cause
End Rhy. Fig. 1
Coda
Outro
Gtr. 1: w/ Rhy. Fig. 1
Fm (Dm)
E♭ (C)
B♭ (G)
Fm (Dm)
E♭ (C)
B♭ (G)
Ahh, ahh, ahh, ahh.
Ahh, ahh, ahh, ahh.
A♭add2 (Fadd2)
E♭ (C)
Begin Fade
Fm (Dm)
E♭sus2 (Csus2)
B♭ (G)
Ahh, ahh, ahh, ahh.
Rhy. Fig. 2
End Rhy. Fig. 2
Rhy. Fig. 3
End Rhy. Fig. 3
Play 5 times and Fade
Gtr. 1: w/ Rhy. Fig. 2, simile
A♭add2 (Fadd2)
E♭ (C)
Gtr. 1: w/ Rhy. Fig. 3
Fm (Dm)
E♭sus2 (Csus2)
B♭ (G)

More Than Words

Words and Music by Nuno Bettencourt and Gary Cherone

Tune down 1/2 step:
(low to high) E♭–A♭–D♭–G♭–B♭–E♭

Intro

Moderately slow ♩ = 96

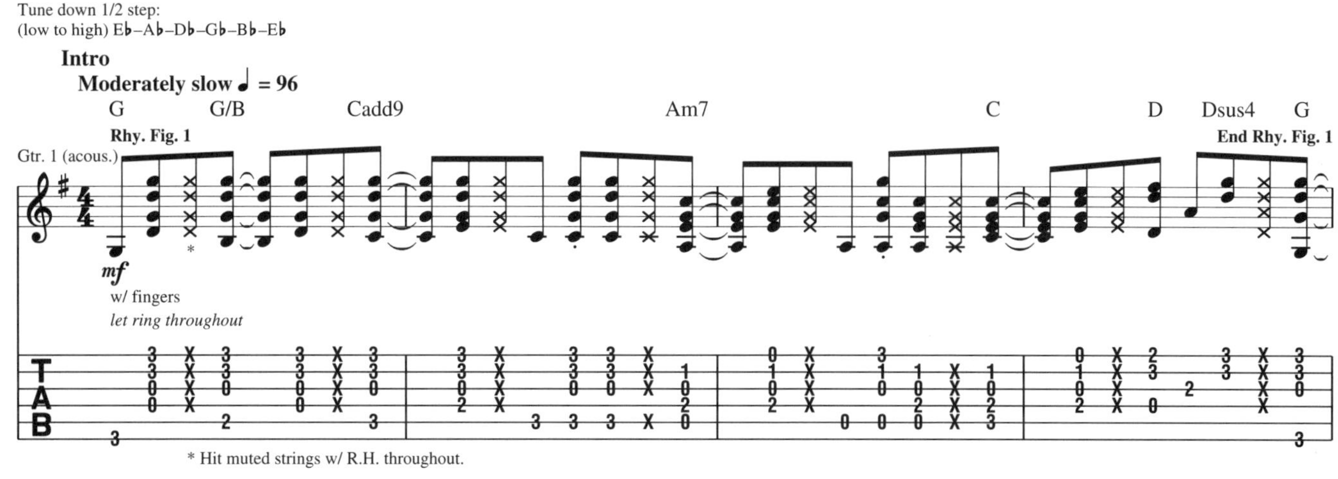

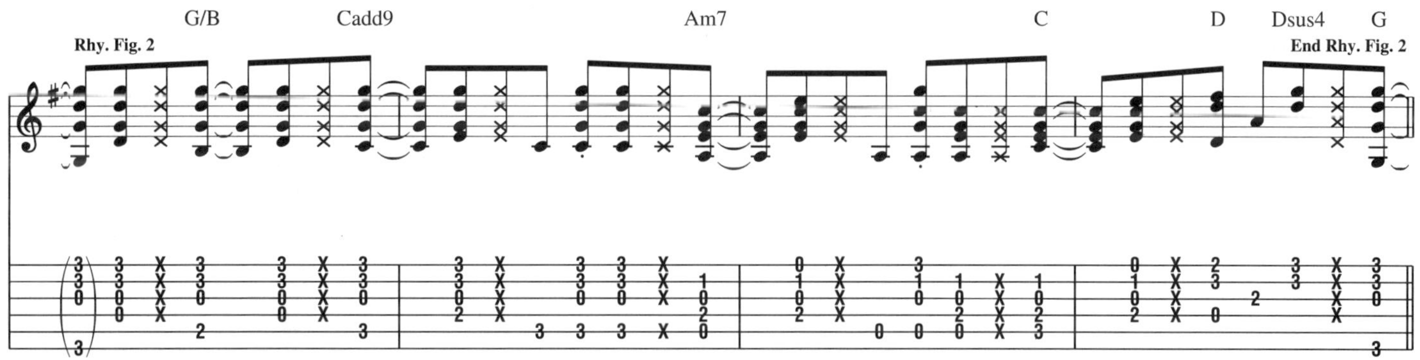

Verse

Gtr. 1: w/ Rhy. Fig. 2

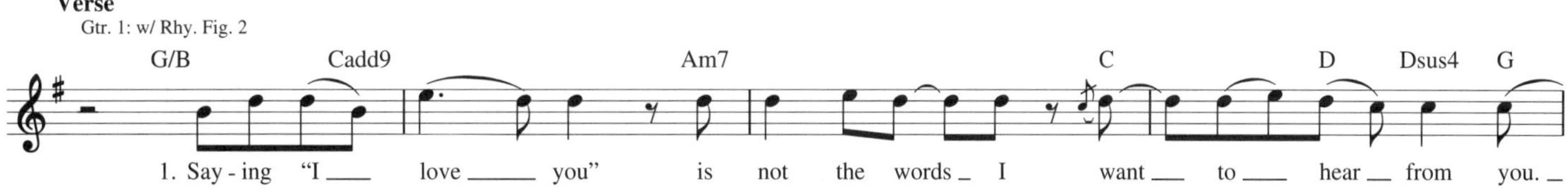

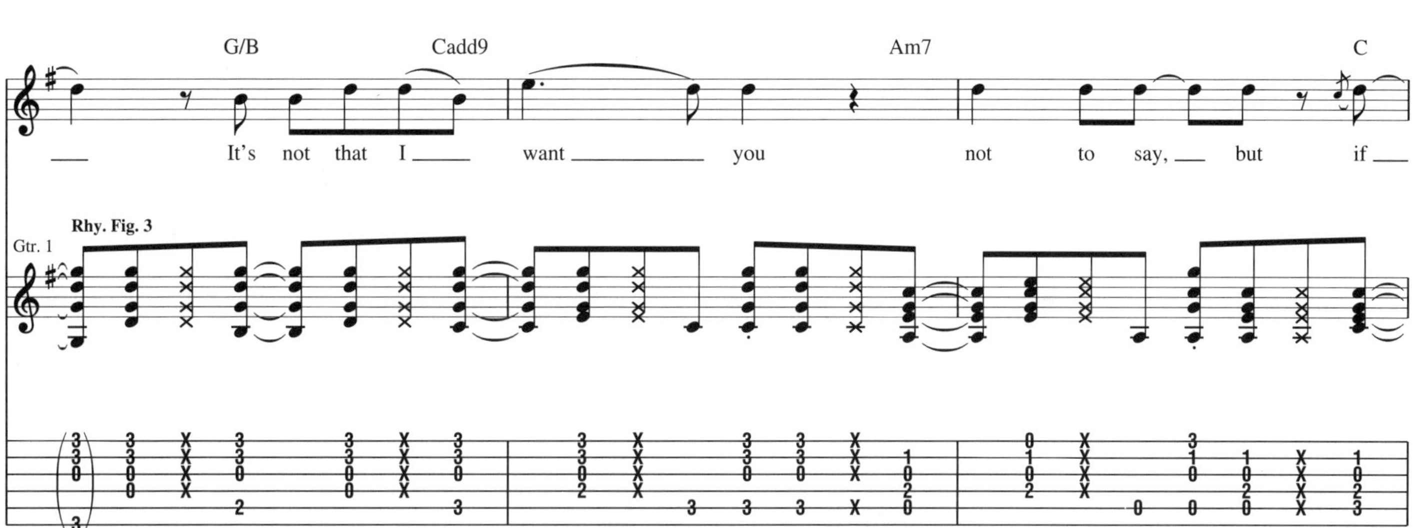

Copyright © 1990 COLOR ME BLIND MUSIC
All Rights Administered by ALMO MUSIC CORP.
All Rights Reserved Used by Permission

D
Dsus4
Em
Am7
you only - ly knew how eas - y
End Rhy. Fig. 3
D7
G
D/F#
Dadd2/F#
Em
Am7
it would be to show me how you feel. More than words
* T
T
* T = Thumb on 6th str.
Chorus
D7
G7
G7/B
C
is all you have to do to make it real.
Rhy. Fig. 4
Cm
G
Em7
Then you would - n't have to say that you love

Am7
D7
G
me, 'cause I'd al - read - y know. What
End Rhy. Fig. 4
Dadd2/F#
Em
Bm
C
would you do if my heart was torn in two?
Rhy. Fig. 5
G/B
Am7
D7
More than words to show you feel that your love
G
for me is real. What would you say

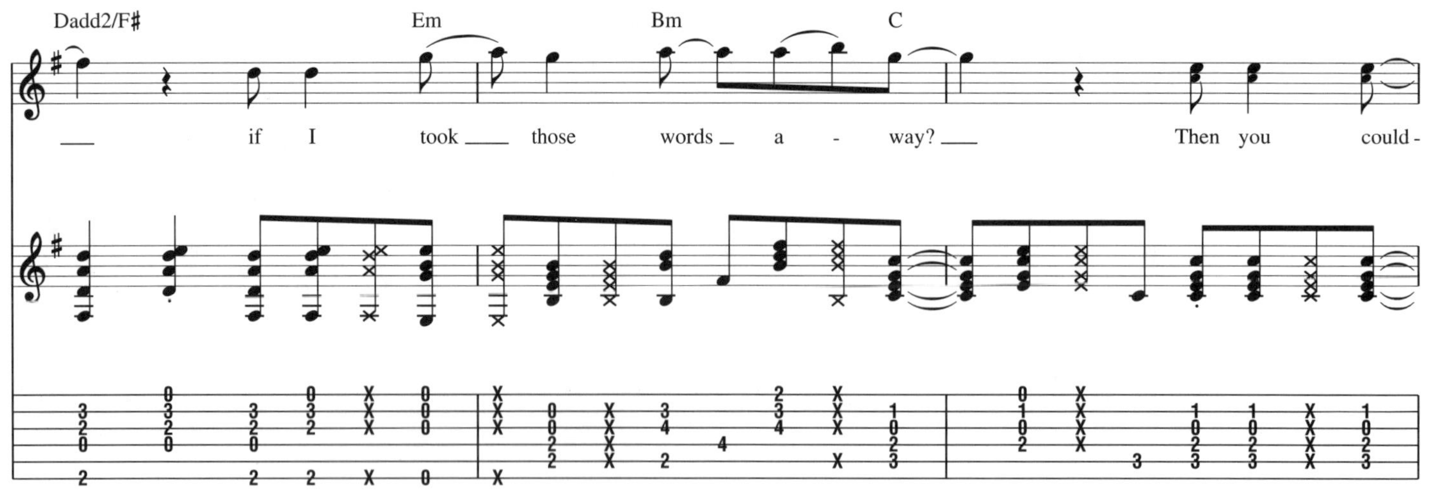

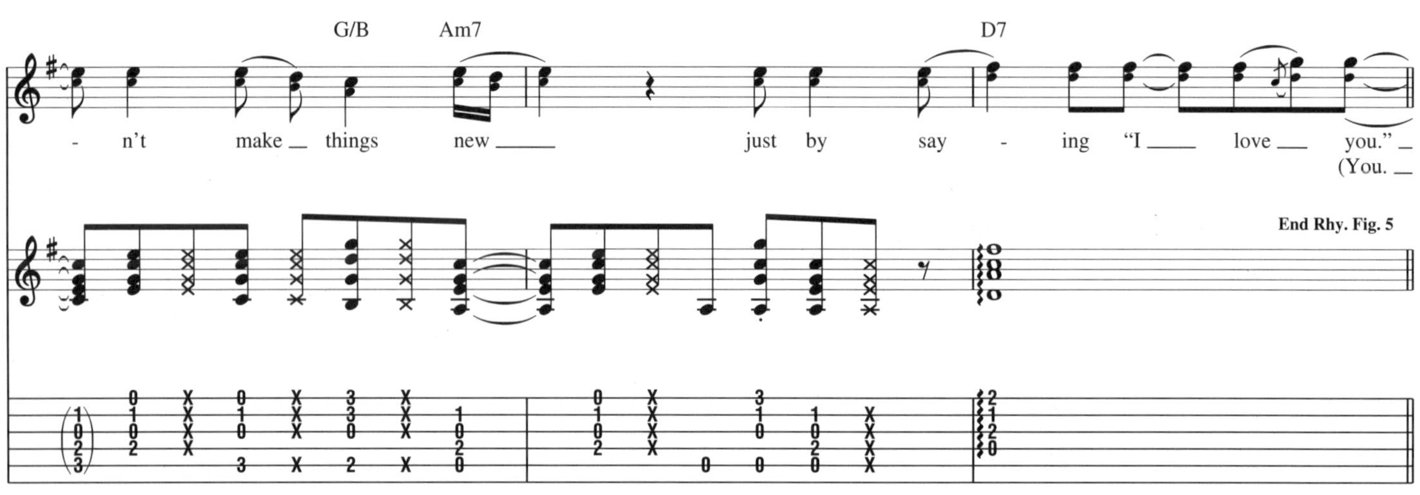

Interlude

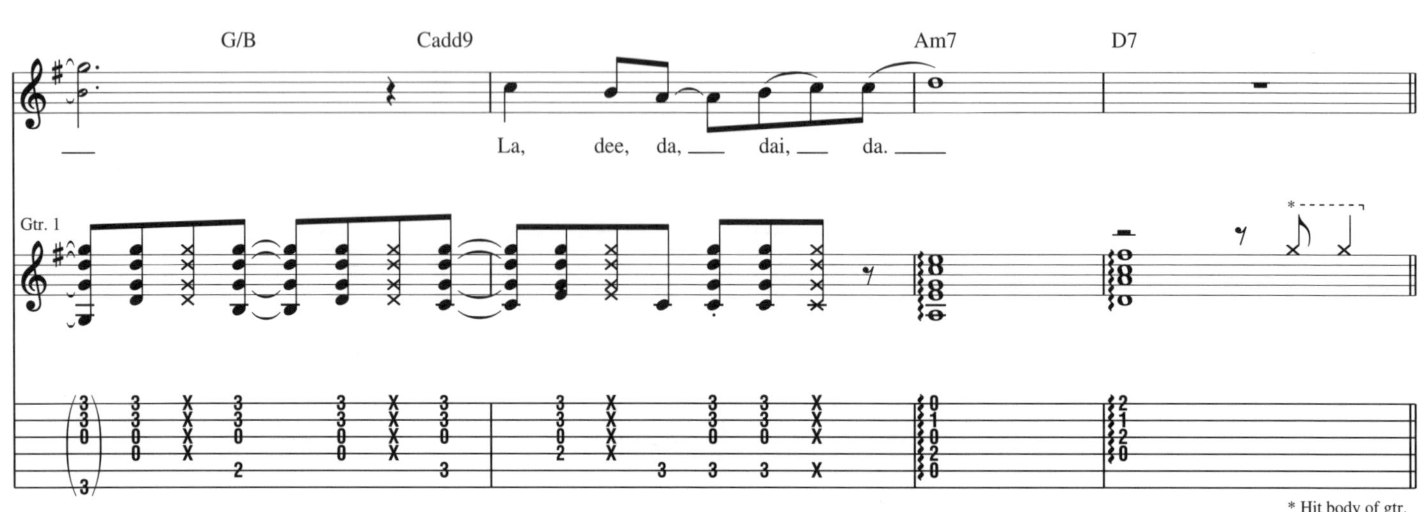

* Hit body of gtr.

Verse

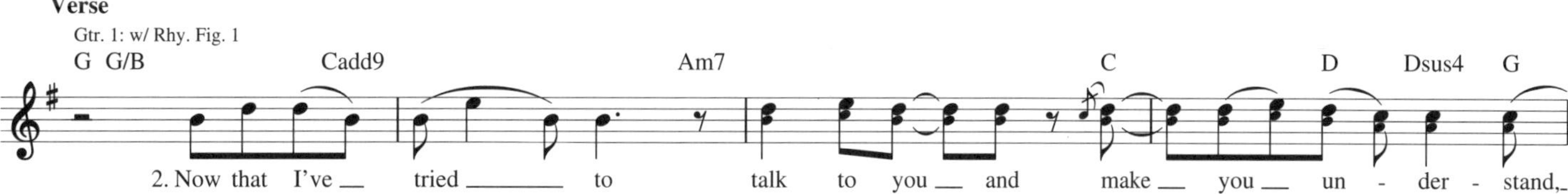

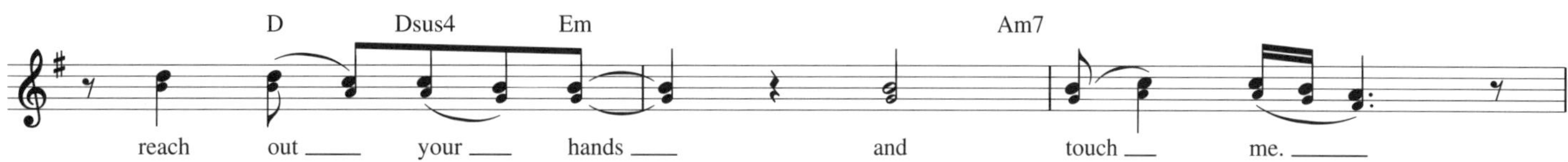

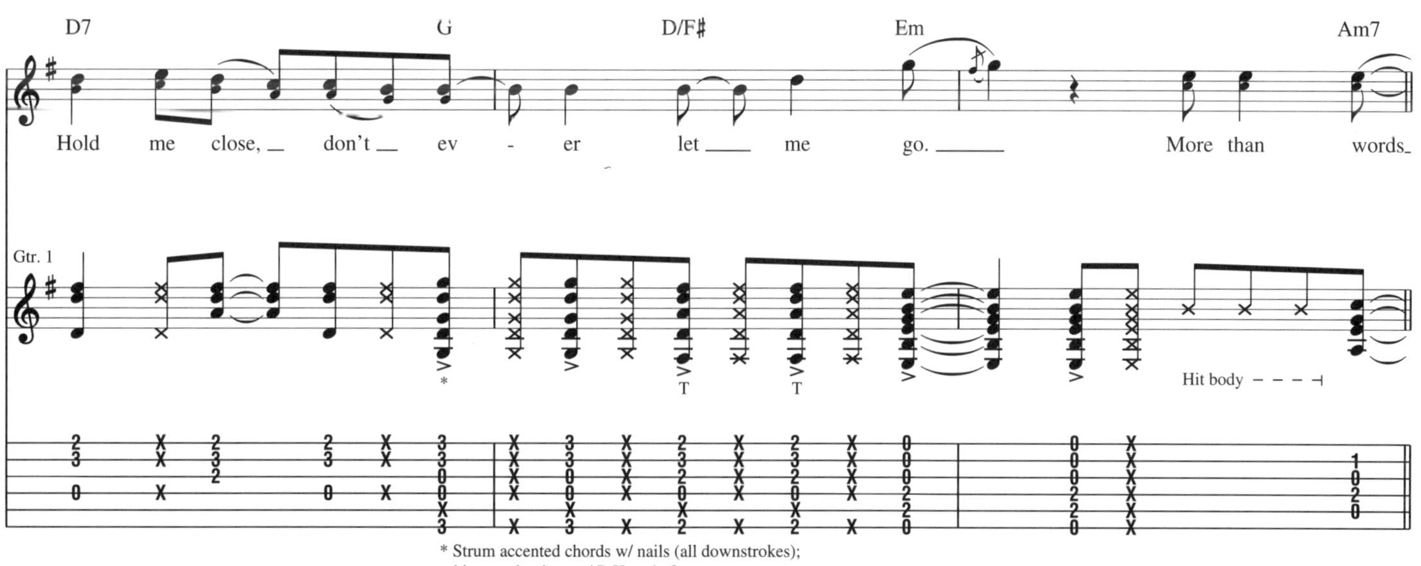

Chorus

Am7
D
D7♭9/A
G
I'd al - read - y know.
What would you do
Gtr. 1
Gtr. 1: w/ Rhy. Fig. 5
Dadd2/F#
Em
Bm
C
G/B
Am7
if my heart was torn in two?
More than words to show you feel
D7
G
that your love for me is real.
What would you say
Dadd2/F#
Em
Bm
C
G/B
Am7
if I took those words a - way?
Then you could - n't make things new
Outro
Gtr. 1: w/ Rhy. Fig. 1
D7
G
G/B
Cadd9
Am7
just by say - ing "I love you."
La, dee, da, dai, dai,
Gtr. 1: w/ Rhy. Fig. 2
C
D
Dsus4
G
G/B
Cadd9
dee, dai, dai, da.
More than words.
Am7
C
D
Dsus4
G
La, dee, da, dai, dai, dee, dai, dai, da.
More than words.

G/B
Cadd9
Am7
La, dee, dai, dai, dai, dee, dai, dai, da.
(La, dee, dai, dai, da. La,
Gtr. 1
* strum
* As before
C
D
Dsus4
G
G/B
Cadd9
Am7
More than words.
La, da, da, dai, da.
da, da, da, da.
La, da, da, dai, da.
strum
Hit body
C
D
G
More than words.
La, da, da, da, da, da.)
Dadd2/F#
Dm(add2)/F
Esus4
rit.
Oo, oo, oo, oo, oo, oo,
rit.

Slower
Am7
rit.
Free time
D
oo.
rit.
accel.
T

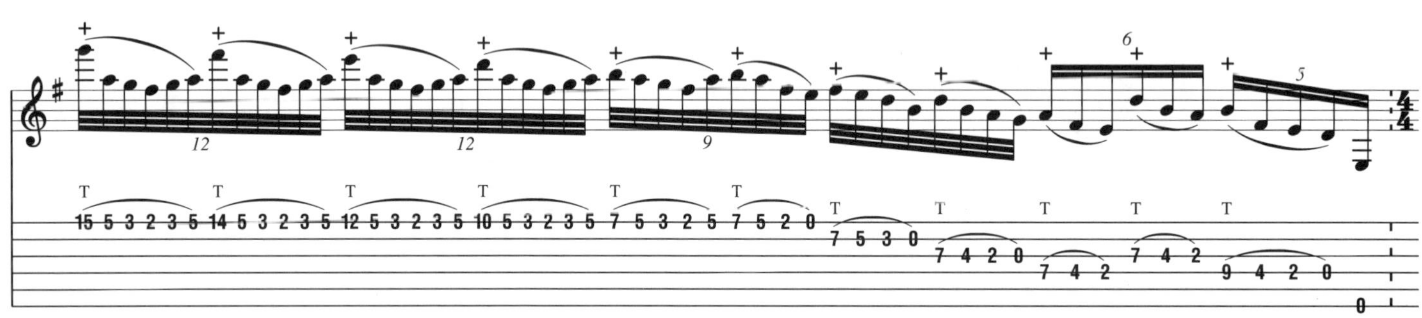

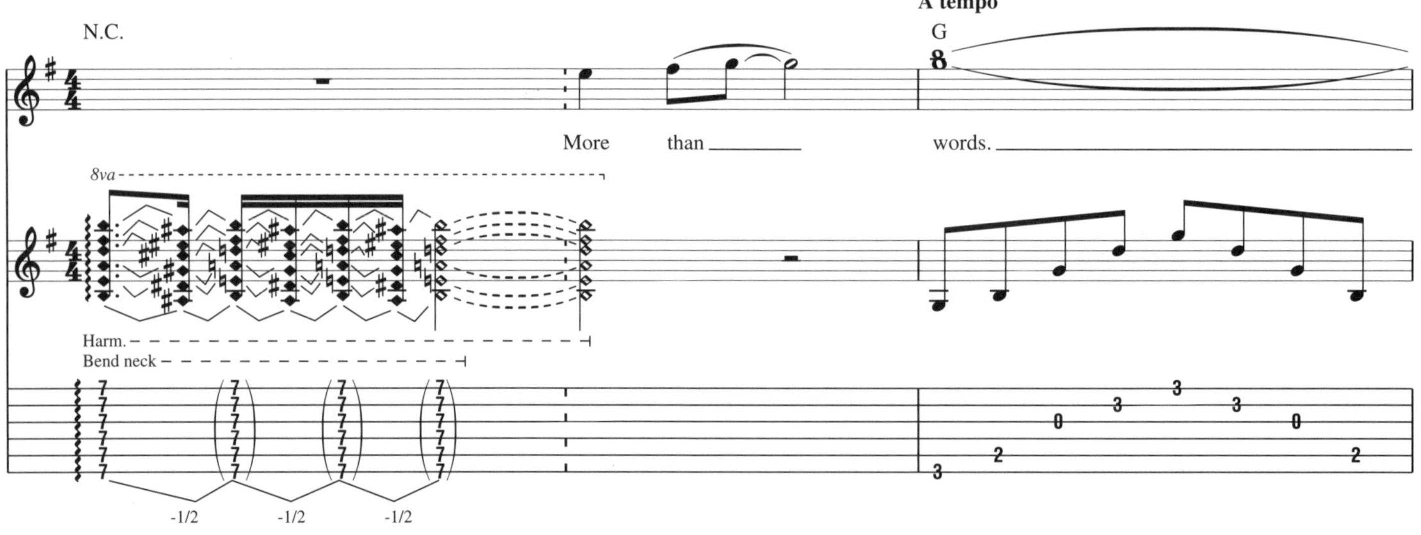
N.C.
A tempo
G
More than
words.
8va
Harm.
Bend neck
-1/2

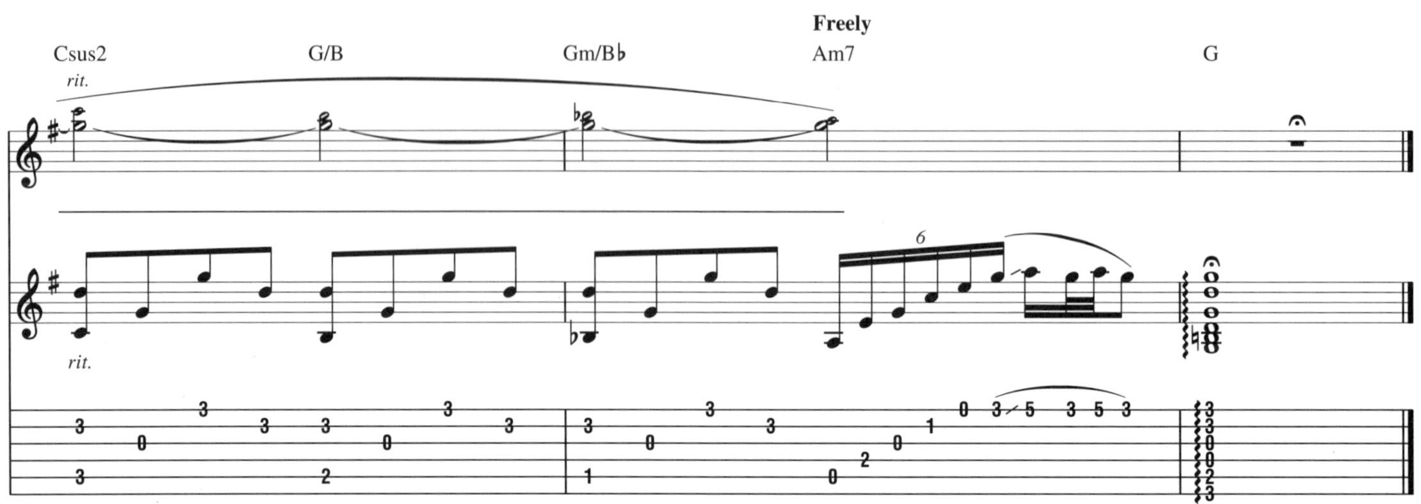
Csus2
G/B
Gm/B♭
Freely
Am7
G
rit.

1979

Words and Music by Billy Corgan

Tune down 1/2 Step:
①=E♭ ④=D♭
②=B♭ ⑤=A♭
③=G♭ ⑥=E♭
Intro
Moderate Rock ♩ = 126
(drums & electronic percussion)
3
w/Voc. echo effect
*Emaj7
Rhy. Fig. 1
E
Gtr. 1
(clean)
*Chord symbols relect implied tonality.
A
End Rhy. Fig. 1
1/2
Verse
Gtr. 1: w/Rhy. Fig. 1, 2¾ times
w/Voc. echo effect
Emaj7
E
A
1. Shake - down nine - teen sev - en nine.
2. June - bug skip - pin' like a stone
Cool kids nev - er have the time.
with the head - lights point - ed at the dawn.
On a live wire right -
We were sure we'd nev -

© 1995 Cinderful Music/Chrysalis Songs (BMI)
All Rights in the USA and Canada administered by Chrysalis Songs (BMI)
All Rights Reserved Used by Permission

1.
F♯m11
B
up off the street; you and I should meet.
er see an end to it all.
Gtr. 1
Rhy. Fig. 2
End Rhy. Fig. 2
2.
𝄋 Chorus
E
Emaj7
E
And I don't e - ven care
Rhy. Fig. 3
A
to shake these zip - per blues.
End Rhy. Fig. 3
1/2
Gtr. 1: w/Rhy. Fig. 3, 1¾ times
E
Emaj7
E
A
And we don't know just where
our bones will rest; to dust, I guess. For- got-

Gtr. 1: w/Rhy. Fig. 2
To Coda
F♯m11
B
- ten and ab - sorbed in - to the earth be - low.
Interlude
Gtr. 1: w/Rhy. Fig. 1
w/Voc. echo effect
4
Verse
Gtr. 1: w/Rhy. Fig. 1, 3 times
w/Voc. echo effect
Emaj7
E
A
Emaj7
E
3. Dou - ble cross the va - cant and the bored.
A
They're not sure just what we have in store.
Emaj7
E
A
Mor - phine cit - y slip - pin' dues
F♯
A
down to see that we
Gtr. 1
Chorus
Gtr. 1: w/Rhy. Fig. 3, 3 times
E
Emaj7
E
A
don't e - ven care, as rest - less as we are.
E
Emaj7
E
A
We feel the pull in the land of a thou - sand guilts.
E
Emaj7
E
A
And poured ce - ment, la - ment - ed and as - sured

Bridge
B5
to the lights and towns
Gtr. 1
Rhy. Fig. 4
C♯m7
Aadd9
be - low.
End Rhy. Fig. 4
Gtr. 1: w/Rhy. Fig. 4, 2 times
B5
C♯m7
Aadd9
Fast - er than the speed of sound.
B5
C♯m7
Aadd9
Fast - er than we thought we'd go,
Gtr. 1: w/Rhy. Fig. 2, last 2 meas.
F♯m11
B
be - neath the sound of hope.
Verse
Gtr. 1: w/Rhy. Fig. 1, 3¾ times
w/Voc. echo effect
Emaj7
E
A
4. Jus - tine nev -

Emaj7
E
- er knew the rules,
A
Emaj7
E
hung down with the freaks and ghouls.
A
No a - pol - o - gies ev - er need be made,
Emaj7
E
A
I know you bet -
Gtr. 1: w/Rhy. Fig. 2
F♯m11
B
D.S. al Coda
- ter than you fake it. To see that we
Outro
Gtr. 1: w/Rhy. Fig. 1, 2 times
w/Voc. echo effect
Coda
Emaj7
E
be - low.
A
Emaj7
E
The street heats the ur - gen - cy of now.
w/electronic percussion
A
E
As you see there's no one a - round.
Gtr. 1
0
0
1
2
2
0

No Excuses

Written by Jerry Cantrell

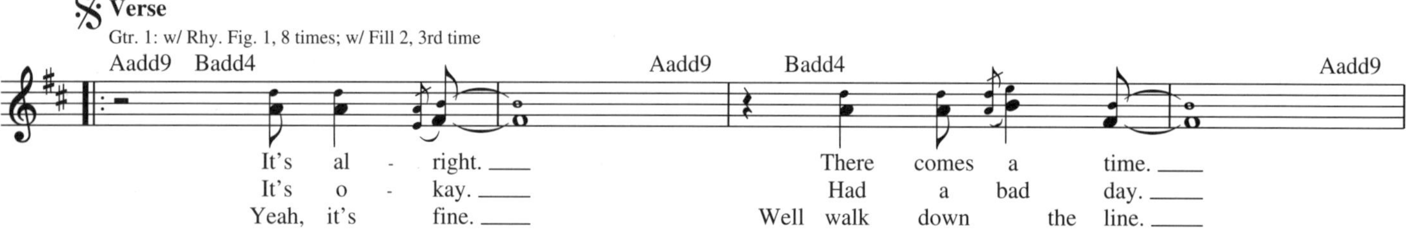

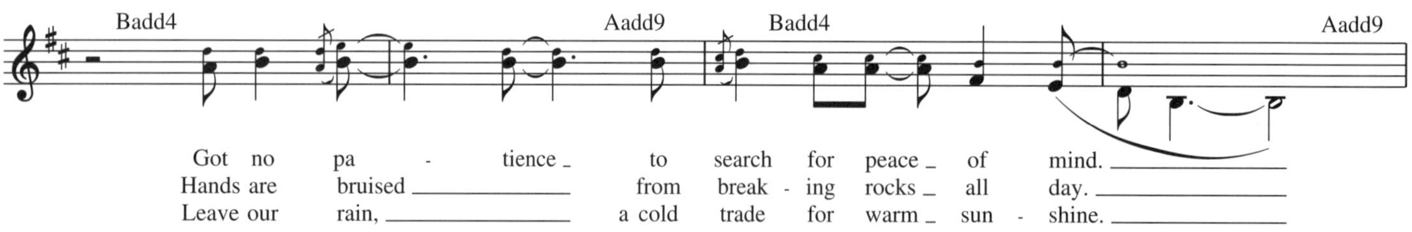

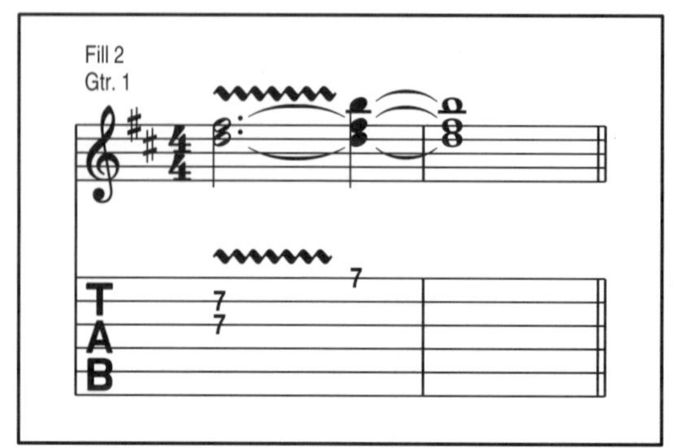

Copyright © 1993 Buttnugget Publishing (ASCAP)
International Copyright Secured All Rights Reserved

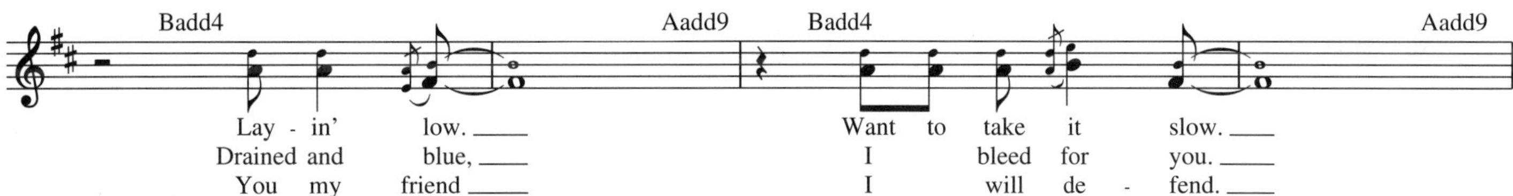
Badd4
Aadd9
Badd4
Aadd9
Lay - in' low.
Want to take it slow.
Drained and blue,
I bleed for you.
You my friend
I will de - fend.

To Coda
Badd4
Aadd9
Badd2
Aadd9
No more hid - ing or dis - guis - ing truths I've sold.
You think it's fun - ny well, you're drown - ing in it too.
And if we change, well, I love you an - y - way.

Chorus
G6
Aadd9
Badd4
Aadd9
Rhy. Fig. 2
Gtr. 1
Ev - 'ry day it's some - thing, hits me all - so cold. You
Gtr. 2 (elec.)
full
full

Gtr. 2: w/ Fill 1, 2nd time (See page 23)
G6
Aadd9
E
Aadd9
End Rhy. Fig. 2
find me sit - tin' by my - self, no ex - cus - es, then I know.
full full

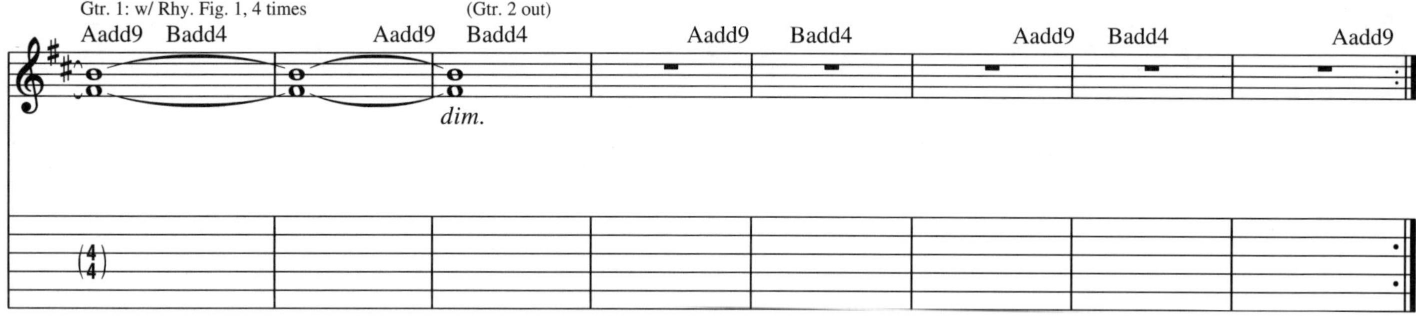
Gtr. 1: w/ Rhy. Fig. 1, 4 times
(Gtr. 2 out)
Aadd9 Badd4 Aadd9 Badd4 Aadd9 Badd4 Aadd9 Badd4 Aadd9
dim.

Guitar Solo

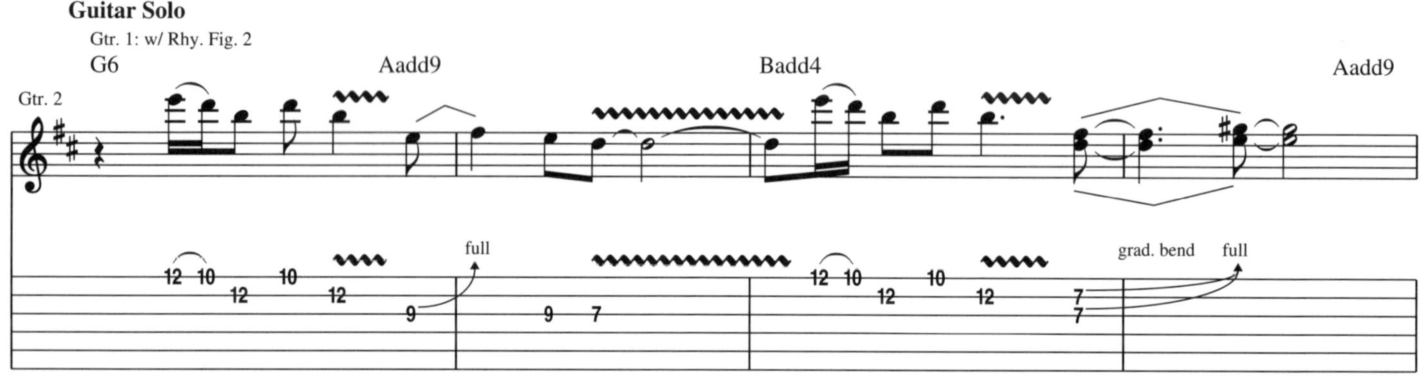
Gtr. 1: w/ Rhy. Fig. 2
G6 Aadd9 Badd4 Aadd9
Gtr. 2
full
grad. bend
full

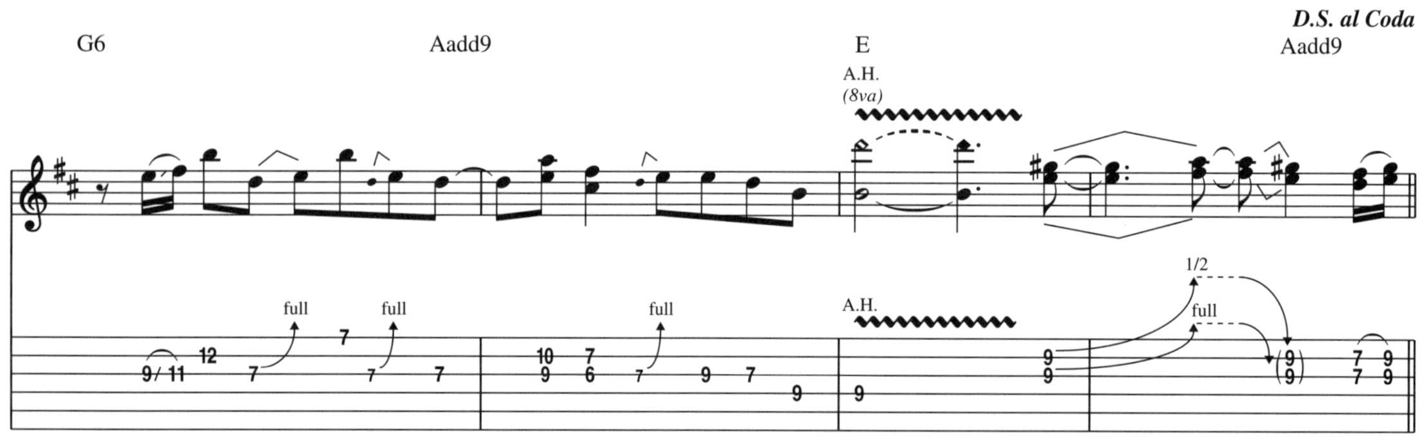
D.S. al Coda
G6 Aadd9 E Aadd9
A.H.
(8va)
full
full
full
A.H.
1/2
full

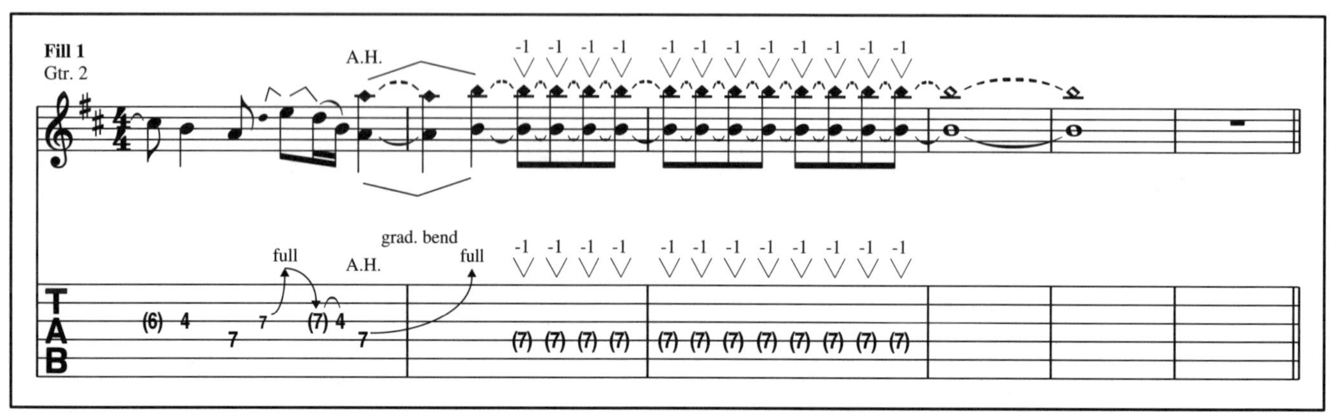
Fill 1
Gtr. 2
A.H.
grad. bend
full
A.H.
full

Coda

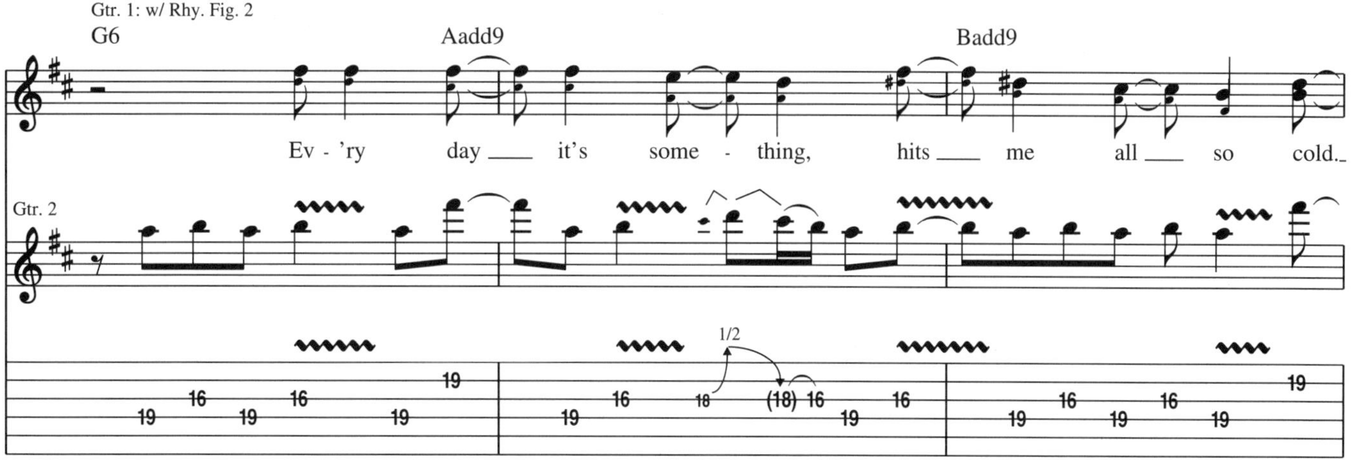
Chorus
Gtr. 1: w/ Rhy. Fig. 2
G6
Aadd9
Badd9
Ev - 'ry day it's some - thing, hits me all so cold.
Gtr. 2
1/2

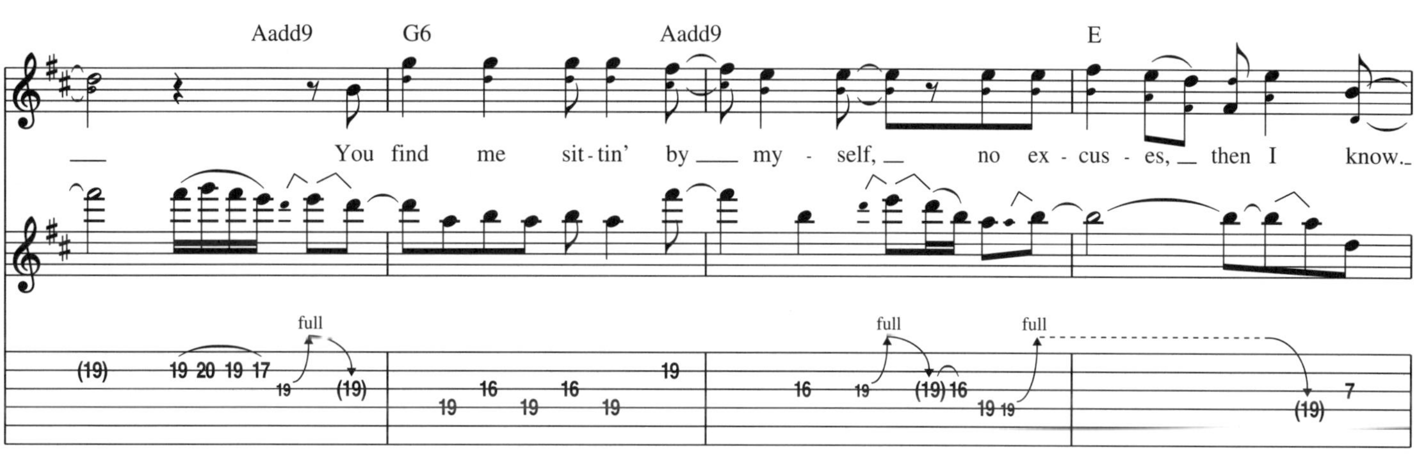
Aadd9
G6
Aadd9
E
You find me sit - tin' by my - self, no ex - cus - es, then I know.
full
full
full

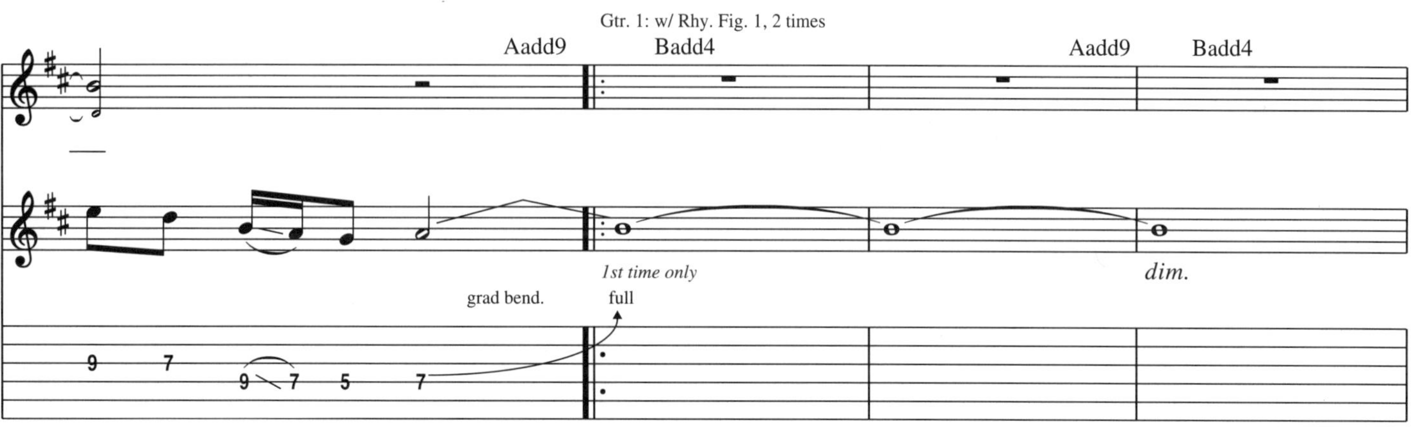
Gtr. 1: w/ Rhy. Fig. 1, 2 times
Aadd9
Badd4
Aadd9
Badd4
1st time only
dim.
grad bend.
full

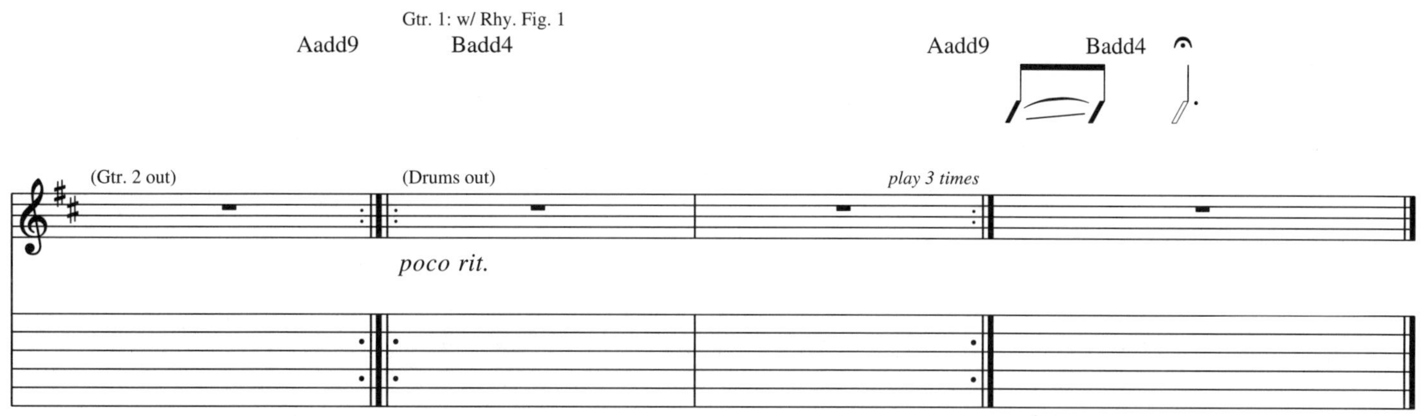
Gtr. 1: w/ Rhy. Fig. 1
Aadd9
Badd4
Aadd9
Badd4
(Gtr. 2 out)
(Drums out)
play 3 times
poco rit.

Santa Monica

Words by Art Alexakis
Music by Art Alexakis and Everclear

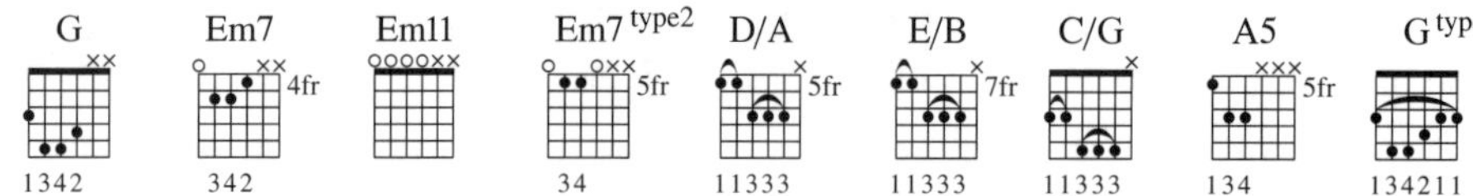

Intro

Moderate Rock ♩ = 100

Gtr. 1 (elec.)

G5 Em7 G5 Em7

mf w/ clean tone

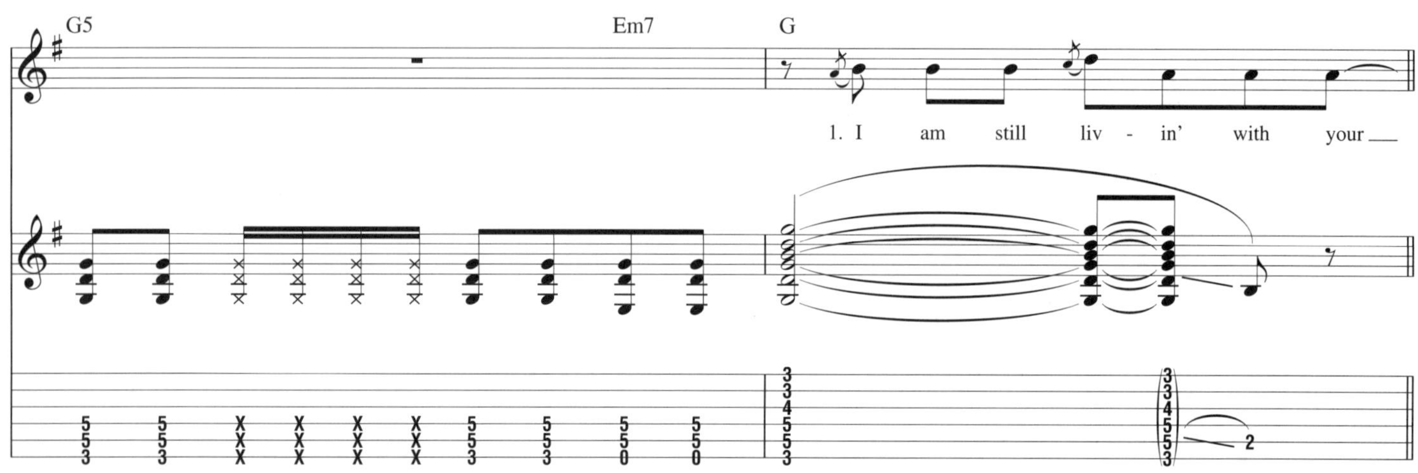

Verse

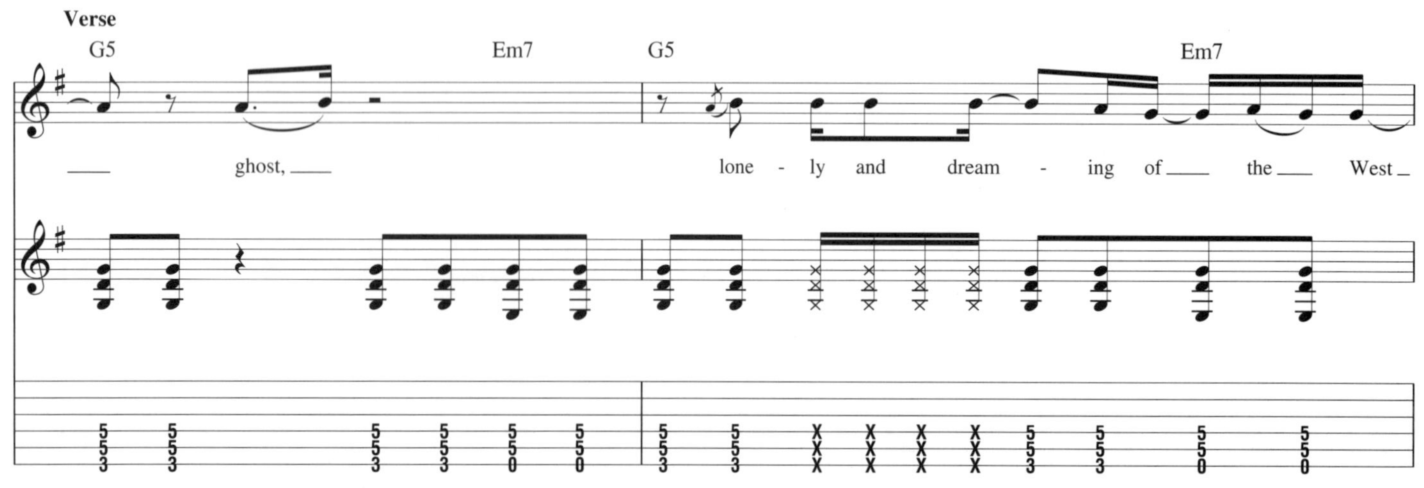

Copyright © 1995 IRVING MUSIC, INC., EVERGLEAM MUSIC, MONTALUPIS MUSIC and COMMONGREEN MUSIC
All Rights Administered by IRVING MUSIC, INC.
All Rights Reserved Used by Permission

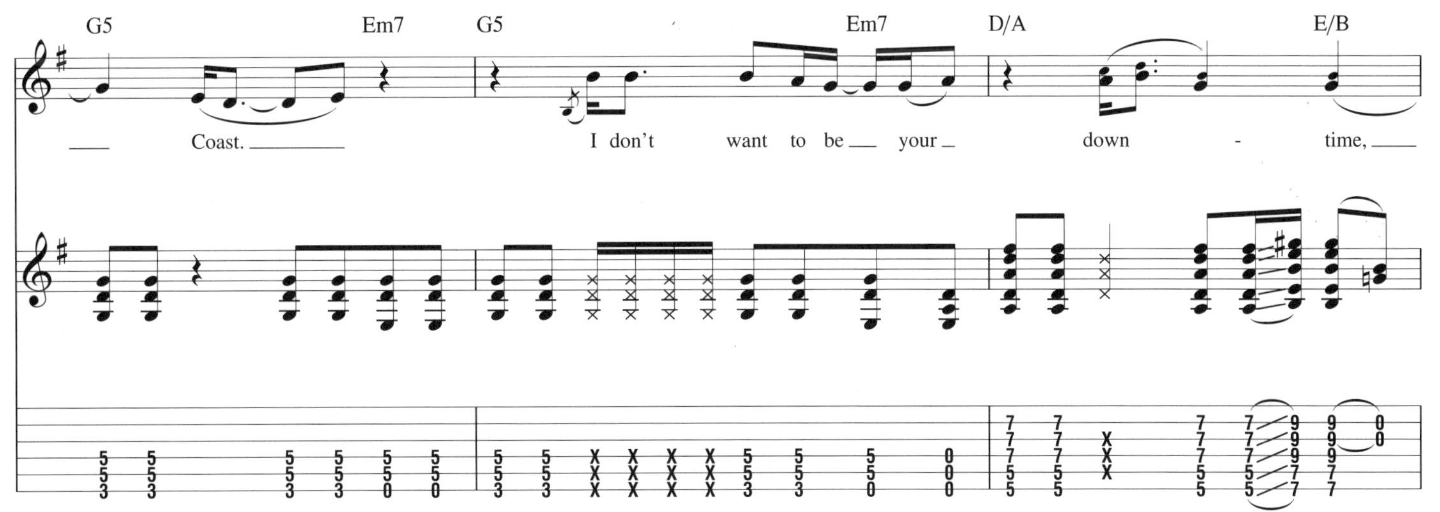
G5 Em7 G5 Em7 D/A E/B
Coast. I don't want to be your down - time,

Gtr. 2: w/ Rhy. Fill 1
C/G A5 G5 Em7 G
I don't want to be your stu - pid game. 2. With my big black boots and an old suit-
(cont. in slashes)

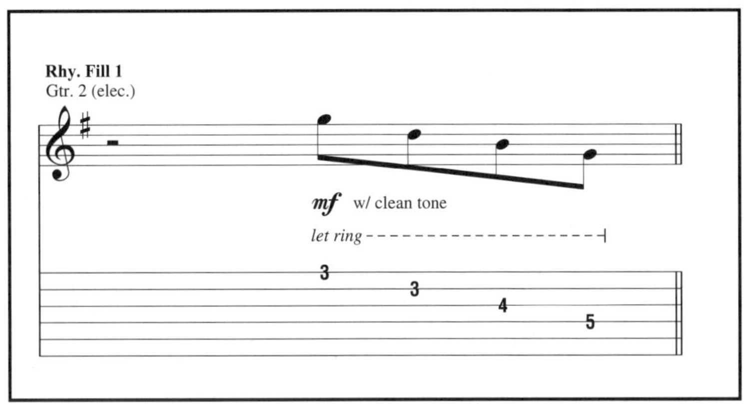
Rhy. Fill 1
Gtr. 2 (elec.)
mf w/ clean tone
let ring

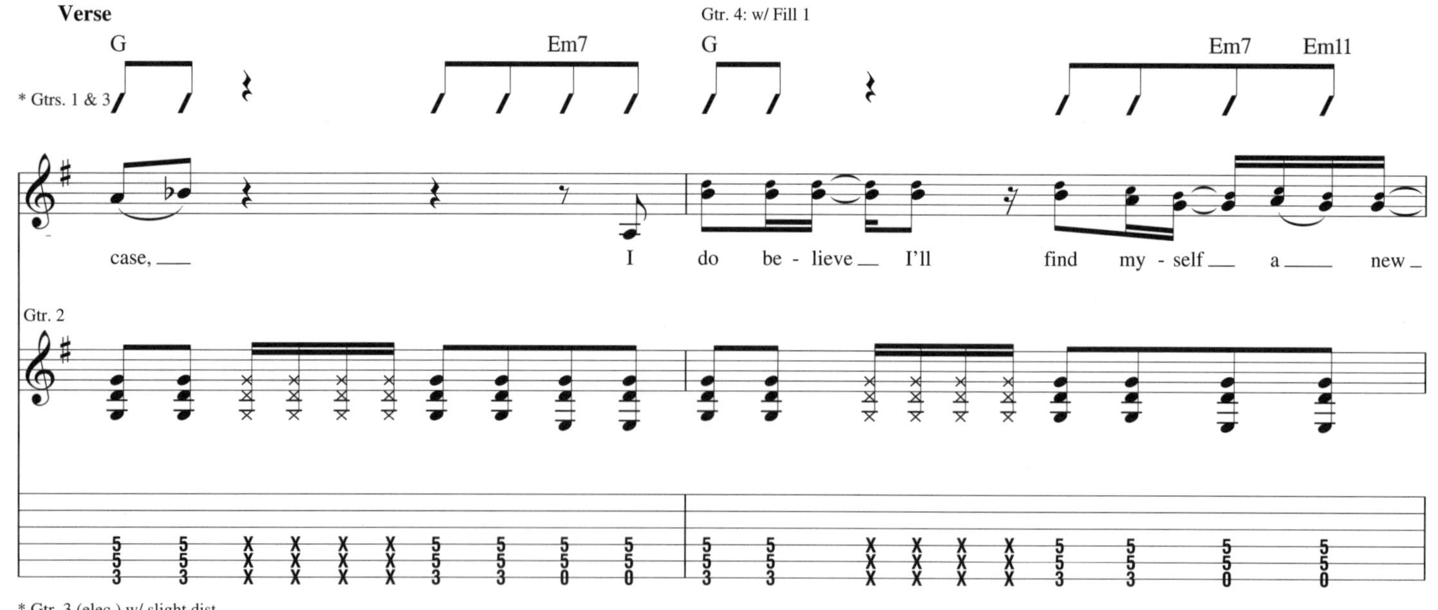
Verse
G
Em7
Gtr. 4: w/ Fill 1
G
Em7
Em11
* Gtrs. 1 & 3
case,
I
do
be - lieve
I'll
find
my - self
a
new
Gtr. 2

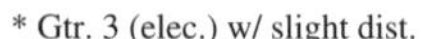
* Gtr. 3 (elec.) w/ slight dist.

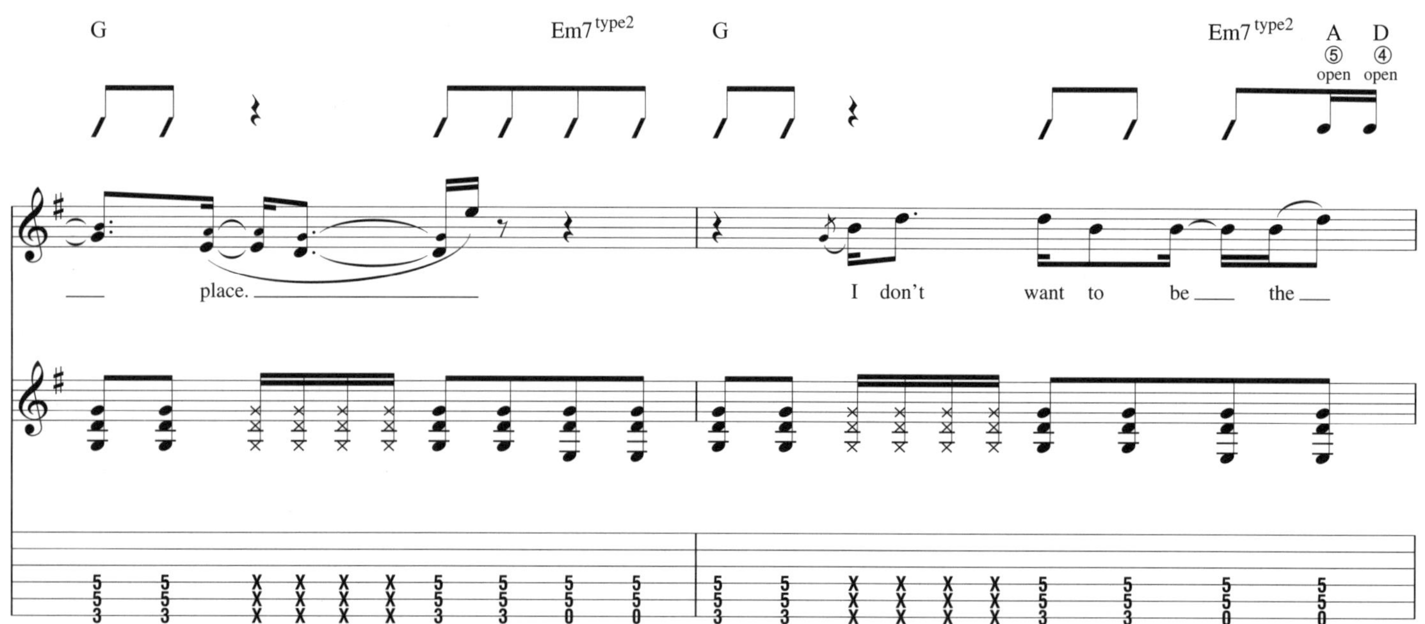
G
Em7 type2
G
Em7 type2
A
D
⑤
④
open
open
place.
I
don't
want
to
be
the

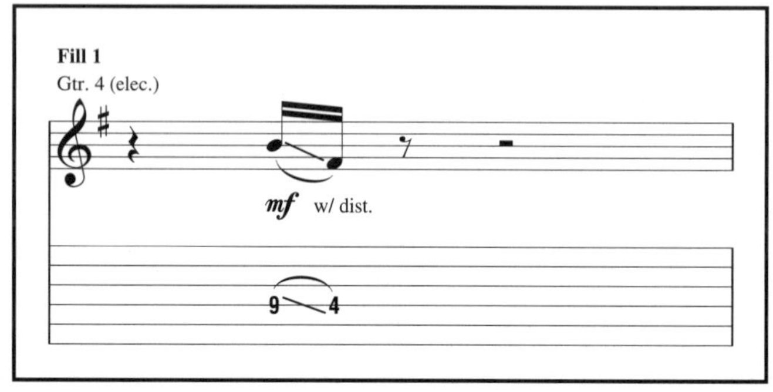
Fill 1
Gtr. 4 (elec.)
mf
w/ dist.

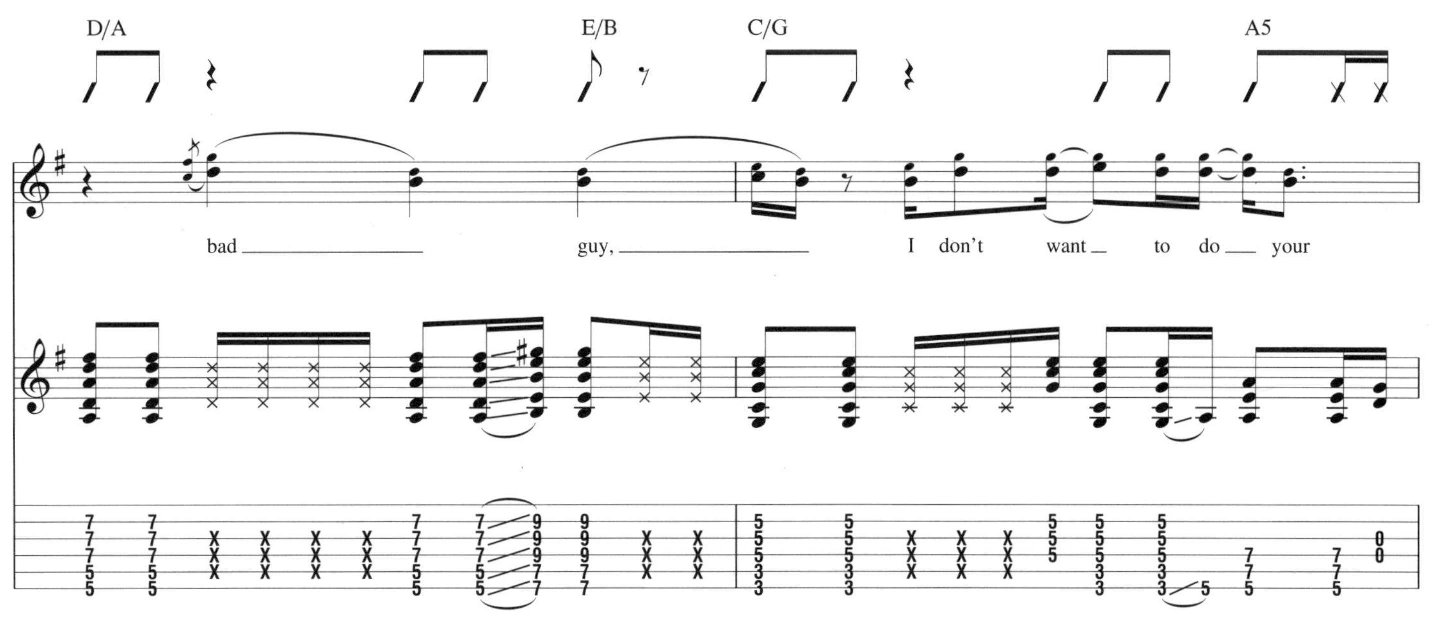
D/A
E/B
C/G
A5
bad
guy,
I don't
want
to
do
your

Gtr. 4: w/ Fill 2
G5
G
Em7
G
E
open
sleep - walk
dance
an - y - more.
I
just
want
to
see
some

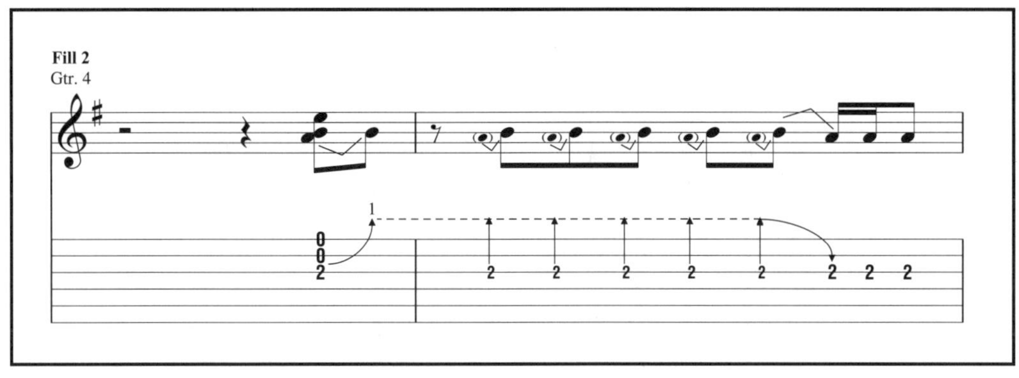
Fill 2
Gtr. 4

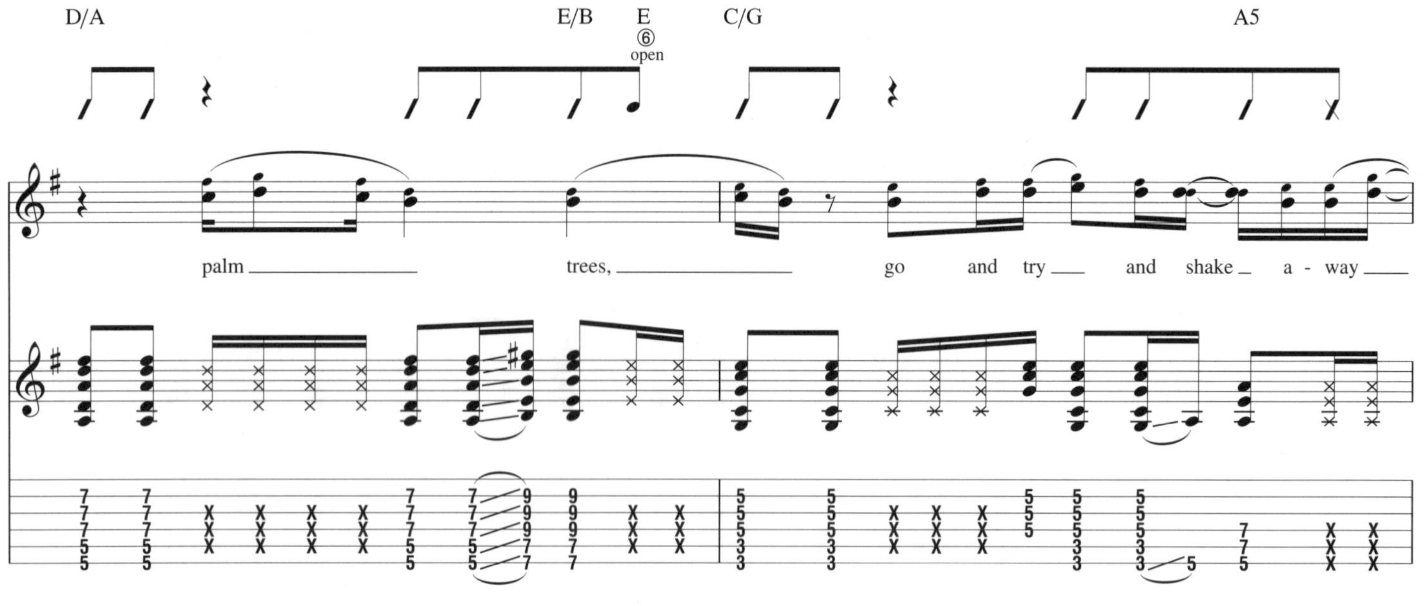
D/A
E/B
E
open
C/G
A5
palm trees, go and try and shake a - way

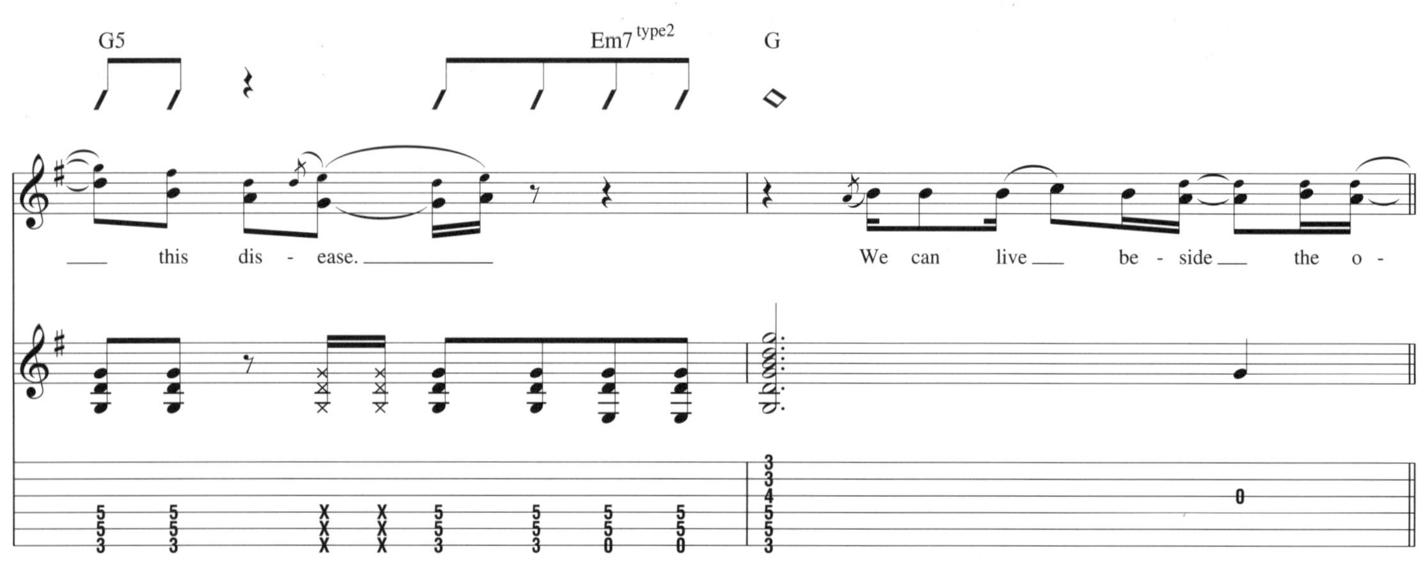
G5
Em7 type2
G
this dis - ease.
We can live be - side the o -

Chorus
Gtr. 2 tacet
C/G
D/A
G
E/B
D/A
- cean, leave the fire be - hind, swim out past the break-
Rhy. Fig. 1
Gtr. 5 (elec.)
mf w/ slight dist.

C/G
G
3fr
1.
G
D/A
C/G
- ers, watch the world die.
We can live be - side the o -
End Rhy. Fig. 1
2.
G5
Em7type2
Em11
G5
Em7type2
Em11
G5
Em7type2
Em11
Gtr. 2: w/ Fill 3
Gtype2
3. I am still dream - ing of your
8va
w/ heavy dist.
fdbk.
steady gliss.
Fill 3
Gtr. 2
⑥ = E♭
w/ heavy dist.
*fdbk.
* Microphonic fdbk., not caused by string vibration.

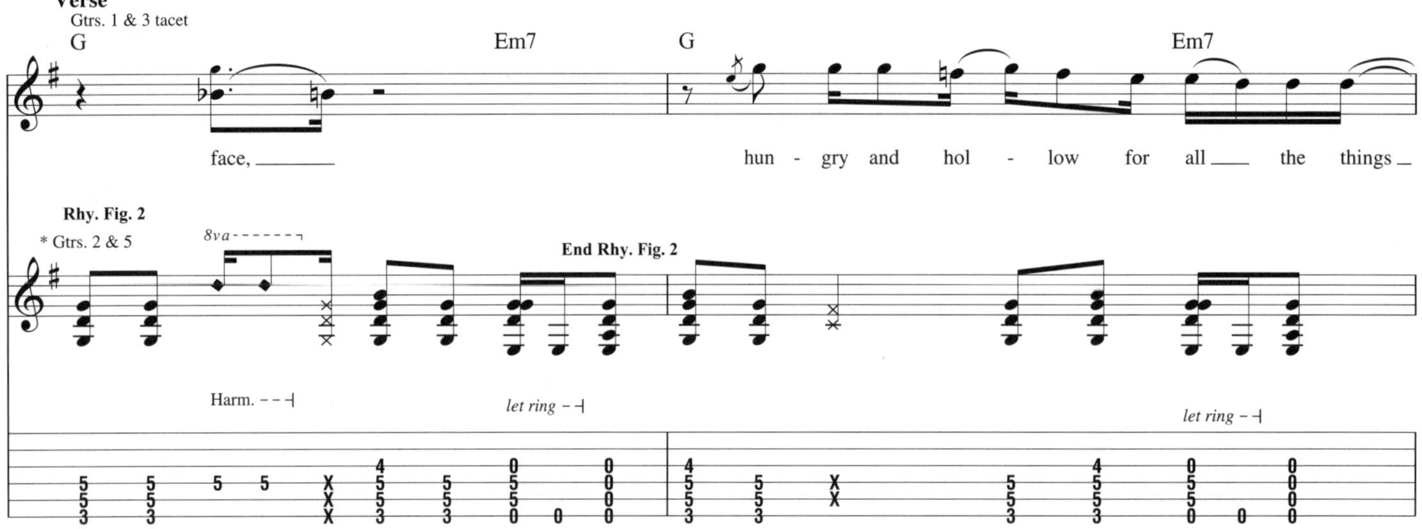

* Two gtrs. arr. for one.

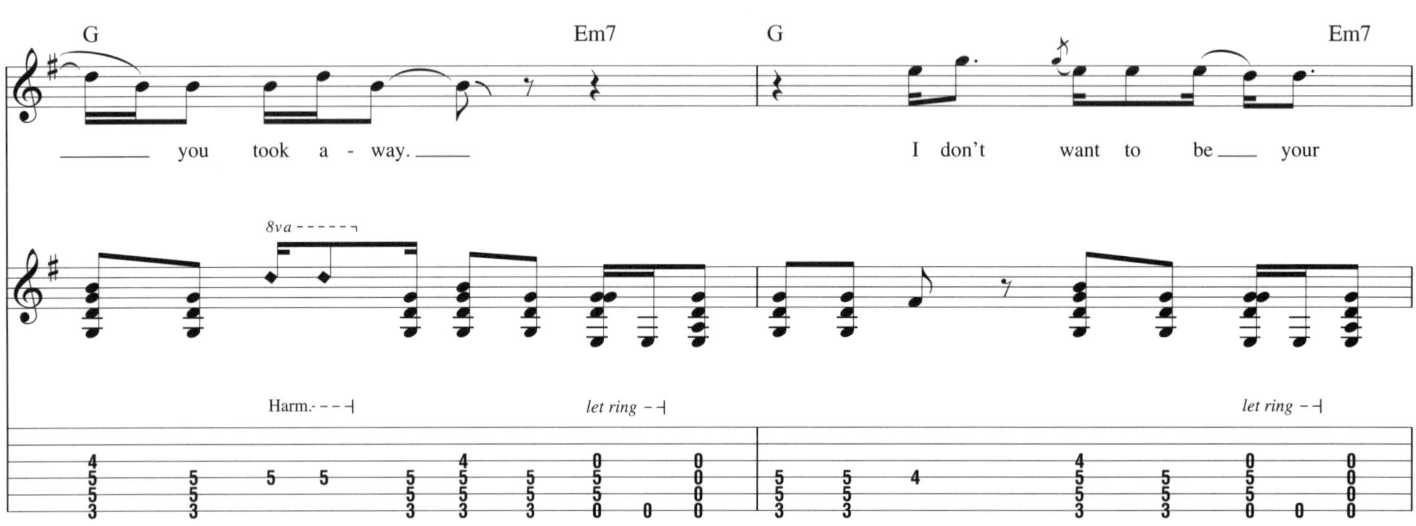

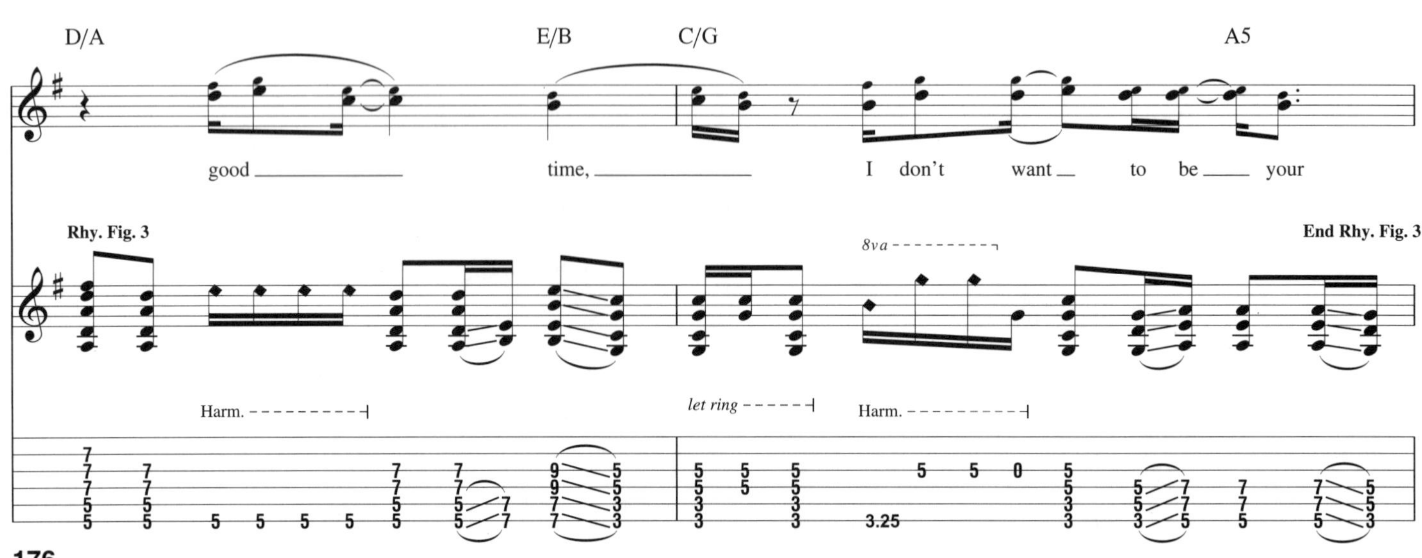

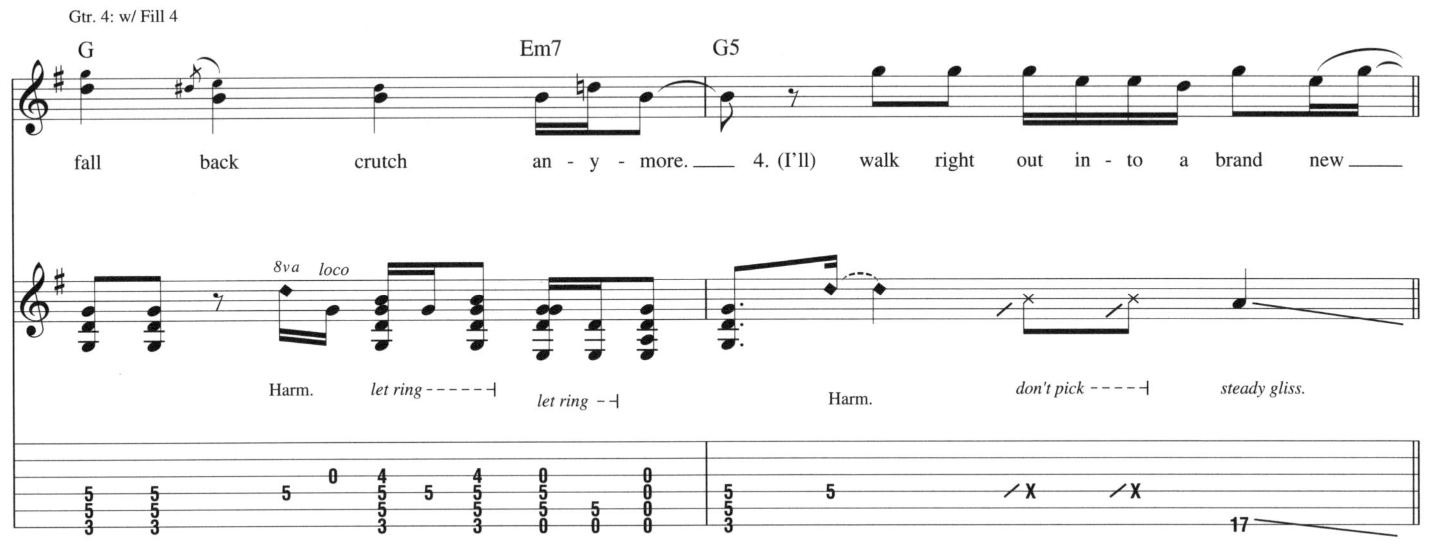
Gr. 4: w/ Fill 4
G
Em7
G5
fall back crutch an - y - more. 4. (I'll) walk right out in - to a brand new
8va loco
Harm.
let ring
let ring
Harm.
don't pick
steady gliss.

Verse

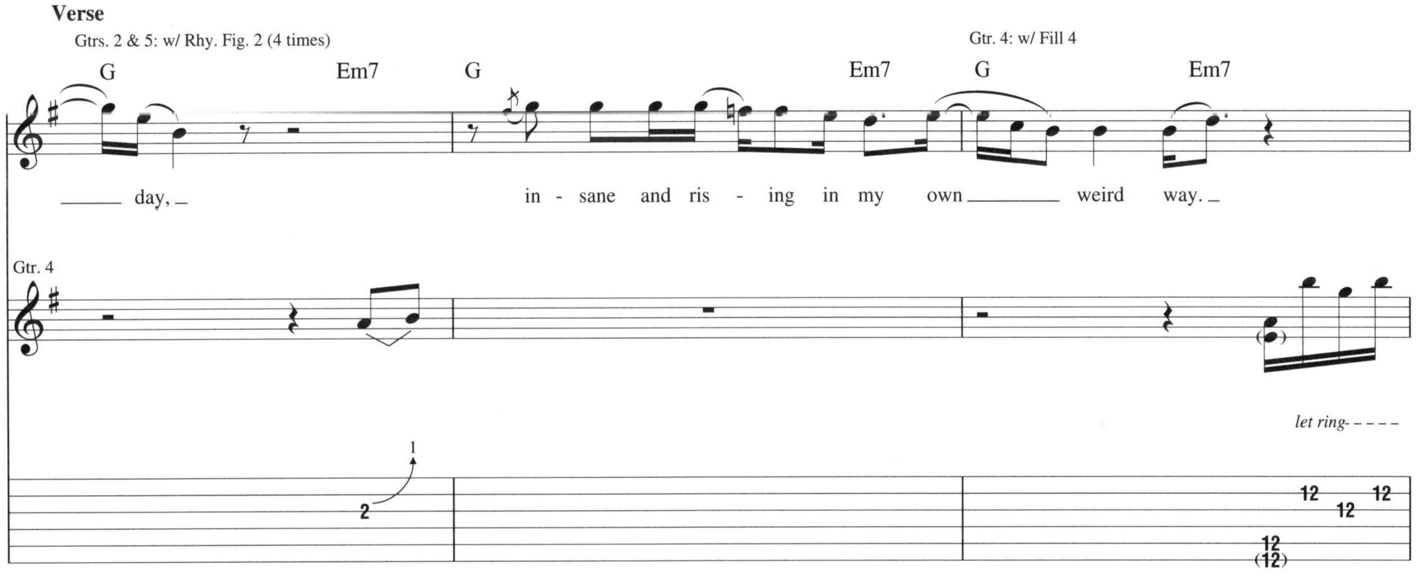
Gtrs. 2 & 5: w/ Rhy. Fig. 2 (4 times)
Gtr. 4: w/ Fill 4
G
Em7
G
Em7
G
Em7
day,
in - sane and ris - ing in my own weird way.
Gtr. 4
let ring

Fill 4
Gtr. 4
hold bend

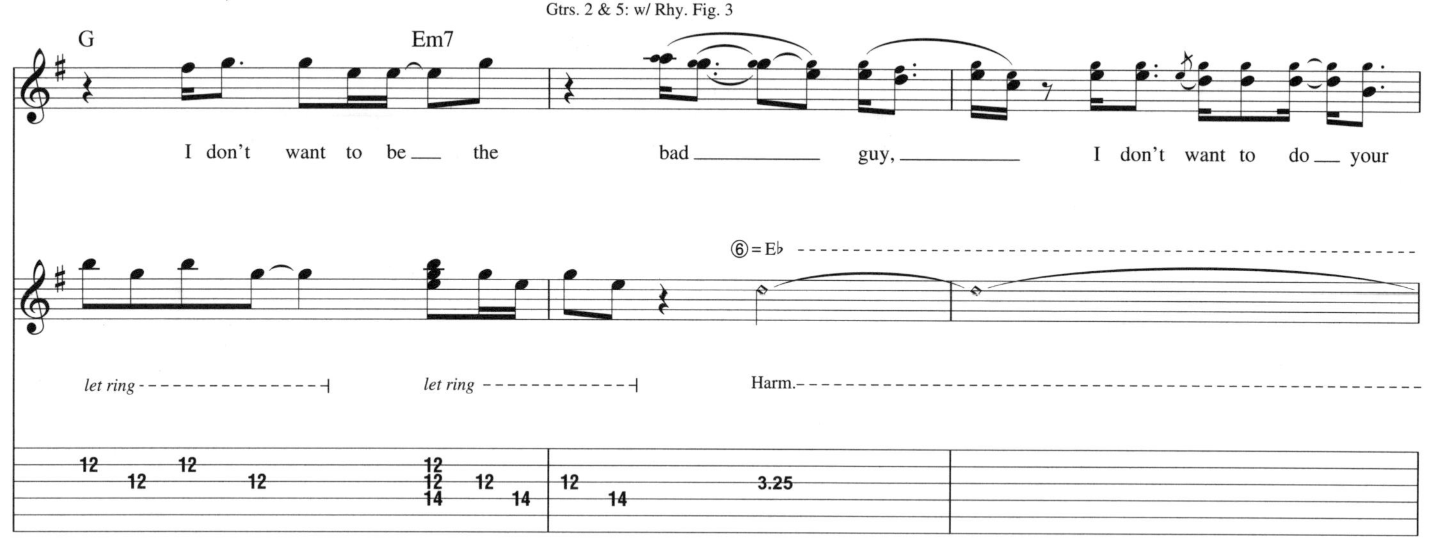
Gtrs. 2 & 5: w/ Rhy. Fig. 3
G
Em7
I don't want to be the bad guy, I don't want to do your
⑥ = E♭
let ring
let ring
Harm.
12 12 12 12 12 12 12 14 12 14 12 14 3.25

Gtrs. 2 & 5: w/ Rhy. Fig. 2 (2 times)
Gtrs. 2 & 5: w/ Rhy. Fig. 3
sleep - walk dance an - y - more. I just want to feel some sun - shine,
Harm.
(3.25)

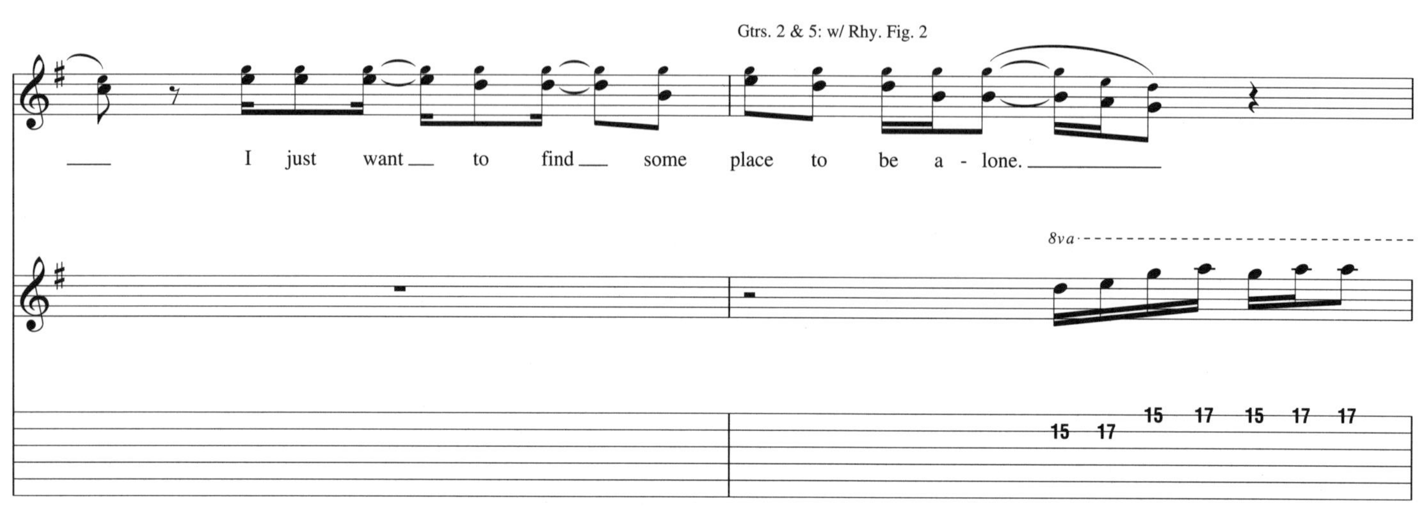
Gtrs. 2 & 5: w/ Rhy. Fig. 2
I just want to find some place to be a - lone.
8va
15 17 15 17 15 17 17

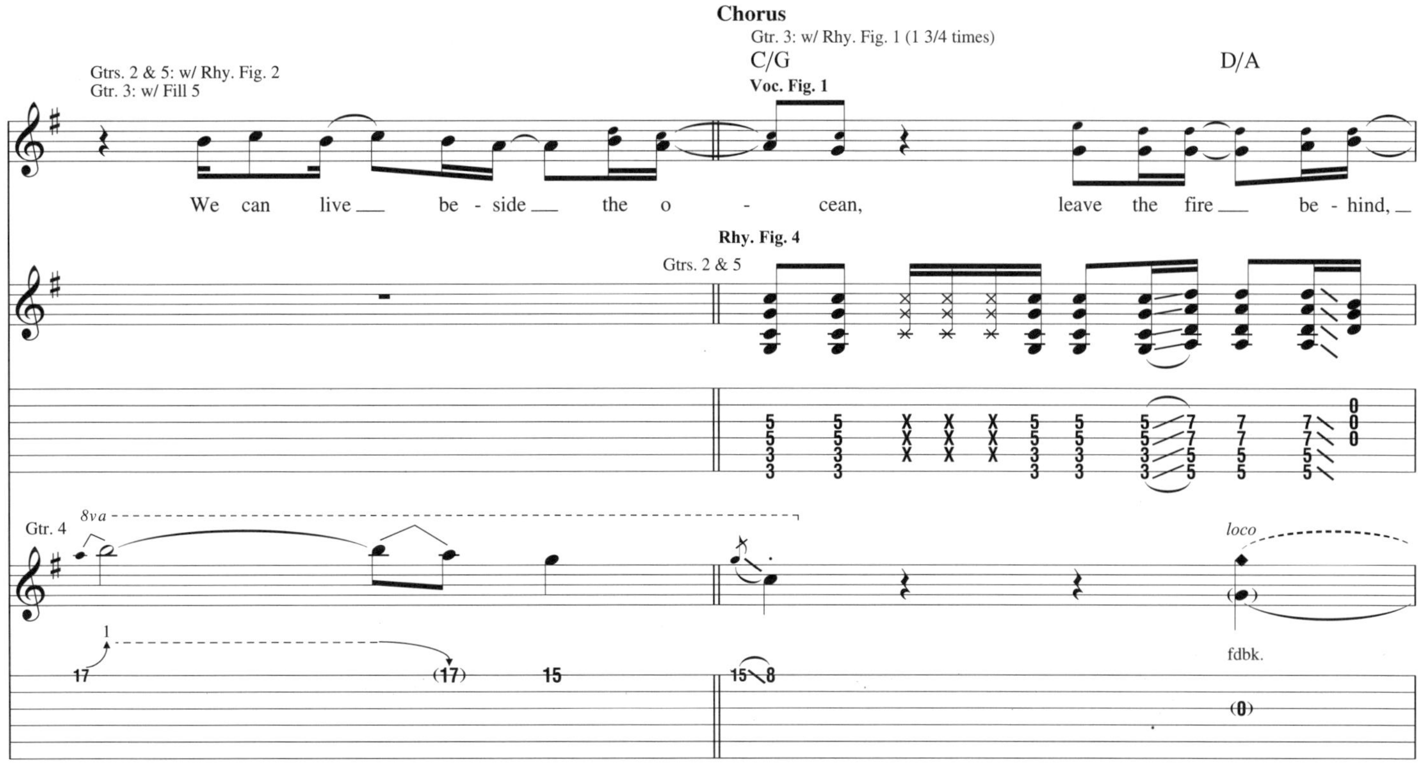
Chorus
Gtr. 3: w/ Rhy. Fig. 1 (1 3/4 times)
Gtrs. 2 & 5: w/ Rhy. Fig. 2
Gtr. 3: w/ Fill 5
C/G
D/A
Voc. Fig. 1
We can live beside the o - cean, leave the fire be - hind,
Rhy. Fig. 4
Gtrs. 2 & 5
Gtr. 4
8va
loco
fdbk.
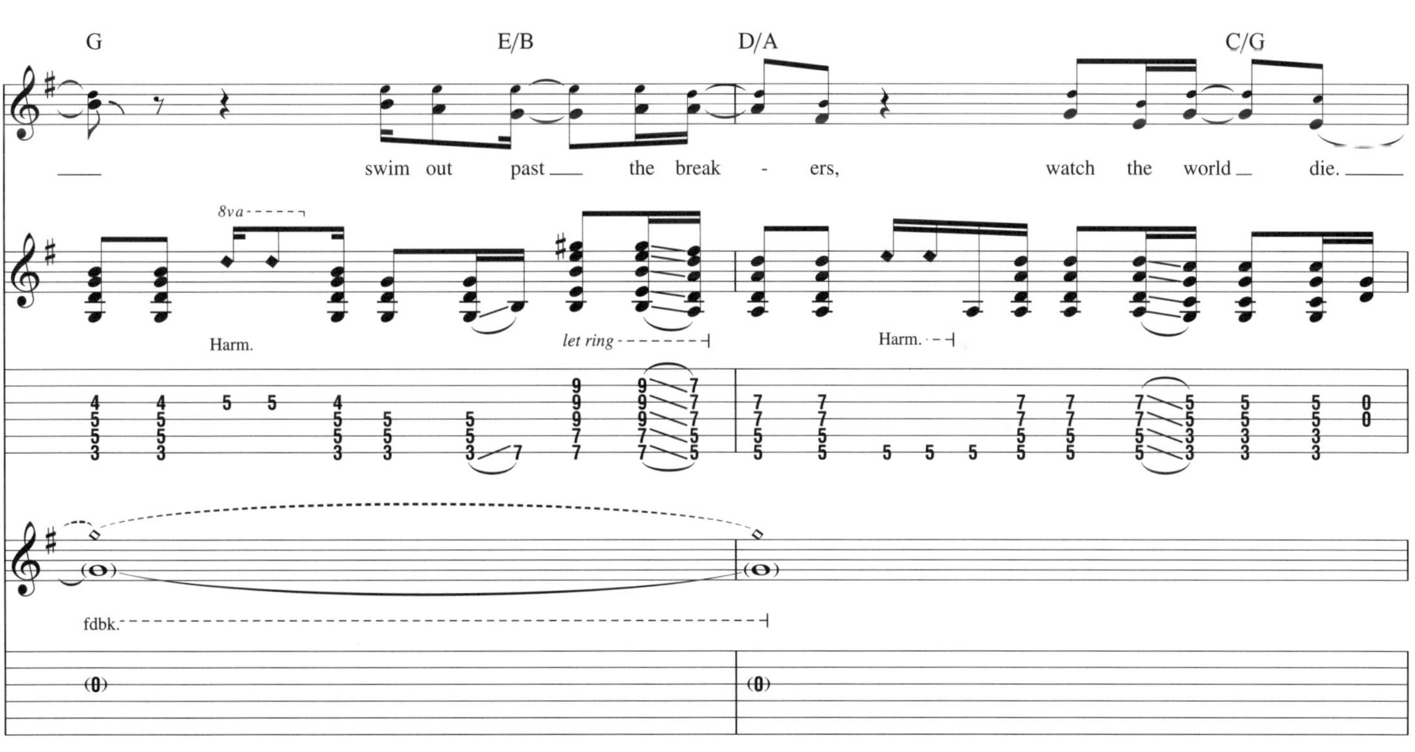
G
E/B
D/A
C/G
swim out past the break - ers, watch the world die.
8va
Harm.
let ring
Harm.
fdbk.
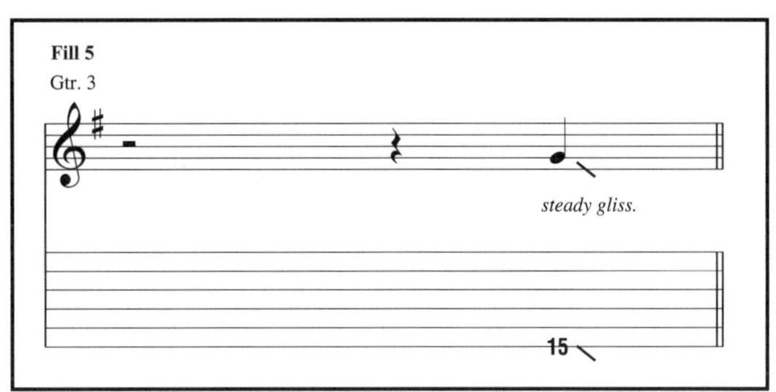
Fill 5
Gtr. 3
steady gliss.

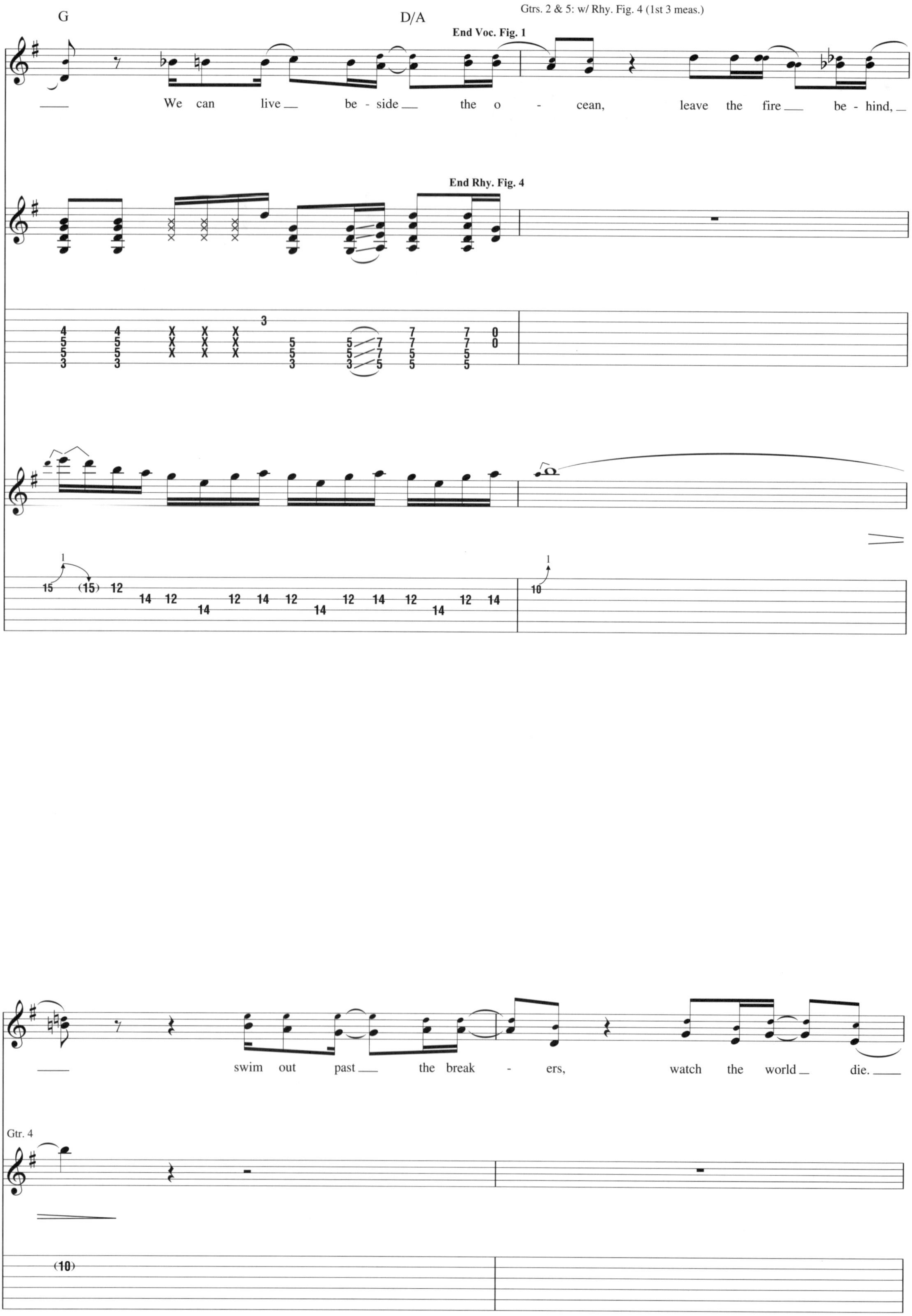

G D/A

Gtrs. 2 & 5: w/ Rhy. Fig. 4 (1st 3 meas.)

End Voc. Fig. 1

We can live beside the o - cean, leave the fire be - hind,

End Rhy. Fig. 4

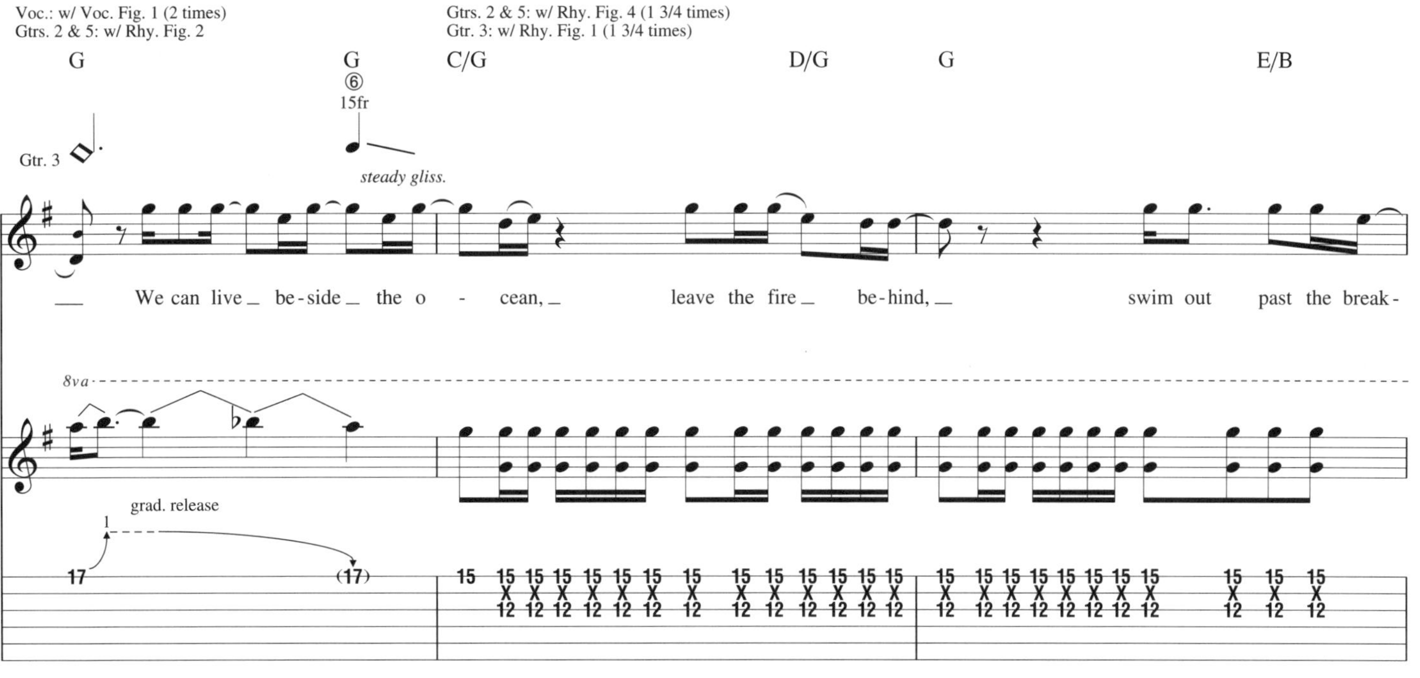
Voc.: w/ Voc. Fig. 1 (2 times)
Gtrs. 2 & 5: w/ Rhy. Fig. 2
Gtrs. 2 & 5: w/ Rhy. Fig. 4 (1 3/4 times)
Gtr. 3: w/ Rhy. Fig. 1 (1 3/4 times)
G G C/G D/G G E/B
15fr
Gtr. 3
steady gliss.
We can live be-side the o - cean, leave the fire be-hind, swim out past the break -
8va
grad. release

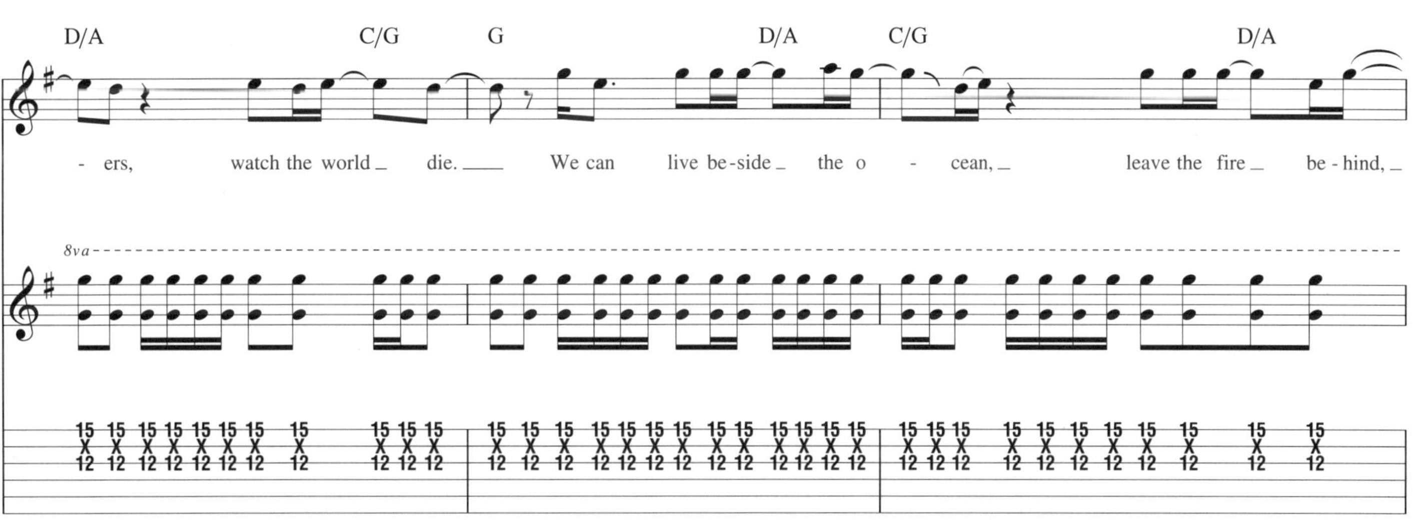
D/A C/G G D/A C/G D/A
- ers, watch the world die. We can live be-side the o - cean, leave the fire be - hind,
8va

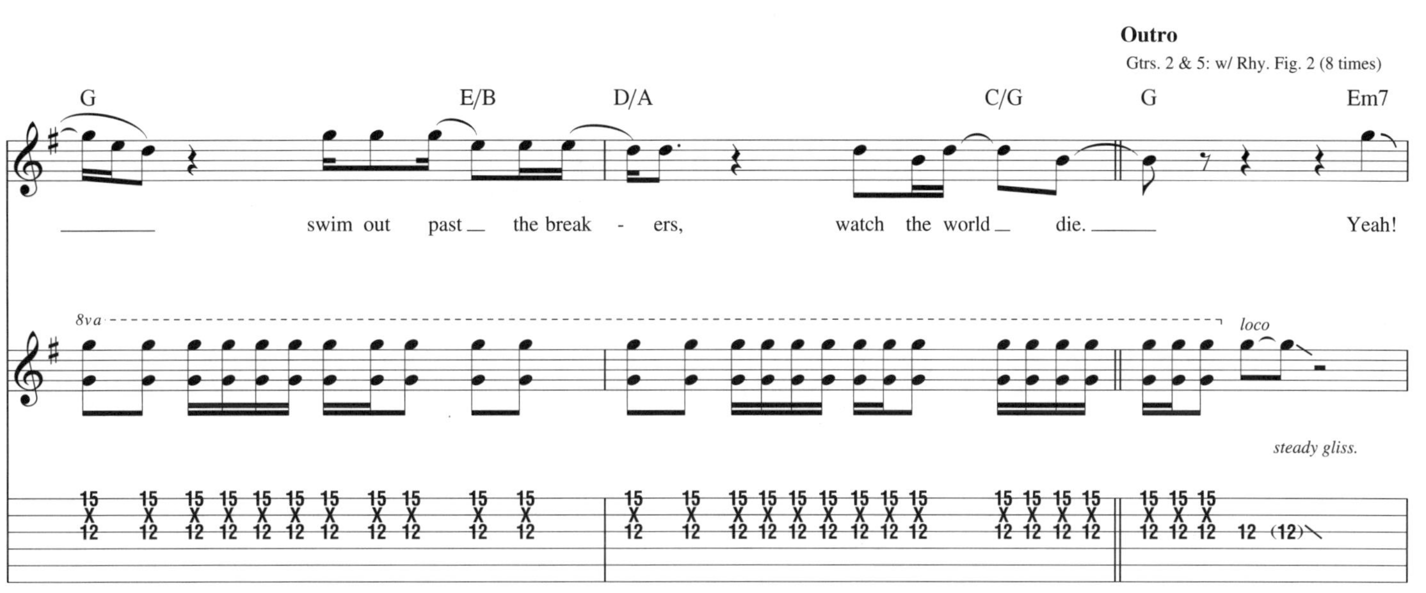
Outro
Gtrs. 2 & 5: w/ Rhy. Fig. 2 (8 times)
G E/B D/A C/G G Em7
swim out past the break - ers, watch the world die. Yeah!
8va
loco
steady gliss.

G
Em7
G
Em7
G
Em7
Yeah, _ watch the world _ die. _
Yeah. _
Yeah, _ watch the world _ die. _
steady gliss.
12 (12) 3

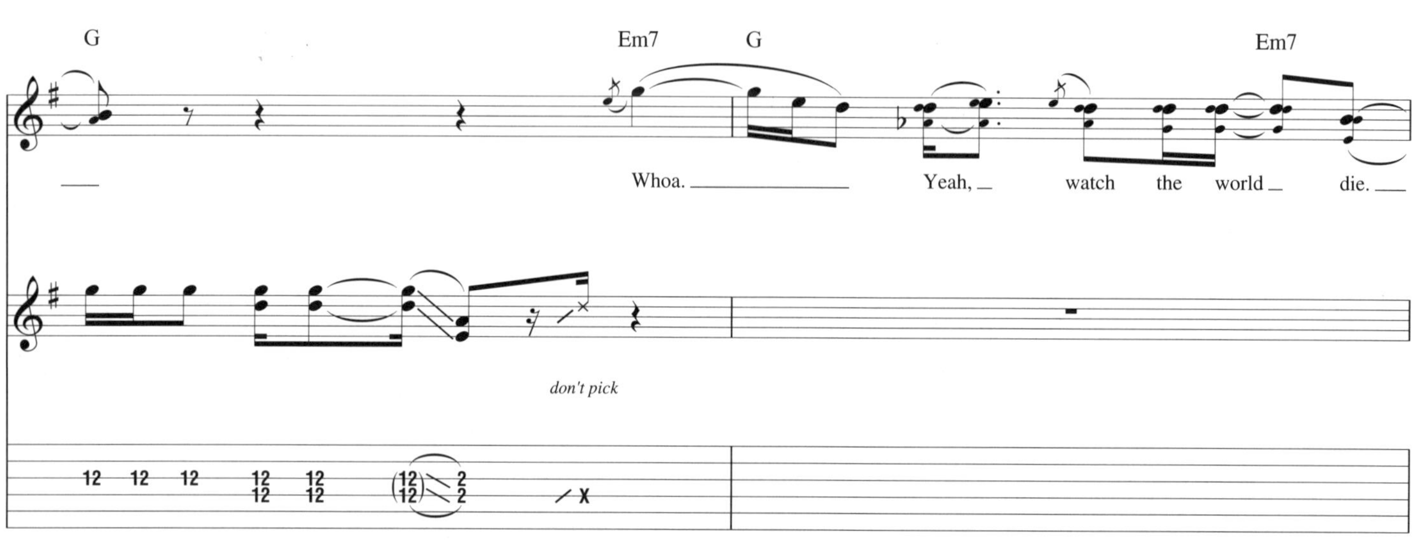
G
Em7
G
Em7
Whoa. _
Yeah, _ watch the world _ die. _
don't pick
12 12 12 12 12 12 12 (12) (12) 2 2 X

G
Em7
G
rit.
Em7
Gtr. 4 tacet
G5
Yeah, _ watch _ the world _ die. _
Gtrs. 2 & 5
don't pick
steady gliss.
rit.
15 12 12 12 (12) (12) (12) X X X 5 5 3 (5) (5) (3)

Spiderwebs

Words and Music by Gwen Stefani and Tony Kanal

*Chord symbols reflect implied tonality.

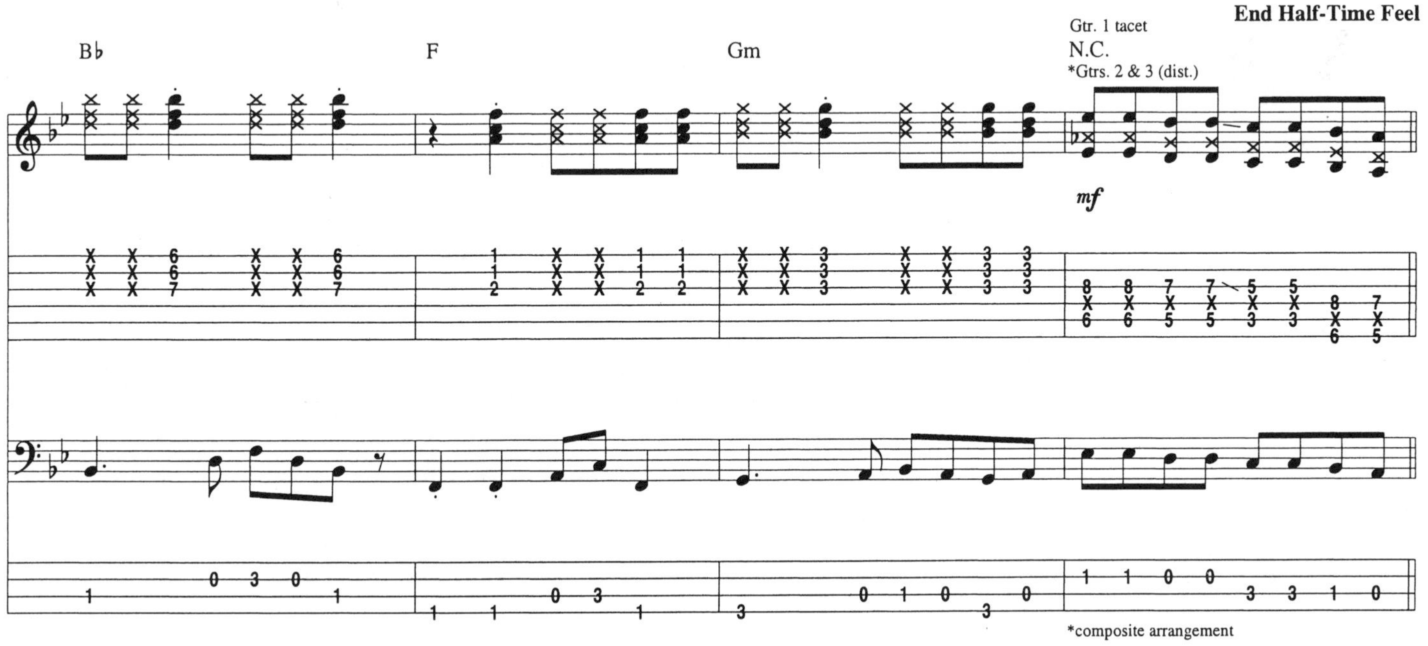

*composite arrangement

© Copyright 1995 by MCA MUSIC PUBLISHING, A Division of UNIVERSAL STUDIOS, INC. and KNOCK YOURSELF OUT MUSIC
All Rights Controlled and Administered by MCA MUSIC PUBLISHING, A Division of UNIVERSAL STUDIOS, INC.
International Copyright Secured All Rights Reserved
MCA Music Publishing

B♭
Bass: w/ Bass Fill 1, 2nd time
1. You
2. You're in -
Riff A
End Riff A
8va
loco
P.M.
P.H.
simile on repeat
pitch: D
Bass Fig. 2
End Bass Fig. 2
simile on repeat

Verse

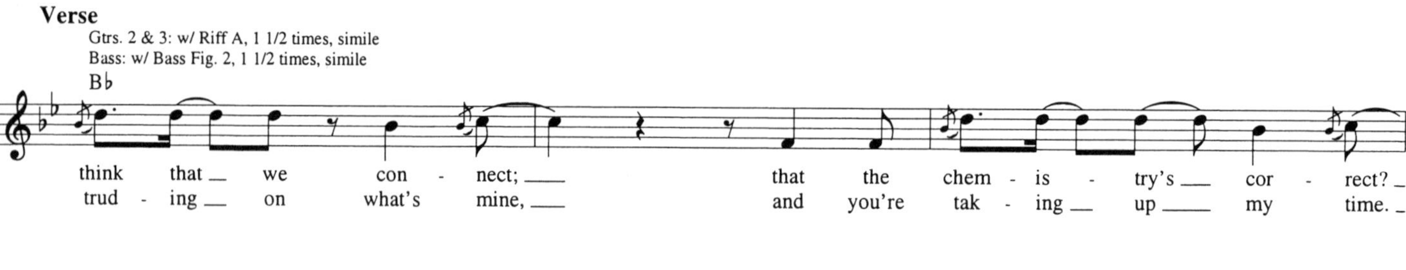
Gtrs. 2 & 3: w/ Riff A, 1 1/2 times, simile
Bass: w/ Bass Fig. 2, 1 1/2 times, simile
B♭
think that we con - nect; that the chem - is - try's cor - rect?
trud - ing on what's mine, and you're tak - ing up my time.

Bass: w/ Bass Fill 2, 2nd time
Your words walk right through my ears, pre - sum - ing
Don't have the cour - age in - side me to tell you,
Bass

Bass Fill 1
Bass

Bass Fill 2
Bass

Pre-Chorus

N.C. Eb5

Gtr. 3

I like what ___ I hear. ___ And now I'm ___
"Please (just) let ___ me be." ___ Com - mu - ni -

Gtrs. 2 & 3

8va loco

P.M. P.H. P.M.

(Gtr. 3 cont. in slash)

Gtr. 2

P.M.

pitch: D

Bass

simile on repeat

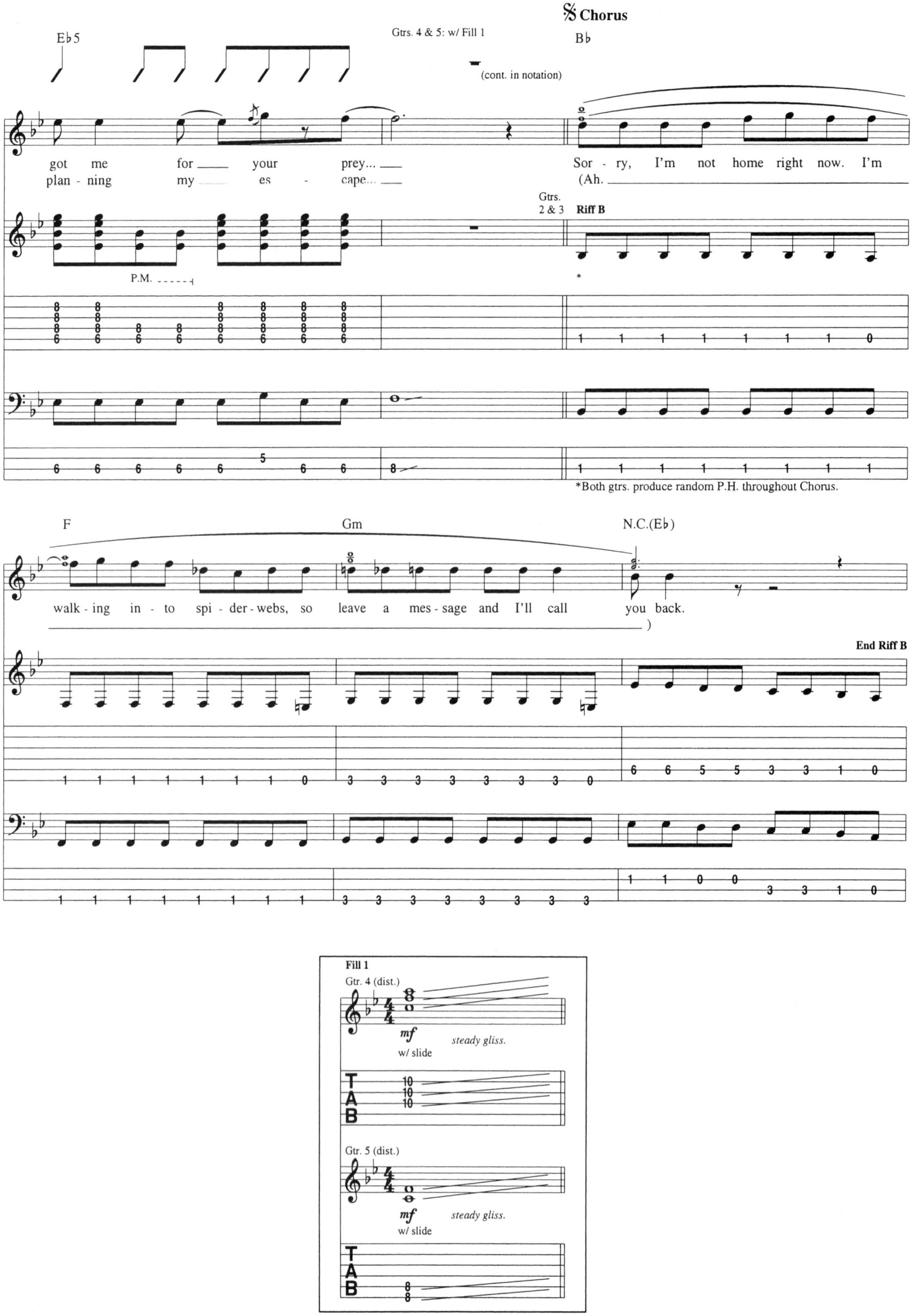

𝄋 Chorus

E♭5 — Gtrs. 4 & 5: w/ Fill 1 (cont. in notation) — B♭

got me for ___ your prey... ___ Sor - ry, I'm not home right now. I'm

plan - ning my ___ es - cape... ___ (Ah. ___

P.M. - - - - -|

Gtrs. 2 & 3 **Riff B**

*Both gtrs. produce random P.H. throughout Chorus.

F — Gm — N.C.(E♭)

walk - ing in - to spi - der - webs, so leave a mes - sage and I'll call you back.

___)

End Riff B

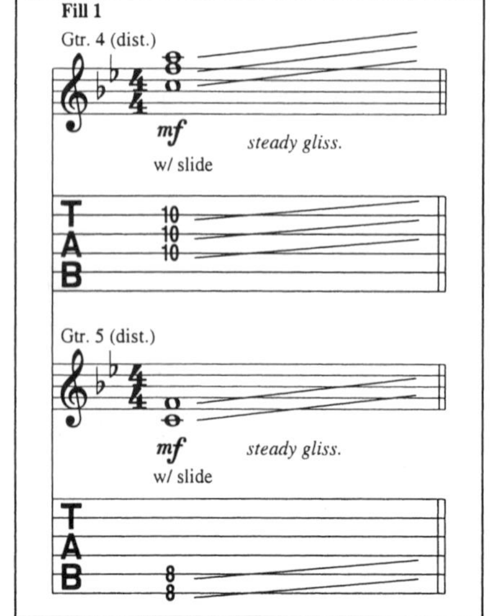

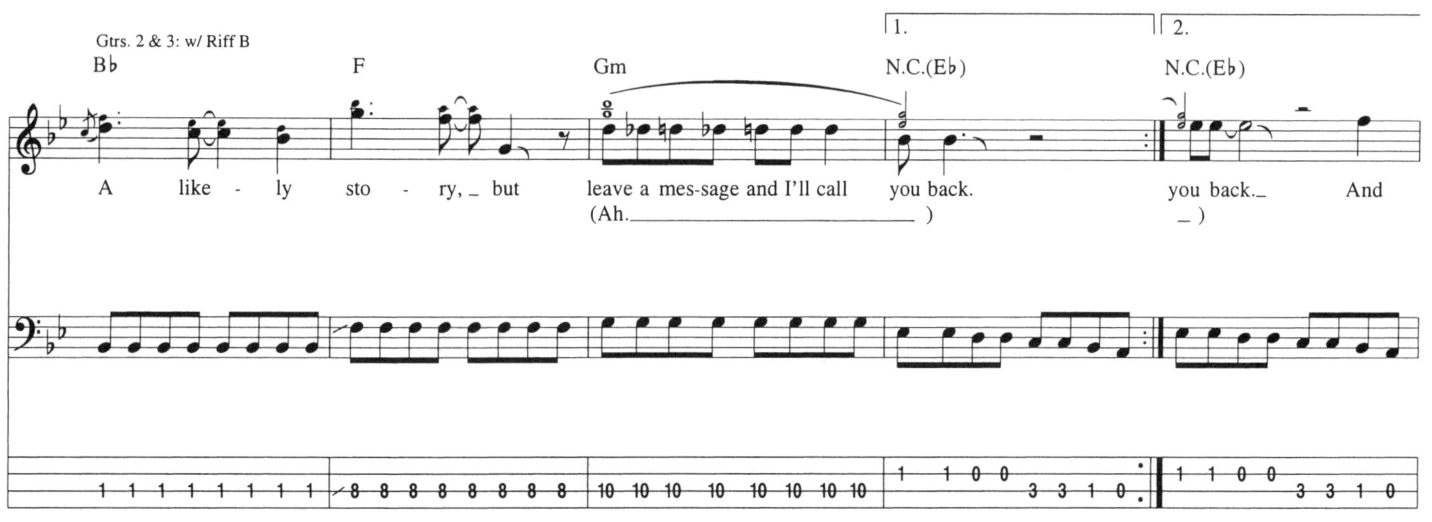

1.
2.
Gtrs. 2 & 3: w/ Riff B
B♭
F
Gm
N.C.(E♭)
N.C.(E♭)
A like - ly sto - ry, but leave a mes-sage and I'll call you back.
(Ah.)
you back. And
)

B♭
F
Gm
N.C.(E♭)
it's all your fault; I screen my phone calls. No
Rhy. Fig. 1
Gtrs. 2 & 3
End Rhy. Fig. 1
Bass Fig. 3
End Bass Fig. 3

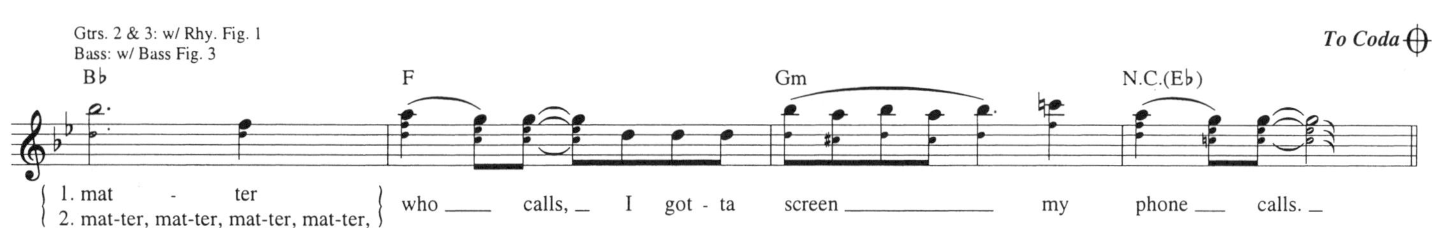

Gtrs. 2 & 3: w/ Rhy. Fig. 1
Bass: w/ Bass Fig. 3
To Coda
B♭
F
Gm
N.C.(E♭)
1. mat - ter
2. mat-ter, mat-ter, mat-ter, mat-ter,
who calls, I got - ta screen my phone calls.

Guitar Solo

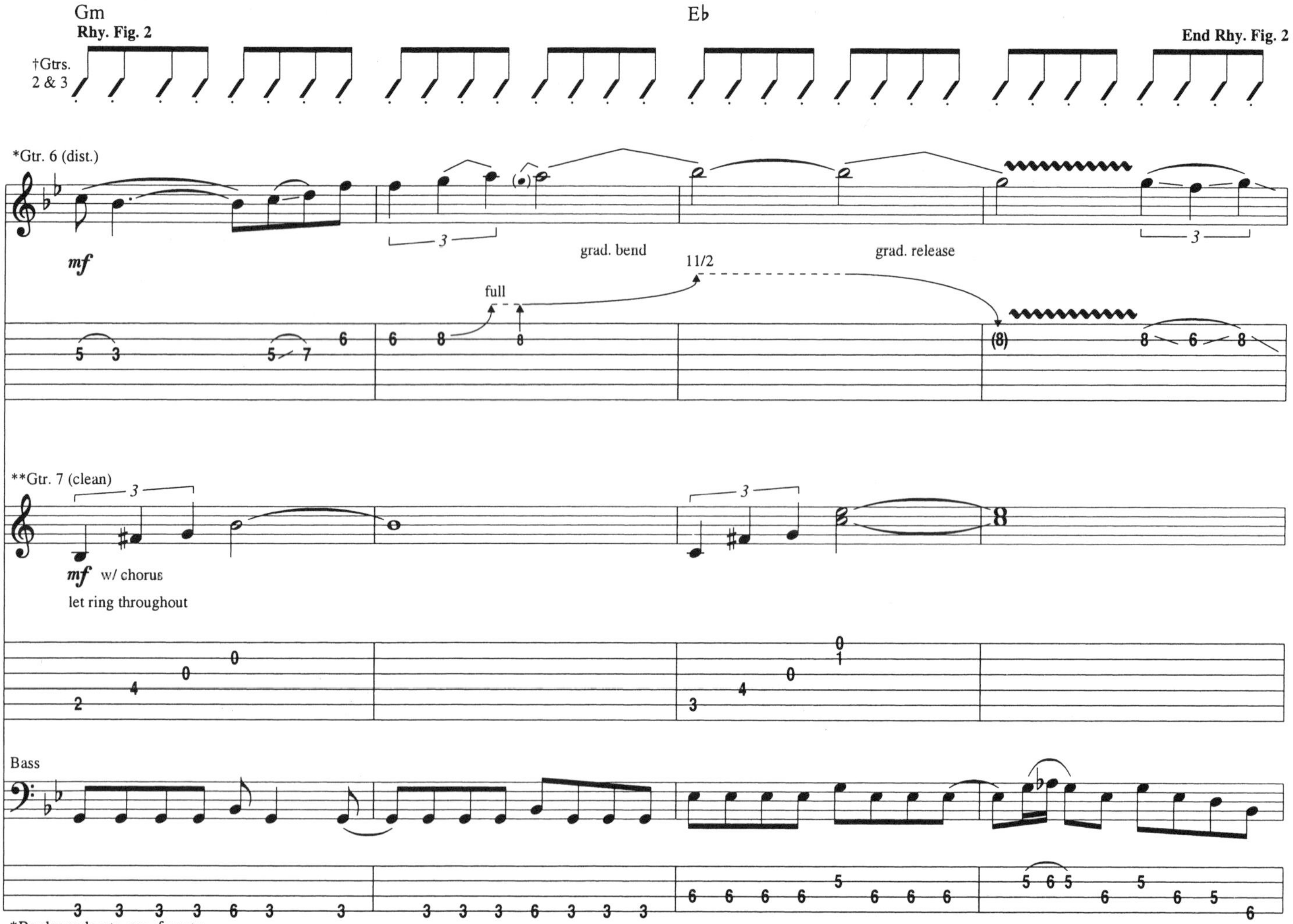

Gm
Rhy. Fig. 2
E♭
End Rhy. Fig. 2
†Gtrs. 2 & 3
*Gtr. 6 (dist.)
mf
grad. bend
11/2
full
grad. release
**Gtr. 7 (clean)
mf w/ chorus
let ring throughout
Bass

*Backwards gtr. arr. for gtr.
**Capo at 3rd fret. Capo becomes "0" in TAB.
†Rhythm is produced by switching toggle switch back & forth between on & off positions.

Gtrs. 2 & 3: w/ Rhy. Fig. 2
Gm
E♭
Gtr. 6
full
Gtr. 7

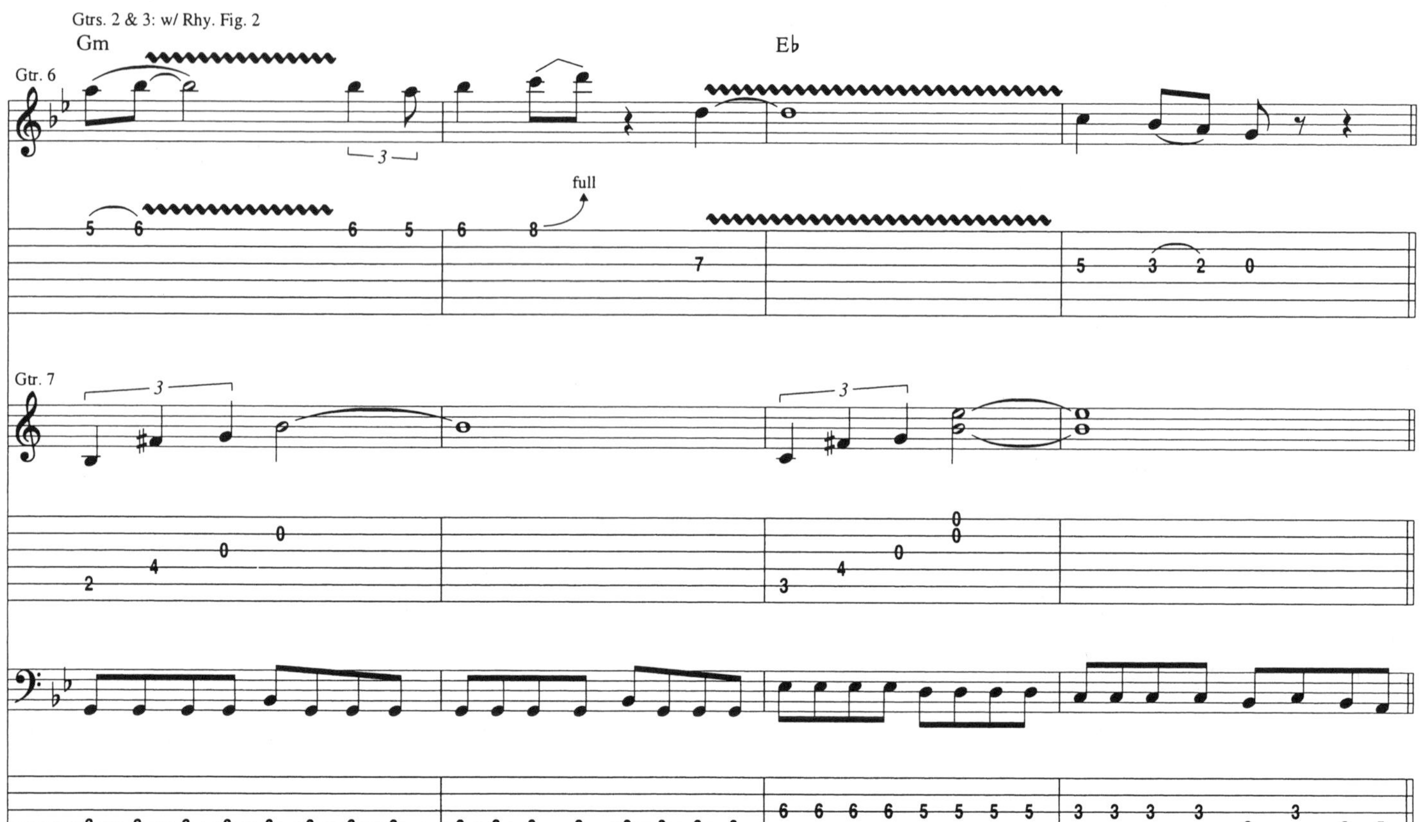

Bridge
Gtrs. 2 & 3: w/ Rhy. Fig. 2, 3 times
Gtr. 6 tacet
Gm
E♭
Now it's gone too deep.
You
(Now it's gone too
Gtr. 7
Gm
E♭
wake me in my sleep.
My
deep.
Wake me in my
Gm
E♭
dreams be - come night - mares
'cause you're
sleep.
Dreams be - come night - mares.

D.S. al Coda
(take 2nd ending)
Gtr. 7 tacet
G5
N.C.(E♭)
ring - ing in my ears.
Ring - ing in my...)
Gtrs. 2 & 3
Gtr. 3
Gtr. 2
divisi
Gtrs. 2 & 3
Coda
Gtrs. 2 & 3: w/ Riff B, 5 3/4 times, simile
B♭
F
Gm
N.C.(E♭)
Oo, a spi - der-web; leave a mes-sage and I'll call you back.
Bass
Bass Fig. 4
End Bass Fig. 4
Bass: w/ Bass Fig. 4
I'm walk - ing in - to spi - der-webs, so leave a mes-sage and I'll call you back.
w/ ad lib. Bkgd. Voc.
It's all your fault; I screen my phone calls.
Bass Fig. 5
End Bass Fig. 5
Bass: w/ Bass Fig. 5, 2 3/4 times
No mat-ter, mat-ter, mat-ter who calls, I got - ta screen my phone calls.

B♭
F
Gm
N.C.(E♭)
It's all your fault.
It's all your fault.
B♭
F
Gm
No mat - ter who calls.
No mat - ter who
Outro
A Tempo
Bass: w/ Bass Fig. 1
Gtrs. 2 & 3 tacet
N.C.(E♭)
rit.
B♭
F
calls.
Oh.
I'm walk - ing in - to
spi - der - webs,
so
8va
Gtrs. 2 & 3
Gtr. 2
Gtr. 3
divisi
rit.
P.H.
full
pitch: D
*Gtrs. 1 & 8 (slight dist.)
mf
Bass
rit.
*composite arrangement
Gm
E♭
w/ ad lib. Lead Voc.
Bass: w/ Bass Fig. 1, simile, till fade
B♭
leave a mes - sage and I'll call you back.
I'm walk - ing in - to
Gtrs. 1 & 8
simile on repeats
Play 5 Times and Fade
F
Gm
E♭
spi - der - webs,
ah, leave a mes - sage and I'll call you back.

Tears in Heaven

Words and Music by Eric Clapton and Will Jennings

Copyright © 1992 by E.C. Music Ltd. and Blue Sky Rider Songs
All Rights for E.C. Music Ltd. Administered by Unichappell Music Inc.
All Rights for Blue Sky Rider Songs Administered by Irving Music, Inc.
International Copyright Secured All Rights Reserved

A7/E
F#7
F#7sus4
F#/A#
Bm7
and car - ry on, 'cause I know I don't be - long
through night and day 'cause I know I just can't stay
D/E
To Coda
A
E/G#
F#m7
F#m7/E
1.
D/F#
E7sus4 E7
here in hea - ven.
here in hea - ven.
2.
A
D/F#
E7sus4 E7
A
Bridge
C
G/B
Am
Time can bring ya down,
D/F#
G
D/F#
Em
D/F#
G
C
G/B
Am
time can bend your knees.
Time can break your heart,

D/F♯ G D/F♯ E A/E E7
have ya beg - gin' please,
beg - gin' please.
T
T
(1) 1 2 0 2 3 0 0 2 2 3
3 0 3 0 3 2 2 3 3 3 3 2 2 2 3 0
0 0 0 1 2 0 1 2 2 3 4 0 0 0
Interlude
A E/G♯ F♯m7 F♯m7/E D/F♯ A E A/E E7
T
T
Chorus
F♯m7 C♯/E♯ A7/E
Be - yond the door
there's peace, I'm sure,
T

F#7
G#m
F#/A#
Bm7
D/E
and I know
there'll be
no more
tears in hea-
A
E/G#
F#m7
F#m7/E
D/F#
E7sus4
E7
ven.
Verse
A
E/G#
F#m7
F#m7/E
3. Would you know
my
name
D/F#
A
E
A/E
E7
A
E/G#
F#m7
if I saw you in hea-ven?
Would you be the same

D.S. al Coda
F♯m7/E
D/F♯
A/E
E
A/E
E7
if I saw you in hea - ven?
T
Coda
A
E/G♯
F♯m7
F♯m7/E
ven.
'Cause I
T
Bm7
D/E
A
E/G♯
F♯m
know I don't be - long here in hea - ven.
T
Freely
F♯m/E
D/F♯
rit.
E7sus4
E7
A
rit.
T
let ring

Two Princes

Words and Music by Spin Doctors

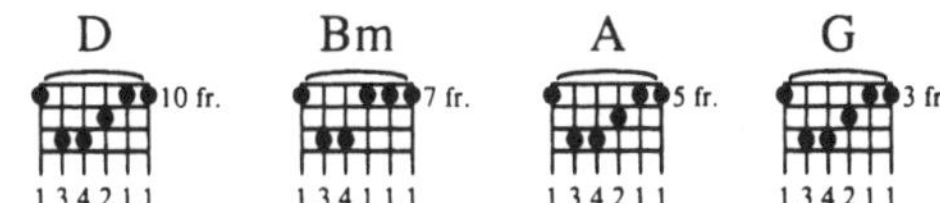

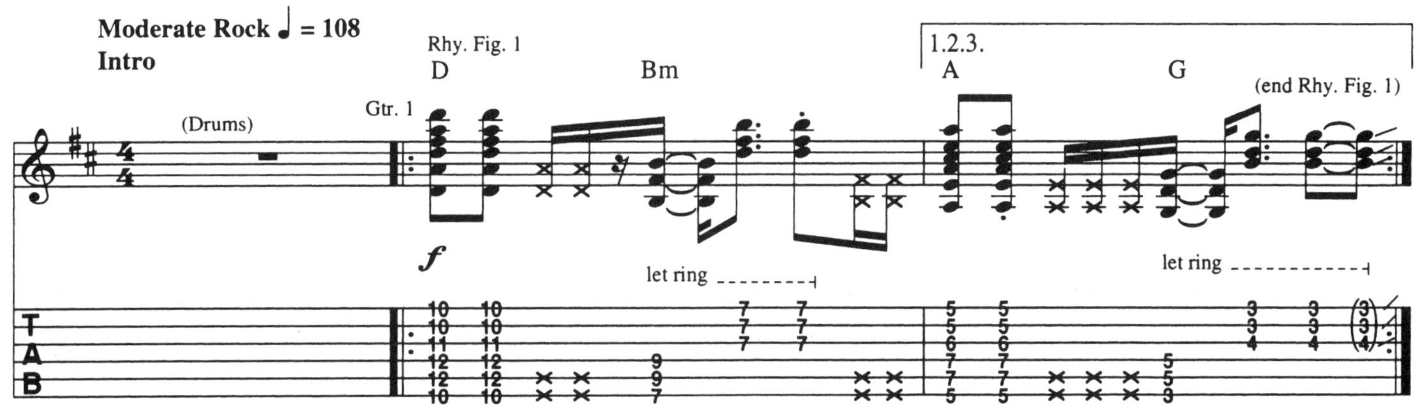

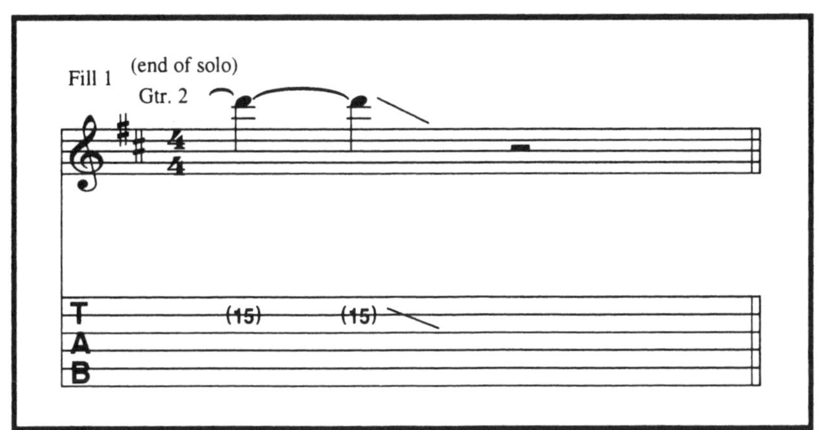

Copyright © 1991 Sony/ATV Songs LLC and Mow B'Jow Music
All Rights Administered by Sony/ATV Music Publishing, 8 Music Square West, Nashville, TN 37203
International Copyright Secured All Rights Reserved

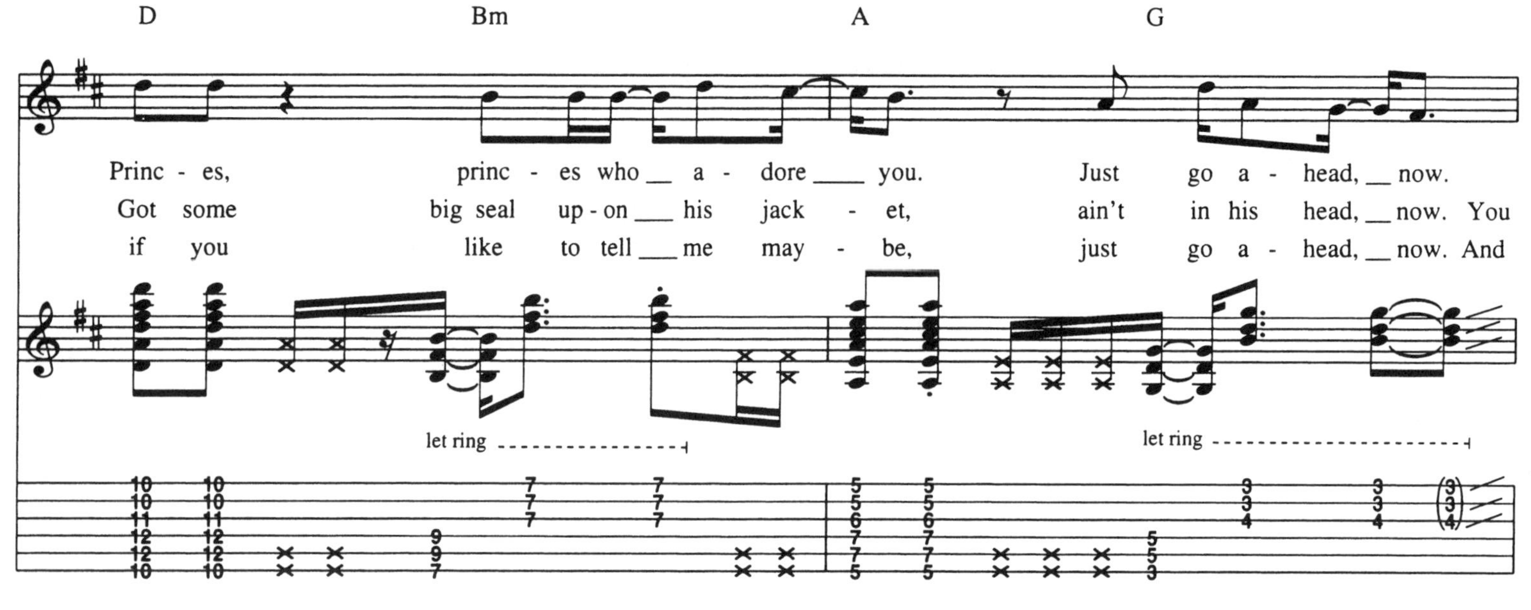
D
Bm
A
G
Princ - es, princ - es who __ a - dore ____ you. Just go a - head, __ now.
Got some big seal up - on __ his jack - et, ain't in his head, __ now. You
if you like to tell __ me may - be, just go a - head, __ now. And
let ring
let ring

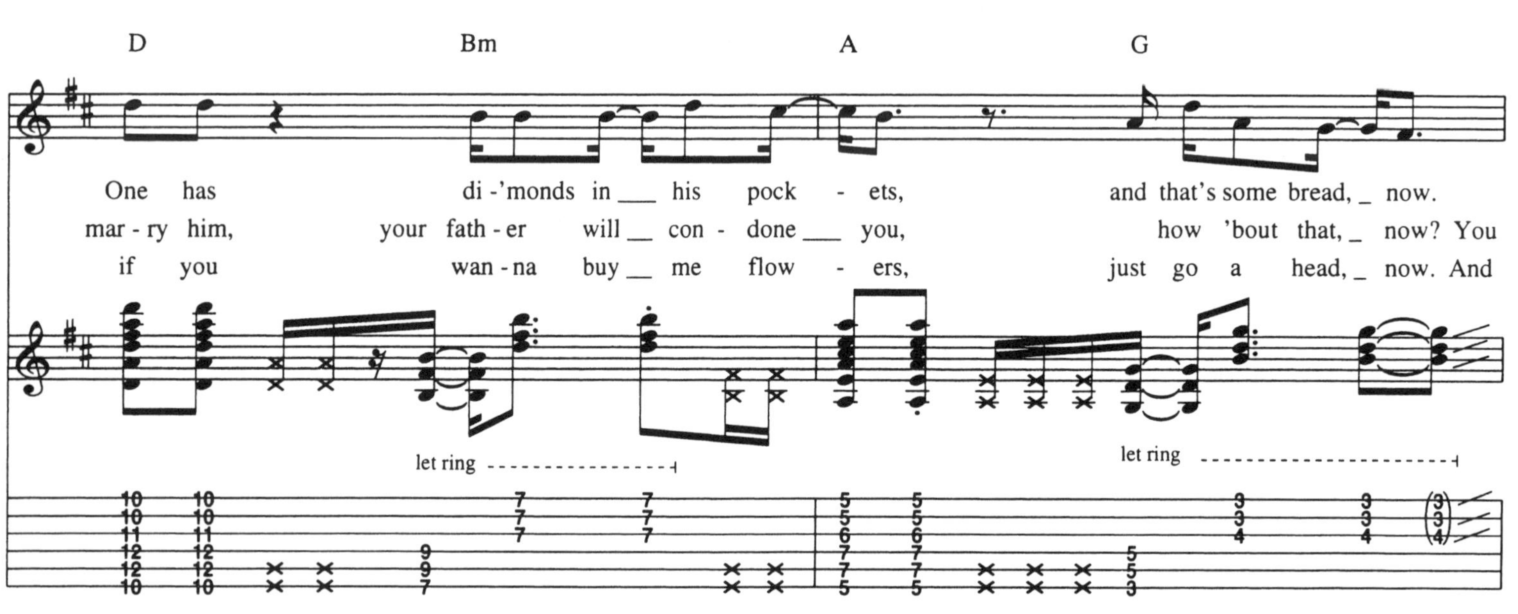
D
Bm
A
G
One has di -'monds in __ his pock - ets, and that's some bread, _ now.
mar - ry him, your fath - er will __ con - done ___ you, how 'bout that, _ now? You
if you wan - na buy __ me flow - ers, just go a head, _ now. And
let ring
let ring

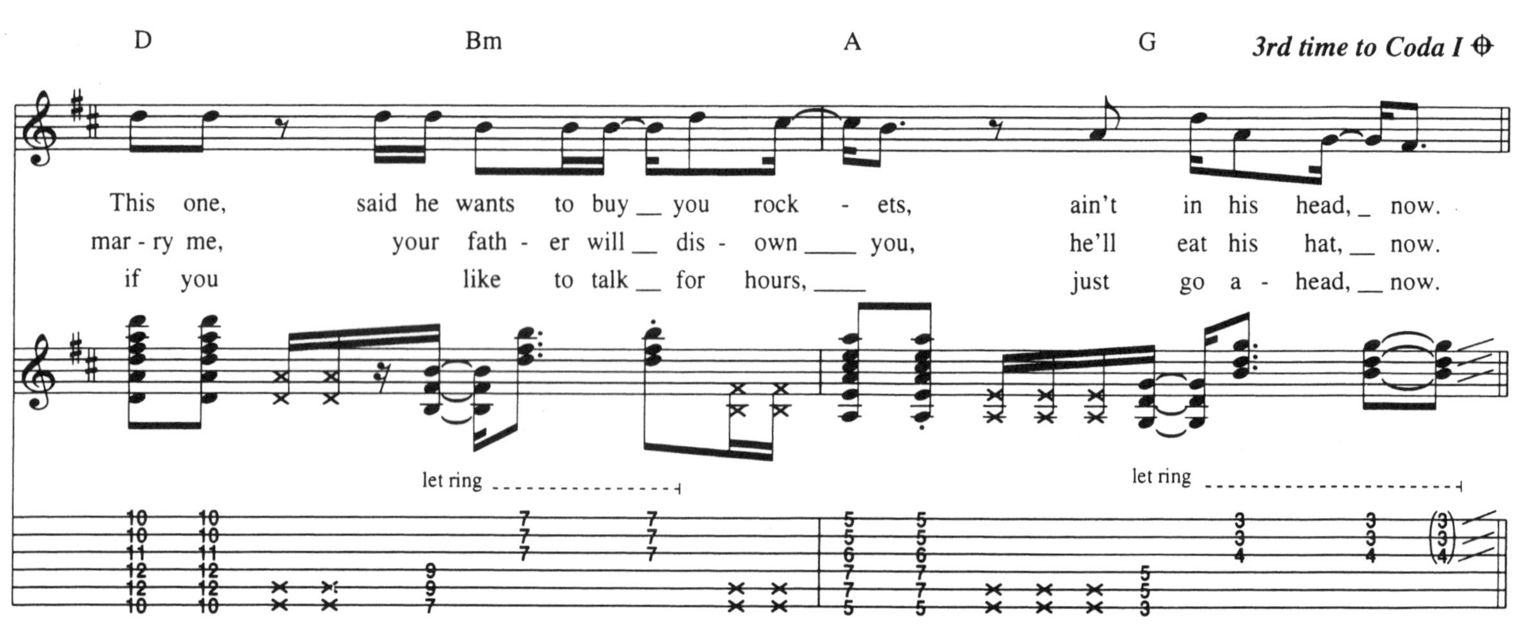
D
Bm
A
G
3rd time to Coda I
This one, said he wants to buy __ you rock - ets, ain't in his head, _ now.
mar - ry me, your fath - er will __ dis - own ____ you, he'll eat his hat, __ now.
if you like to talk __ for hours, ____ just go a - head, __ now.
let ring
let ring

1.
D
Bm7
A
G
Yeah, yeah, yeah. De de de
Rhy. Fig. 2
let ring
D
Bm7
A
G
dit. D-be, be be de. Be-dee-dl-y de-bu du-bu du-bu du-bu du-bu du-bu du-bu du-bu.
(end Rhy. Fig. 2)
let ring
2.
G
D
G
Mar-ry him or mar-ry me. I'm the one that loves you ba-by, can't you see? I ain't
Rhy. Fig. 3
A
2nd time to Coda II
got no fu-ture or fam-'ly tree, but I know what a prince and lov-er ought to be.
(end Rhy. Fig. 3)

D. S. al Coda I
Coda I
Guitar Solo
I know what a prince and lov - er ought to be. __ Said. . .
Gtr. 1
Gtr. 2
D
Bm
A
G
1/2
full
hold bend
w/Rhy. Fig. 3 (Gtr. 1)

A
hold bend
hold bend
let ring
full
full
full
Gtr. 1
A
D. S. (take 2nd ending) al Coda II
Said. . .
(cont. in Fill 1)
hold bend
let ring
let ring
full
full
full
1/2
full
1/2
full
Coda II
A
C5 A5 N.C.
D
N.C.
I know what a prince and lov - er ought to be.
Said if you want to call me ba -
(Gtr. tacet)
1/4
by, just go a - head, now. And if you like to tell me may - be, just go a - head now. And
if you wan - na buy me flow - ers, just go a - head, now. And if you like to talk for hours,
w/Rhy. Fig. 2 (2 times)
D
Bm7
A
G
just go a - head, now. And if you want to call me ba - by, just go a - head, now. And

D Bm7 A G D Bm7
if you like to tell _ me may - be, just go a - head, _ now. And if you like to buy _ me flow -
A G D Bm7 A G
ers, just go a - head, _ now. And if you like to talk _ for hours, ___ just go a - head, _ now.
w/Rhy. Fig. 1 (4 times)
D Bm A G
If you want to call me ___ ba - by, just go a - head, _ now.
D Bm A G
And if you'd like to tell ___ me ___ may - be, just go a - head, ___ now.
D Bm A G D Bm
If you want to buy me flow - ers, just go a - head, _ now. And if you like to talk for hours, _
w/Rhy. Fig. 2 (2 times)
A G D Bm7 A G
_ just go a - head, _ now. Oh, ___ ba - by. Oh, _
(Just go a - head, _ now.)
D Bm7 A G D Bm7
___ oh, ___ just, just go a - head, ___ now. Oh, ___ your _ maj -
(Just go a - head, ___ now.)
A G D Bm7
es - ty, ___ come on _ for - get ___ the king ___ and
(Just go a - head, _ now.)
A G D Bm7 A G
w/Rhy. Fig. 1
(cont. Lead voc. ad lib)
Repeat and fade
mar - ry me. ___ (Just go a - head, _ now.)
(Just go a - head, _ now.)

What I Got

Words and Music by Brad Nowell, Eric Wilson and Floyd Gaugh

© Copyright 1996 by MUSIC CORPORATION OF AMERICA, INC., GASOLINE ALLEY MUSIC and LOU DOG PUBLISHING
All Rights Controlled and Administered by MUSIC CORPORATION OF AMERICA, INC.
International Copyright Secured All Rights Reserved

D5 G5 D5 G5 D5 G5

Got to find a rea - son why my mon-ey's all gone. __ I ____ got a Dal - ma - tion, and

D5 G5 D5 G5 D5 G5

I can still _ get high. _ I ____ can play the gui - tar like a moth - er - fuck - in' ri - ot.

Gtr. 2 (acous.)

Fill 1 **End Fill 1**

f

Gtr. 1

End Riff A

P.S. *

* Pick slide unintentionally sounds open strings.

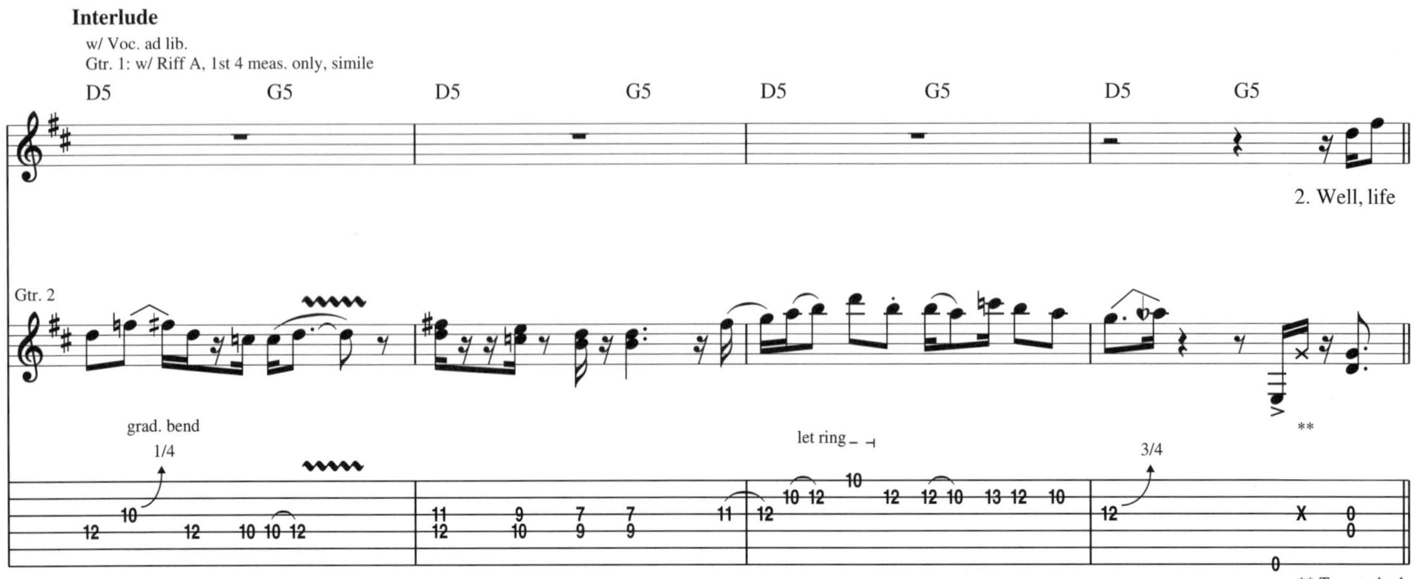

Verse
Gtr. 1: w/ Riff A, simile
Gtr. 2 tacet
D5 G5 D5 G5
is (too short) so love the one you got 'cause you might get run o - ver or you might get shot.
3. Why, I don't cry when my dog runs a - way. I don't get an - gry at the bills I have to pay.

D5 G5 D5 G5
Nev - er start no stat - ic, I just get it off my (chest.) Nev - er had to bat - tle with no bul - let - proof (vest.)
I don't get an - gry when my mom smokes pot, hits the bot - tle and moves right to the rock.

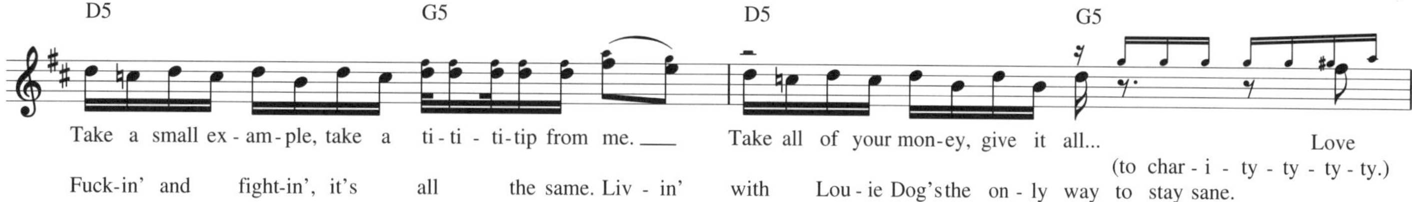
D5 G5 D5 G5
Take a small ex - am - ple, take a ti - ti - ti-tip from me. Take all of your mon-ey, give it all... Love
(to char - i - ty - ty - ty - ty.)
Fuck-in' and fight-in', it's all the same. Liv - in' with Lou - ie Dog's the on - ly way to stay sane.

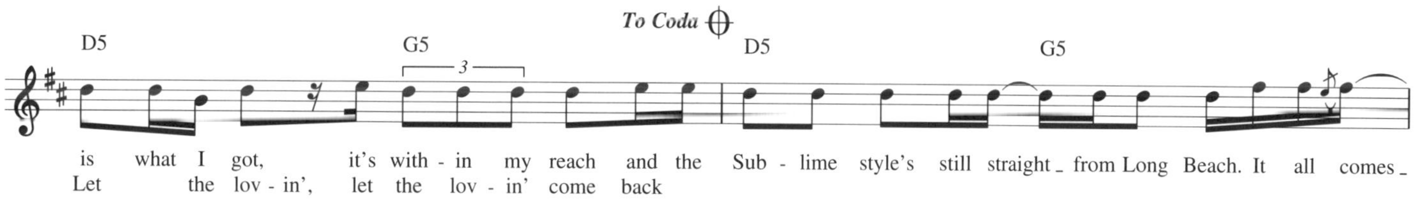
To Coda
D5 G5 D5 G5
is what I got, it's with - in my reach and the Sub - lime style's still straight from Long Beach. It all comes
Let the lov - in', let the lov - in' come back

D5 G5 D5 G5
back to you, you fin - 'ly get what you de - serve. Try and test that, you're bound to get served.

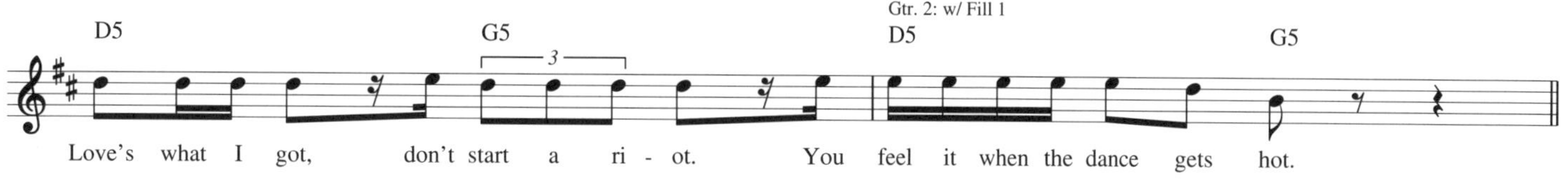
Gtr. 2: w/ Fill 1
D5 G5 D5 G5
Love's what I got, don't start a ri - ot. You feel it when the dance gets hot.

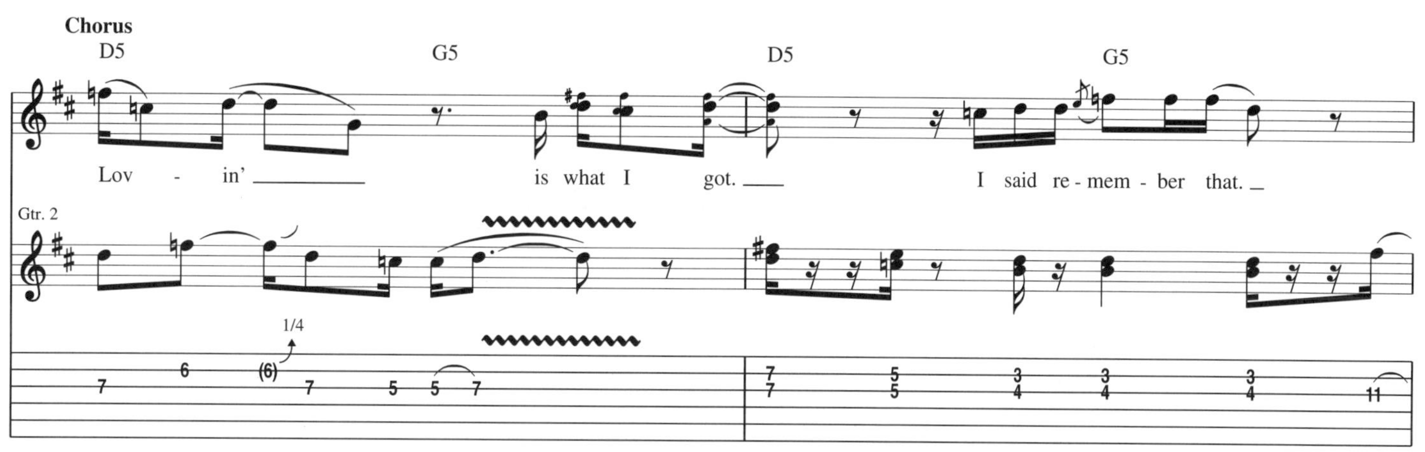
Chorus
D5 G5 D5 G5
Lov - in' is what I got. I said re - mem - ber that.
Gtr. 2
1/4

D5
G5
D5
G5
Lov - in' is what I got, and re-mem - ber that.
1/2
1/2
D5
G5
D5
G7
Lov - in' is what I got. I said re-mem - ber that.
Gtr. 2
mf
let ring
let ring
let ring
Gtr. 1
D
G5
D
G7
D.S. al Coda
Lov - in' is what I got, I got, I got, I got.
let ring
1/4
let ring

Coda
Interlude
D5
C5
G5
to me.
Riff B
'Cause
End Riff B
Chorus
lov - in' is what I got. I said re-mem - ber that. Lov-
P.S.
string noise
Gtr. 1: w/ Riff B, last 2 meas. only, simile
- in' is what I got, and re-mem- ber that. Lov - in' is what I got.
Gtr. 1: w/ Riff B, simile
I said re-mem-ber that. Lov - in' is what I got, I got, I got, I got.
Outro
Gtr. 1
G7
D
N.C.
Slower ♩ = 88

Wonderwall

Words and Music by Noel Gallagher

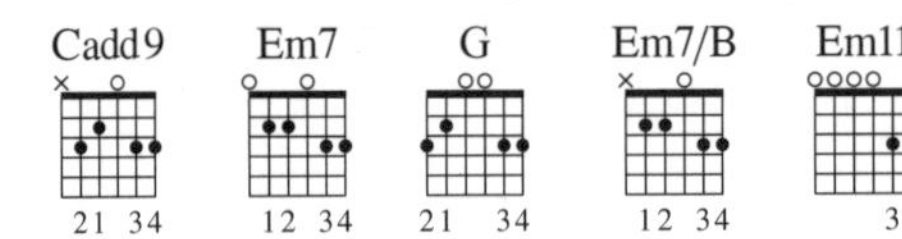

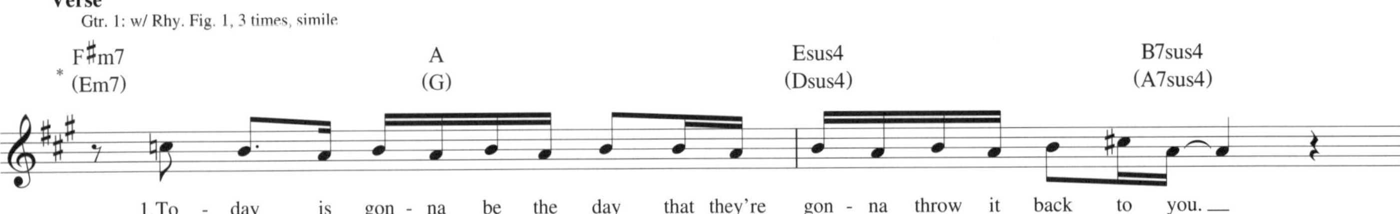

* Symbols in parentheses represent chord names respective to capoed guitars.
Symbols above reflect actual sounding chords.

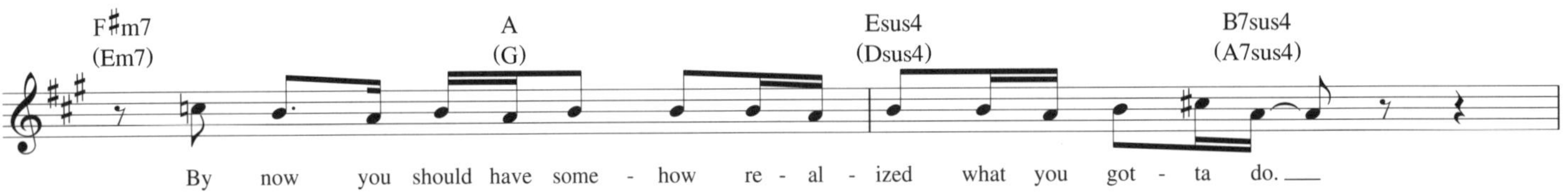

Copyright © 1995 Sony Music Publishing United Kingdom and Creation Songs Ltd.
All Rights Administered by Sony/ATV Music Publishing, 8 Music Square West, Nashville, TN 37203
International Copyright Secured All Rights Reserved

Verse
Gtr. 1: w/ Rhy. Fig. 1, 4 times, simile
F#m (Em7) A (G) Esus4 (Dsus4) B7sus4 (A7sus4)
2. Back - beat, the word is on the street that the fire ___ in your heart is out. ___
3. To - day was gon - na be the day, but they'll nev - er throw it back to you. ___
F#m7 (Em7) A (G) Esus4 (Dsus4) B7sus4 (A7sus4)
I'm sure you've heard it all be - fore, but you nev - er real - ly had a doubt. ___
By now you should have some - how re - al - ized what you're not to do. ___
F#m7 (Em7) A (G) Esus4 (Dsus4) B7sus4 (A7sus4)
I don't be - lieve ___ that an - y - bod - y feels the way I do ___ a - bout you now. ___
F#m7 (Em7) A (G) Esus4 (Dsus4) B7sus4 (A7sus4)
And all ___
And all ___
Pre-Chorus
*D (C) E (D) F#m7 (Em7)
___ the roads ___ we have ___ to walk ___ are wind - ing, and all ___
___ the roads ___ that lead ___ you there ___ were wind - ing, and all ___
Gtrs. 1 & 2 (clean)
mf
let ring throughout
* Chord symbols reflect overall harmony.
D (C) E (D) F#m7 (Em7)
___ the lights ___ that lead ___ us there ___ are blind - ing.
___ the lights ___ that light ___ the way ___ are blind - ing.

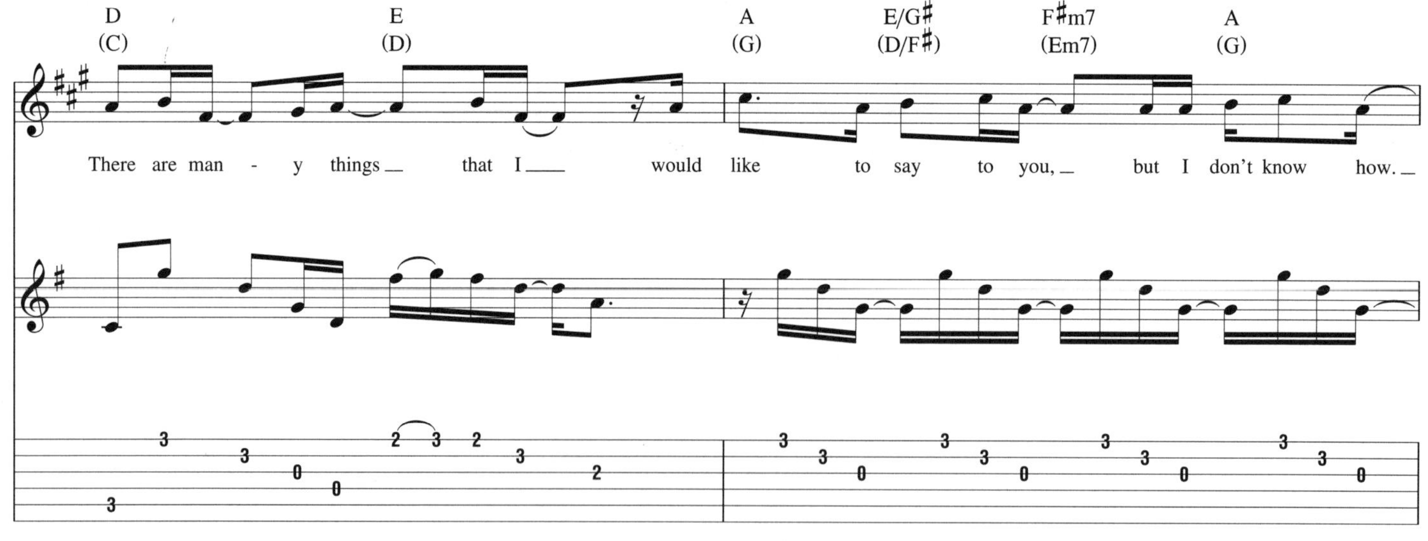
D
(C)
E
(D)
A
(G)
E/G♯
(D/F♯)
F♯m7
(Em7)
A
(G)
There are man - y things that I would like to say to you, but I don't know how.

B7sus4
(A7sus4)
Be-cause
I said
(cont. in slash)
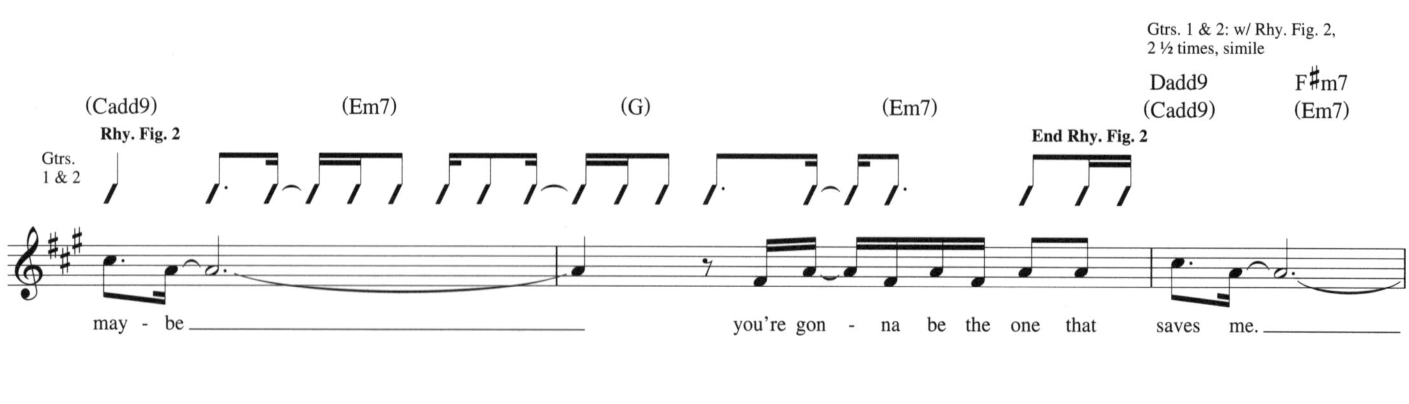
Gtrs. 1 & 2: w/ Rhy. Fig. 2,
2 ½ times, simile
(Cadd9)
(Em7)
(G)
(Em7)
Dadd9
(Cadd9)
F♯m7
(Em7)
Rhy. Fig. 2
Gtrs.
1 & 2
End Rhy. Fig. 2
may - be you're gon - na be the one that saves me.
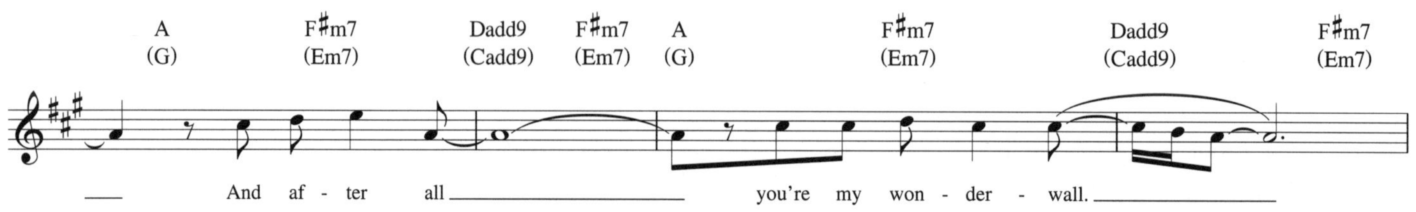
A
(G)
F♯m7
(Em7)
Dadd9
(Cadd9)
F♯m7
(Em7)
A
(G)
F♯m7
(Em7)
Dadd9
(Cadd9)
F♯m7
(Em7)
And af - ter all you're my won - der - wall.

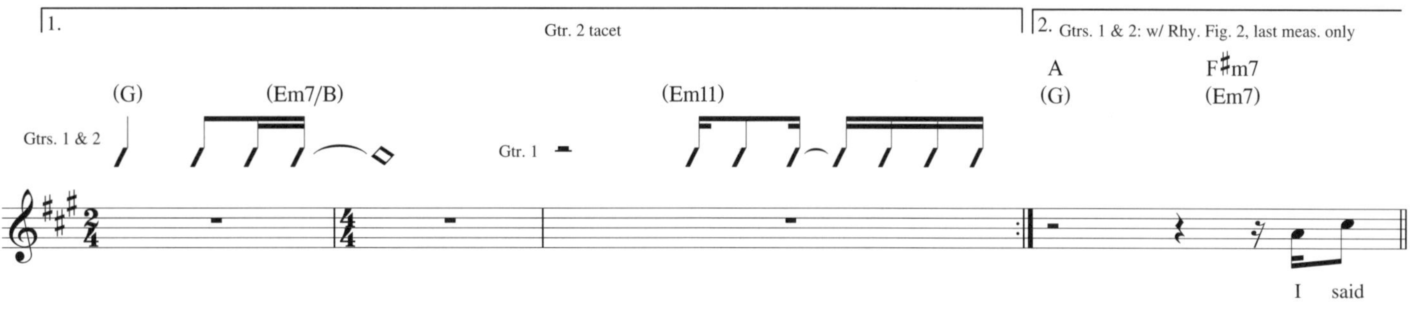
1.
Gtr. 2 tacet
2. Gtrs. 1 & 2: w/ Rhy. Fig. 2, last meas. only
(G) (Em7/B) (Em11)
A (G) F#m7 (Em7)
Gtrs. 1 & 2
Gtr. 1
I said

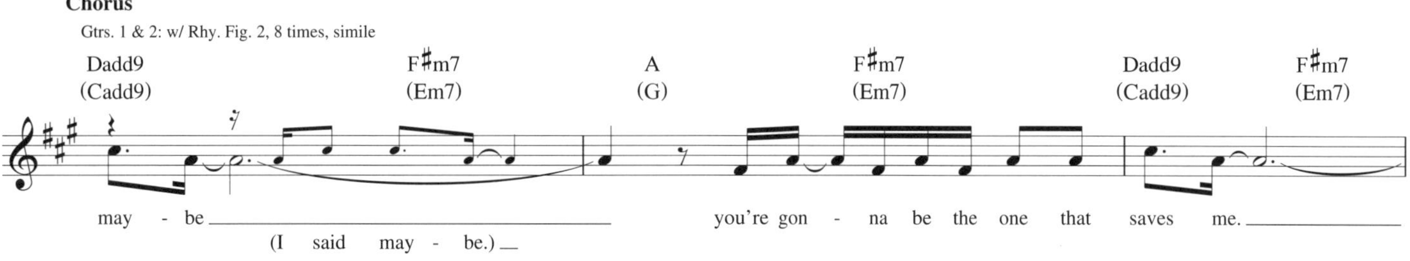
Chorus
Gtrs. 1 & 2: w/ Rhy. Fig. 2, 8 times, simile
Dadd9 (Cadd9) F#m7 (Em7) A (G) F#m7 (Em7) Dadd9 (Cadd9) F#m7 (Em7)
may - be you're gon - na be the one that saves me.
(I said may - be.)

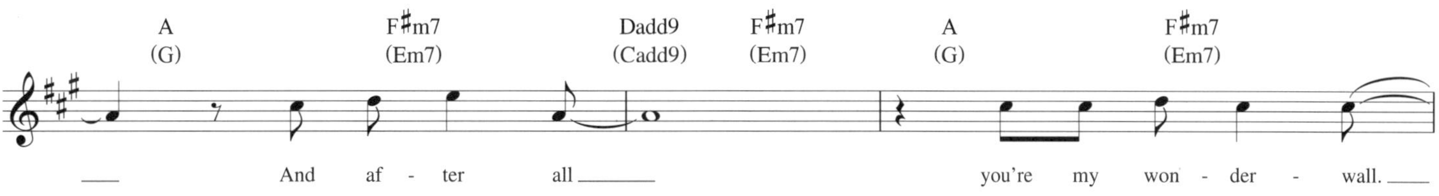
A (G) F#m7 (Em7) Dadd9 (Cadd9) F#m7 (Em7) A (G) F#m7 (Em7)
And af - ter all you're my won - der - wall.

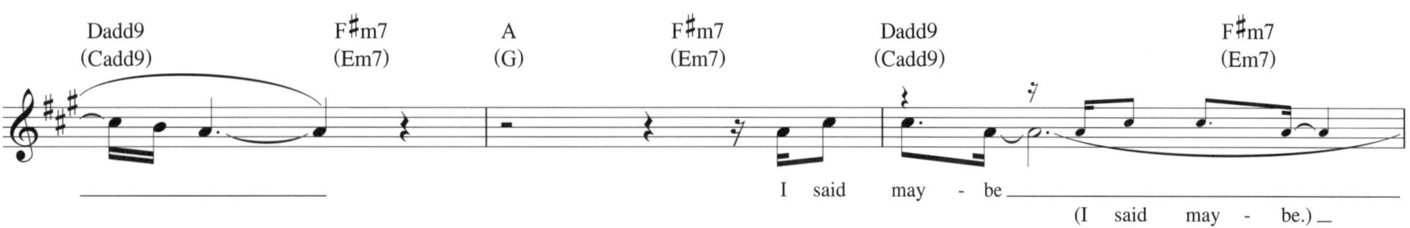
Dadd9 (Cadd9) F#m7 (Em7) A (G) F#m7 (Em7) Dadd9 (Cadd9) F#m7 (Em7)
I said may - be
(I said may - be.)

1., 2.
A (G) F#m7 (Em7) Dadd9 (Cadd9) F#m7 (Em7) A (G) F#m7 (Em7)
you're gon - na be the one that saves me. You're gon - na be the one that
(Saves me.)

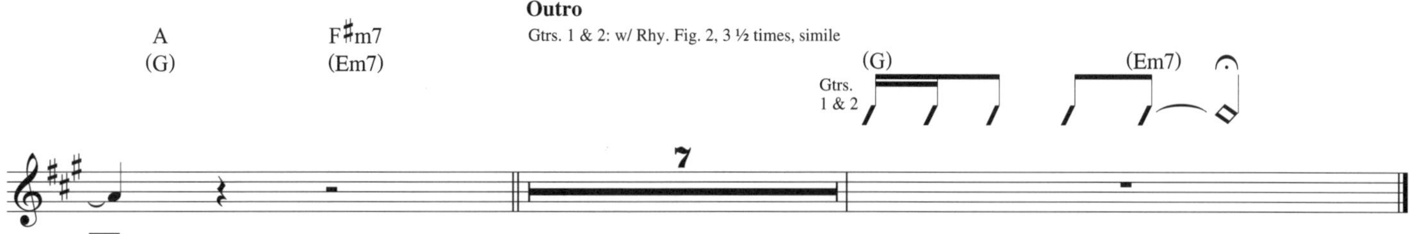
3.
Outro
Gtrs. 1 & 2: w/ Rhy. Fig. 2, 3 ½ times, simile
A (G) F#m7 (Em7) (G) (Em7)
Gtrs. 1 & 2
7

You Oughta Know

Lyrics by Alanis Morissette
Music by Alanis Morissette and Glen Ballard

© Copyright 1995 by MUSIC CORPORATION OF AMERICA, INC., VANHURST PLACE, MCA MUSIC PUBLISHING,
A Division of UNIVERSAL STUDIOS, INC. and AEROSTATION CORPORATION
All Rights for VANHURST PLACE Controlled and Administered by MUSIC CORPORATION OF AMERICA, INC.
All Rights for AEROSTATION CORPORATION Controlled and Administered by MCA MUSIC PUBLISHING, A Division of UNIVERSAL STUDIOS, INC.
International Copyright Secured All Rights Reserved
MCA Music Publishing

Pre-Chorus
F♯m7
Rhy. Fig. 1
Gtr. 3 (fuzz)
mf
1., 2. love that you gave, that we made was-n't a - ble to make it e-nough for you to be o -
3. joke that you laid in the bed that was me and I'm not gon-na fade as soon as you close
Gtr. 1
Gtr. 2 (clean)
mp
let ring throughout
B
End Rhy. Fig. 1
pen wide, no.
your eyes, and you know it.
And ev -
And ev -

Gtr. 3: w/ Rhy. Fig. 1
F♯m7
- 'ry time _ you speak _ her name _ does she know _ how you told _ me you'd hold me un - til
- 'ry time _ I scratch _ my nails _ down some - one else - 's back, I hope you
B
you died, 'til you died? But your still a - live. And I'm here ____
feel it. Well, can you feel it? Well, I'm here ____
(cont. in slash)
Chorus
F♯
E
A
B^II
Rhy. Fig. 2
End Rhy. Fig. 2
Gtr. 1
____ to re - mind ___ you ___ of the mess ___ you left _ when you went a - way. It's not
Gtr. 3
Rhy. Fig. 2B
End Rhy. Fig. 2B
Gtr. 2
Rhy. Fig. 2A
End Rhy. Fig. 2A
mf

To Coda 1
To Coda 2
Gtrs. 1, 2 & 3: w/ Rhy. Figs. 2, 2A & 2B
F#
E
A
B
fair to de - ny me of the cross I bear that you gave to me. You, you, you
Verse
Gtr. 2 tacet
B
Gtr. 1
(cont. in notation)
F#m7
Gtr. 3
mp
B/F#
ought-a know. 2. You seem ve - ry well, things look peace -
Gtr. 3
(Gtr. 3 cont. in slash)
Gtr. 1
Gtr. 2
divisi
F#m7
B/F#
- ful. I'm not quite as well, I thought you should know.
F#m7
Did you for - get a - bout me, Mis - ter Du - plic - i - ty? I hate to

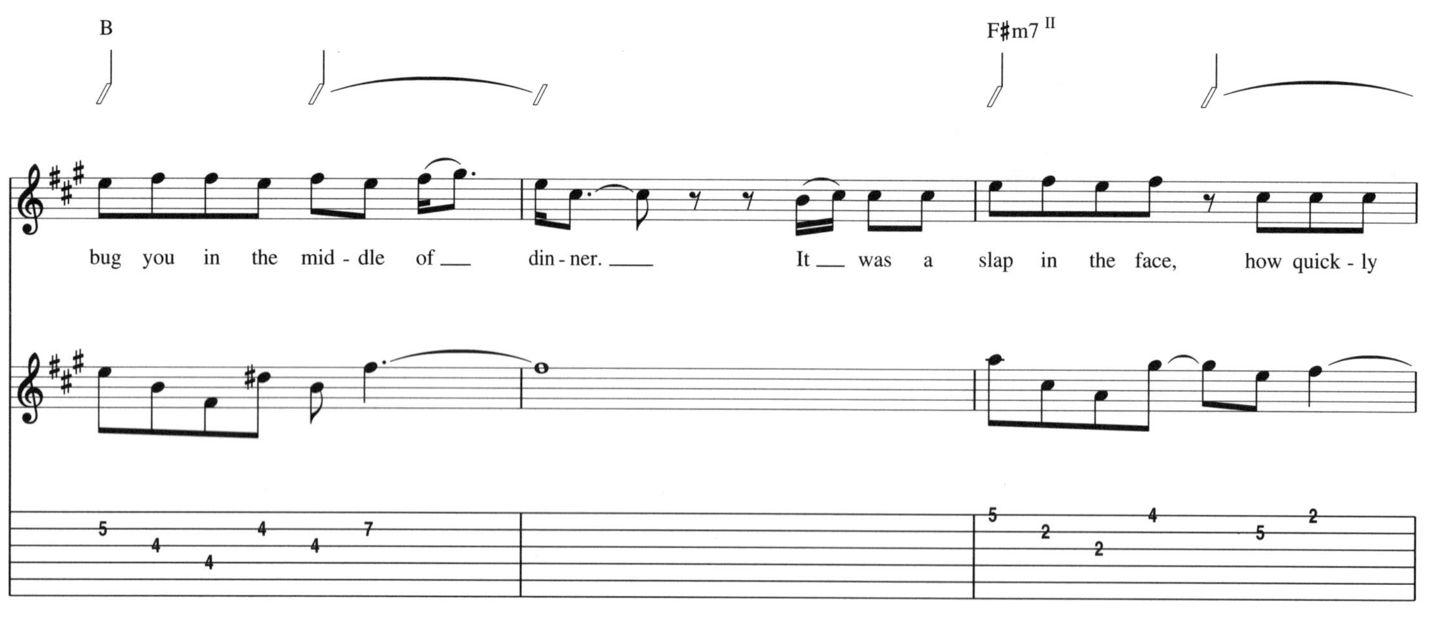
B
F#m7 II
bug you in the mid - dle of dinner. It was a slap in the face, how quick - ly

D.S. al Coda 1
B
I was re - placed and are you think - ing of me when you fuck her? 'Cause the

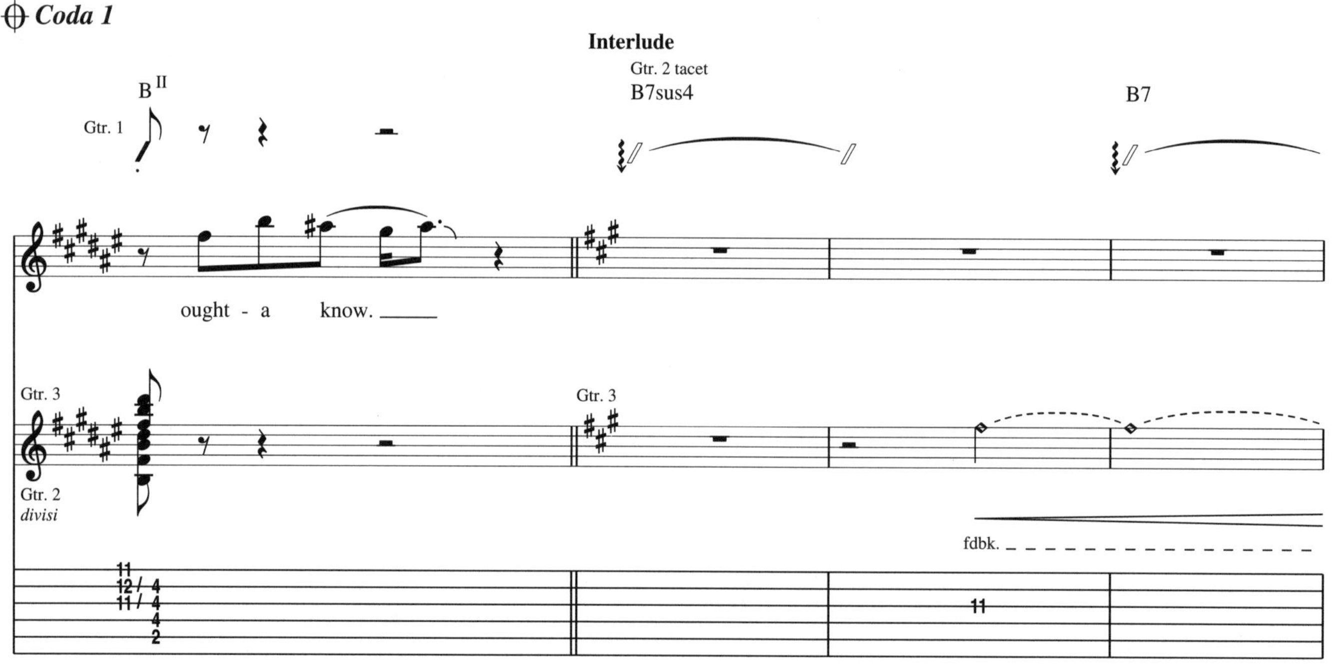
Coda 1
Interlude
Gtr. 2 tacet
B II
B7sus4
B7
Gtr. 1
ought - a know.
Gtr. 3
Gtr. 2
divisi
fdbk.

B7sus4
Ah.
w/ bar
w/ bar
fdbk.
(11)
(11)
(11)
(11)
(11)
(11)
-1
pitch: E
-1/2
D♯
-1
D
B7
F♯m/B
Ah.
Ah.
fdbk.
fdbk.
(11)
(0)
(11)
(11)
-3/4
-1
-1/2
-1/2
pitch: E
D♯
pitch: D♯
C♯
Gtr. 3 tacet
B^type2
B7
Ah.
Ah.
Ah.
D.S. al Coda 2
F♯m/B
Ah.
Ah.
Ah.
'Cause the

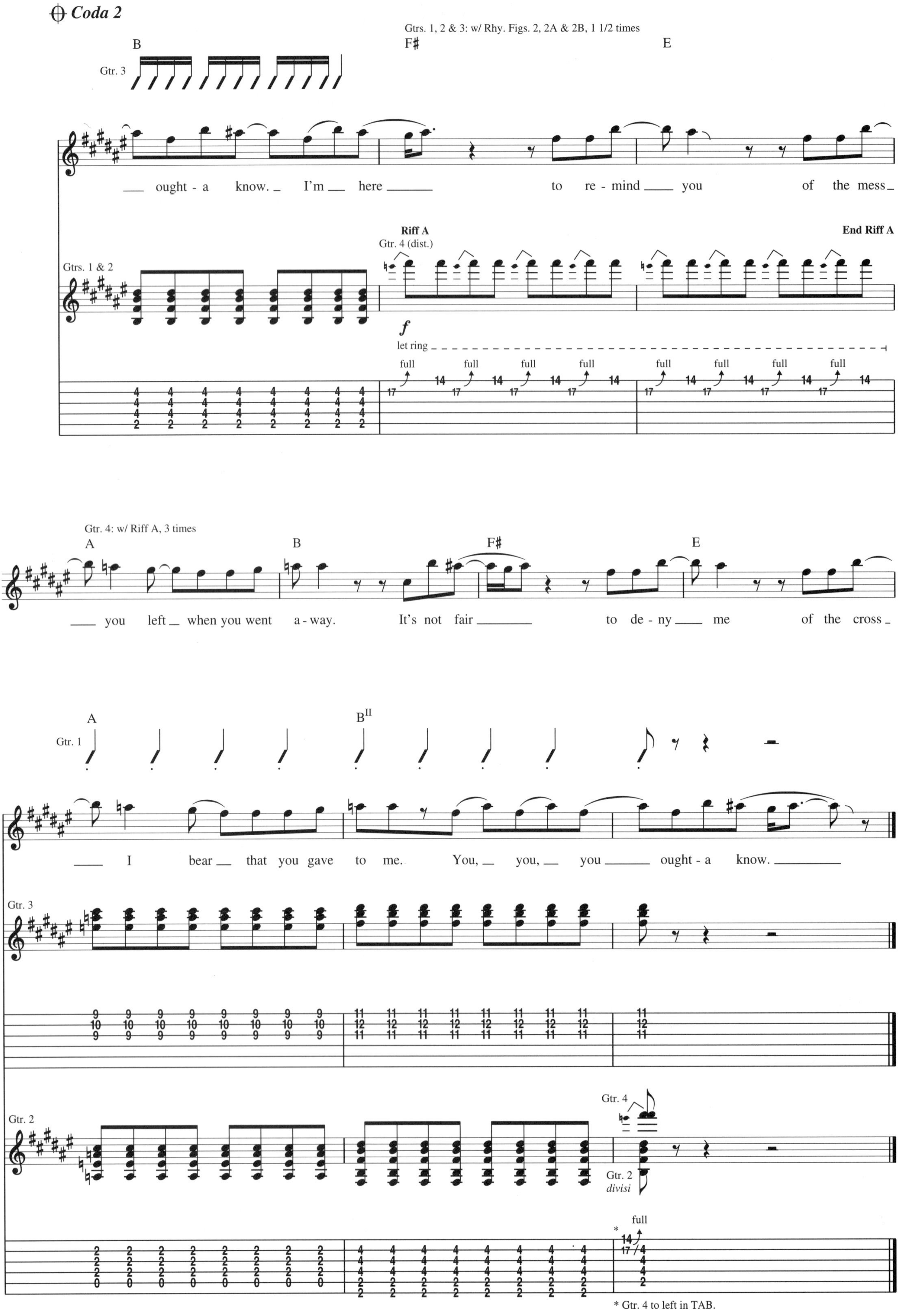

Coda 2

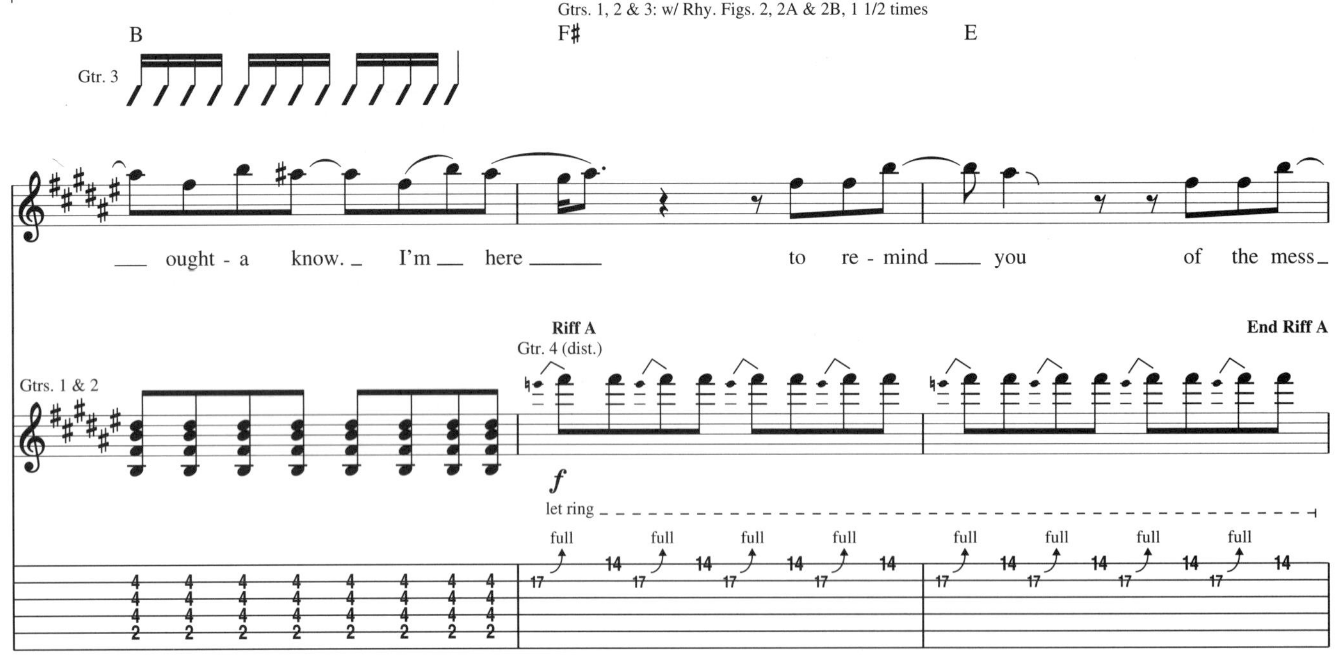

A B^II

Gtr. 1

I bear that you gave to me. You, you, you ought - a know.

Gtr. 3

Gtr. 2

Gtr. 4

Gtr. 2 *divisi*

full

* Gtr. 4 to left in TAB.

Zombie

Lyrics and Music by Dolores O'Riordan

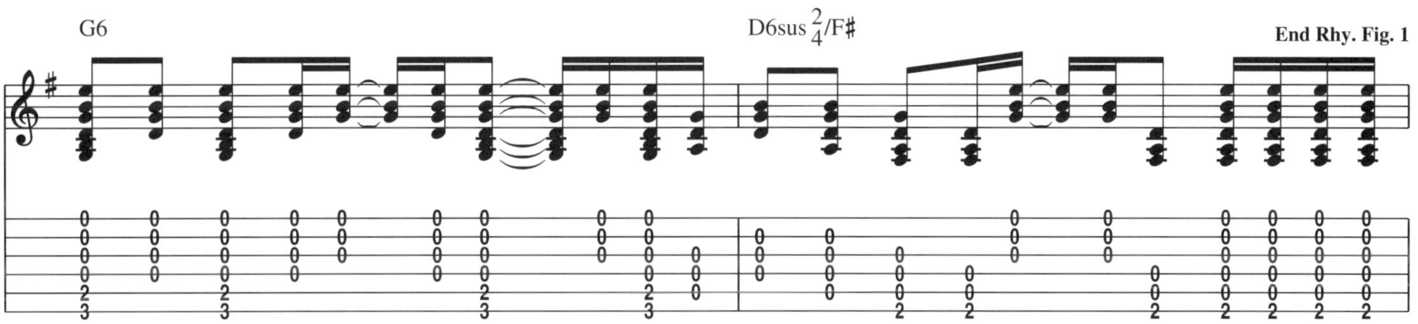

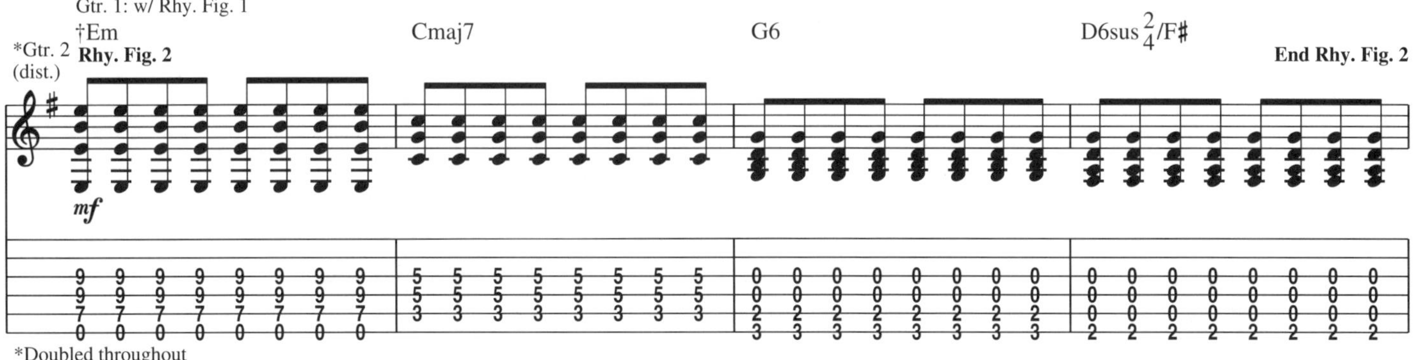

*Doubled throughout

†Chord symbols reflect combined tonality.

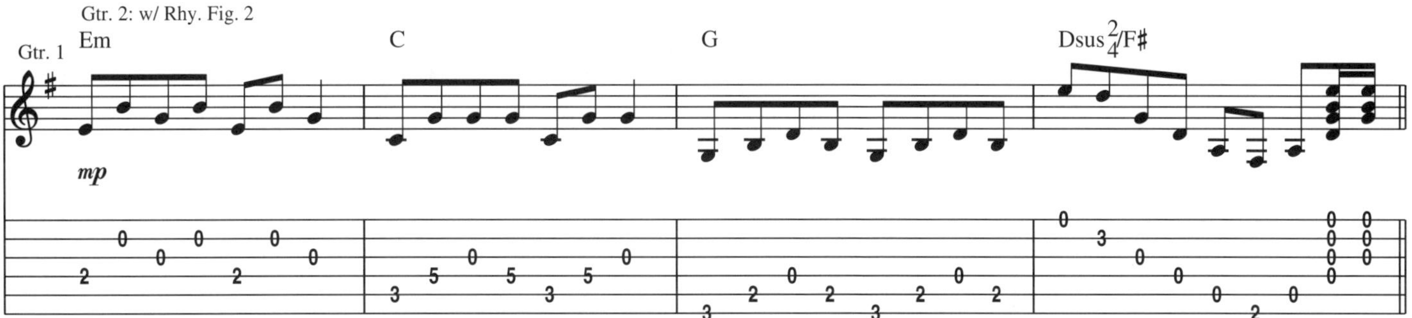

Copyright © 1994 Island Music Ltd.
All Rights for the U.S. and Canada Administered by Songs Of PolyGram International, Inc.
International Copyright Secured All Rights Reserved

Gtr. 2
Em
C
Gtr. 2 tacet
Gtr. 3 (dist.)
G
Dsus 2/4/F#
mf
Gtr. 1
Verse
Gtr. 3: w/ Fill 1
*Em
Cmaj7
G6
Dsus 2/4/F#
Em
1. An-oth - er head hangs low - ly, child is slow - ly tak - en.
2. An-oth - er moth - er's brak - in' heart is tak - ing o - ver.
Gtr. 1
*Chord symbols represent combined tonality of gtr. and bass.
Cmaj7
G6
And the vio - lence caused such si - lence, who are we mis - tak -
When the vio - lence caus - es si - lence, we must be mis - tak -
Fill 1
Gtr. 3
TAB

Dsus 2/4/F♯
Em
Cmaj7
en? But you see, it's not me, it's not my ___ fam - i - ly. ___ In your head, _
en. It's the same old ___ theme since _ nine - teen - six - teen. ___ In your head, _
G6
Dsus 2/4/F♯
Em
___ in your head they are fight - ing ___ with their tanks, and their bombs _ and their bombs _
___ in your head they're still fight - ing ___ with their tanks, and their bombs _ and their bombs _
Cmaj7
G6
Dsus 2/4/F♯
___ and their guns. ___ In your head. ___ in your head they are cry - ing ___ in your
___ and their guns. ___ In your head. ___ in your head they are dy - ing ___
Chorus
Gtr. 1 tacet
Gtr. 2: w/ Rhy. Fig. 2, 3 times, simile
E5
C5
G
head, ___ in your head, ___ zom - bie, ___ zom - bie, ___ zom - bie, _
Dsus4/F♯
E5
C5
___ hey, ___ hey. ___ What's in your head, ___ in your head, ___ zom - bie, _

1.
G
Dsus4/F♯
E5
zom - bie, zom - bie? Hey, hey, hey, oh, doo, doo, doo, doo,

C5
G
Dsus4/F♯
doo, doo, doo, doo, doo, doo, doo, doo, doo, doo, doo, doo.

2.
E5
C5
G
Dsus4/F♯
oh, oh, oh, oh, oh, oh, hey, oh, ya, ya.

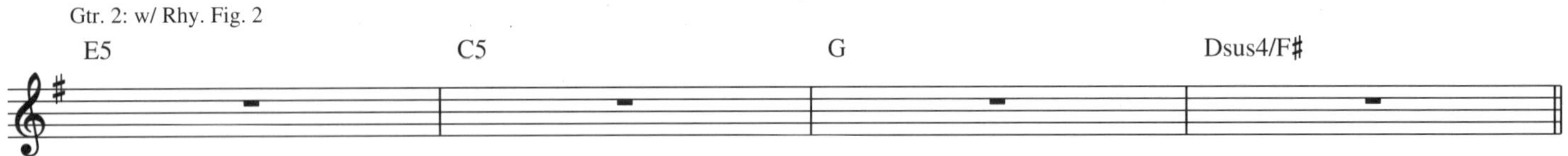

Gtr. 2: w/ Rhy. Fig. 2
E5
C5
G
Dsus4/F♯

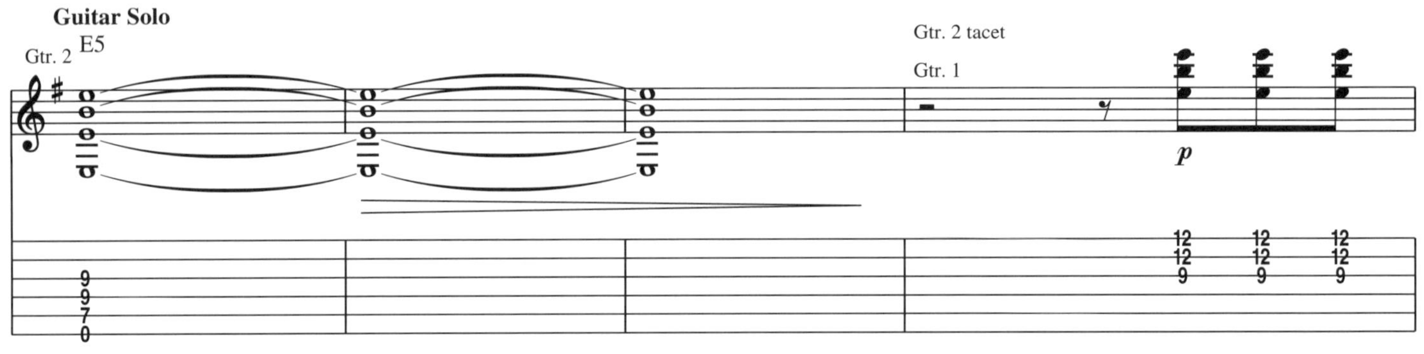

Guitar Solo
Gtr. 2
E5
Gtr. 2 tacet
Gtr. 1
p

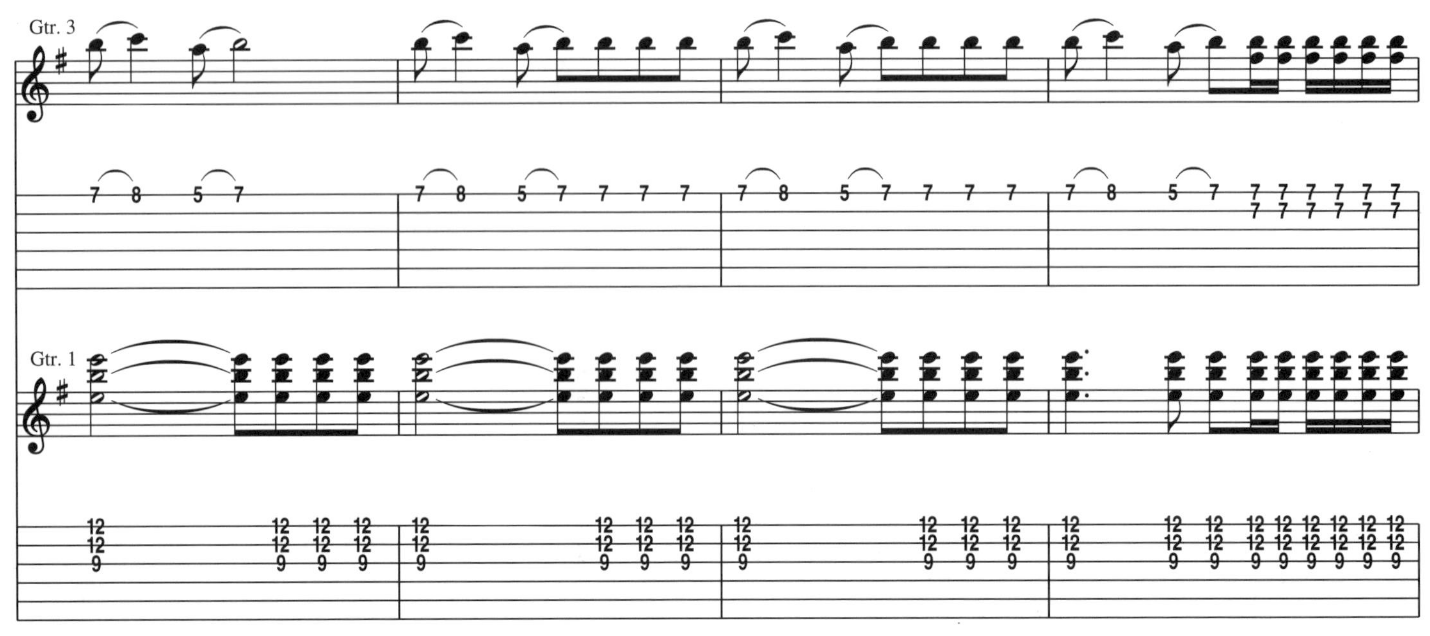

Gtr. 3
Gtr. 1

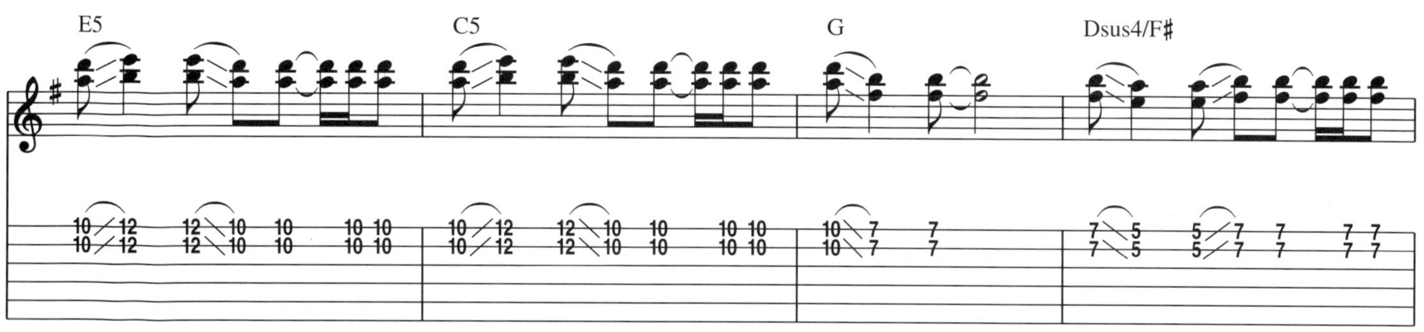

Outro

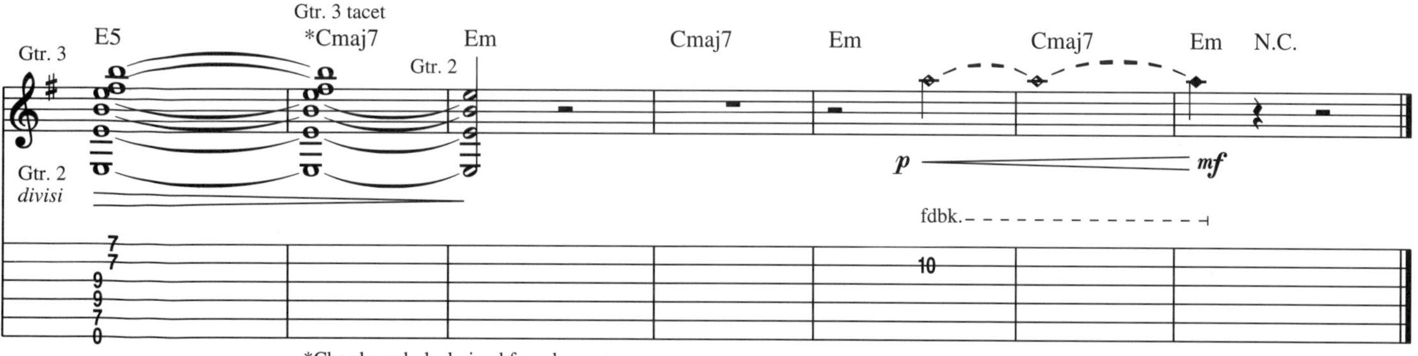

*Chord symbols derived from bass.

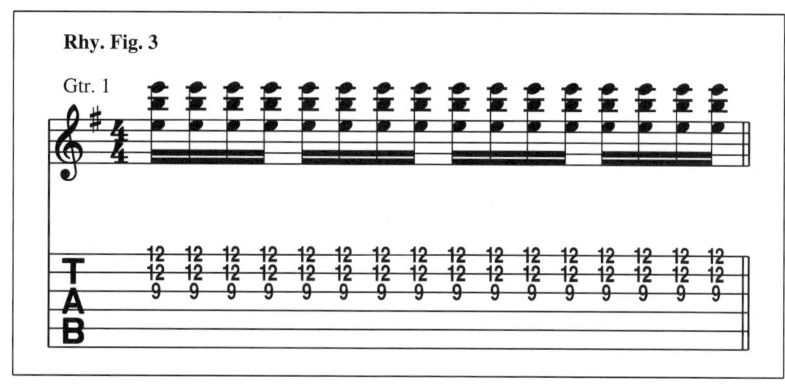